The Charlton Standard Catalogue

CHINTZ

Third Edition

By
Susan Scott

W.K. Cross
Publisher

The Charlton Press
Birmingham, Michigan Toronto, Ontario

Canadian Cataloguing In Publication Data

Scott, Susan, 1948 -
        The Charlton standard catalogue of Chintz
3rd ed.
Previous editions written by Linda Eberle and Susan Scott
Includes index.
ISBN 0-88969-228-3

1. Chintzware - Catalogs. I. Eberle, Linda, Charlton standard catalogue of Chintz. II. Title.

NK4085.E23 1999   738.2'7   C99-931281-2

EDITORIAL

Editor   W. K. Cross
Graphic Technician   Davina Rowan

ACKNOWLEDGEMENTS

The Charlton Press wishes to thank those who have helped and assisted with the third edition of the *Charlton Standard Catalogue of Chintz*.

Contributors to the Third-Edition

The publisher would like to thank the following collectors and dealers who graciously supplied photographs, price lists, shape names and other valuable information for the third edition, for which we are profoundly grateful.

Beverley and Beth Adams, England; **Jill Boyland**, Australia; **Dianne Brackett**, California; **Sharon Brown**, Virginia; **Gilda Bullock**, Ontario; **Yvonne Butorac**, Ontario; **Toni Cardwell**, New Zealand; **Betsy Clark**, Maryland; **Jonathan Daltrey**, England ;**Vikki Davis**, New York; **Cheryl Daysh**, Rhode Island; **Patricia Dennis**, New Mexico; **Leslie Domeyer**, California; **Carolyn Evers**, Oregon; **Jane Fehrenbacher**, California; **Felicity Finburgh**, England; **Mary Finegan**, North Carolina; **Cheryl Fullerton**, Australia; **Ken and Diana Glibbery**, England; **Laurie Goldberg**, Maryland; **Wanda Green**, Florida; **Ann Gregorovich**, Indiana; **Bill Hansen**, California; **Mary Jane Hastings**, Illinois; **Pierre Hébert**, Quebec; **Bonnie Heller**, New York; **Bill Hogan**, Ontario; **Joy Humphreys**, England; **Luanne Jones**, Oklahoma; **Char Jorgenson**, California; **Curt Leiser**, Washington; **Andrew Mattijssen**, The Netherlands; **Muriel Miller**, England; **Fritz Mueller**, British Columbia; **Phil Neilsen**, Ontario; **Steve and Jennifer Phillips**, Texas; **Diane Plotek**, Quebec; **Marilyn Richardson**, British Columbia; **Diana Richman**, California; **Ann Sachar**, Ontario; **Carol Saunders**, California; **David and Barbara Shestak**, California; **Britt Smith**, Ontario; **Karen Stopper**, Oregon; **Khris Sundvahl**, Minnesota; **Dave Timney**, British Columbia; **Judy van der Walt**, Wyoming; **Sheryl Vogt**, Australia ; **John Webber**, England; **Mark Wilkinson** and **Michael Jeffery, Christies**, England; **Ruth Whittaker**, Texas; **Diane Wofford**, Texas; **Linda Feldman**, Michigan; **Carolyn Fox**, California; **Dave Timney**, British Columbia, **Debra Gable**, Vermont

A SPECIAL NOTE TO COLLECTORS

The Charlton Press has an ongoing commitment to excellence and completeness in the production of all its reference works. We will consider editorial additions or corrections regarding colourways, varieties, or dating of patterns. Your help in providing new or previously unobtainable data on any aspect of Chintz collecting will be considered for inclusion in subsequent editions. Those providing information will be acknowledged in the contributors section of this catalogue.

Please send your contributions together with your name, address and phone number to our editorial offices in Toronto:

**Printed in Canada
in the Province of Manitoba**

The Charlton Press

Editorial Office
2040 Yonge Street, Suite 208, Toronto, Canada. M4S 1Z9
Telephone (416) 488-1418 Fax: (416) 488-4656
Telephone (800) 442-6042 Fax: (800) 442-1542
www.charltonpress.com e-mail: chpress@charltonpress.com

A Cheerful Effect

Glowing With Poppies and Corn.

" Poppies and Corn" Cretonne, price 1/11½d. per yard, 31 inches wide, from Messrs. J. J. Allen, Ltd., The Quadrant, Bournemouth.

Warm comfort is the first impression given by this cheery sitting-room in spite of its northern aspect.

The corn and poppy hangings were especially chosen as fit companions to the red lacquered furniture, and together they give a sunny appearance.

Warm golden brown is in the carpet, and the black Wedgwood vases on the mantelshelf strike a strong note against the buff walls.

And for a cosy tea there is a gay "Fantasy" tea set !

The " Fantasy" Tea Set, 11 9d. for 21 pieces.

TABLE OF CONTENTS

"CHEADLE"
A new chintz pattern by
ROYAL WINTON OF ENGLAND

The distinctive brilliance of color and fine glazing of Royal Winton ware are exemplified in this fine new pattern. Typically British, who are renowned for their ability to produce fine chintzware. The shapes are traditionally conservative, reflecting the restraint of good taste and old-world charm. "CHEADLE" is a riot of rose, blue and yellow bloosoms, green leaves, and is highlighted in gold. You will like it, and we predict volume sales for you.

OPEN STOCK FOR PROMPT SHIPMENT, f.o.b., Phila., Pa.

#1 Tea Cup and Saucer..$12.00 doz.	#7 Fruit Saucer 5½"....$ 6.00 doz.	#14 Open Sug. & Cream.$21.00 doz.
3 B. & B. Plates 7".... 4.50 "	9 Salad Bowl 9½"..... 24.00 "	15 Cov'd Sug. & Cream. 30.00 "
4 Salad Plates 8".... 9.00 "	12 Teapot, 4 cup....... 30.00 "	16 Platter 11" .... 21.00 "
5 Luncheon Plates 9"... 12.00 "	13 Teapot, 6 cup....... 36.00 "	17 Baker 9" .... 18.00 "
6 Dinner Plates 10".... 15.00 "		

EBELING & REUSS COMPANY
Established 1886
MAIN OFFICE, 707 CHESTNUT ST., PHILADELPHIA 6, PA.

NEW YORK 10	CHICAGO 54	LOS ANGELES 14
225 Fifth Ave.	1557 Merchandise Mart	527 W. 7th Street

PREFACE

I find it difficult to believe that it is only two years since the second edition of *The Charlton Standard Catalogue of Chintz* was launched at the Chintz Convention in Orlando, Florida. The world of chintz has changed so much in two years, partly as a result of the explosion in the production of new chintz, but mainly because of the ever-expanding reach of the Internet, including the advent of eBay and other online auction sites, and a wonderful array of chintz web sites and chat lines.

Very few people ask what you mean when you ask for chintz these days. Christie's South Kensington put chintz on the front cover of their auction catalogue in August 1997 and held their first all-chintz auction. At the same time, IKEA in England ran a campaign 'Chuck out your Chintz' and go modern. Almost every newspaper in England including the financial papers picked up the story and suggested if you were going to throw out your chintz, they would be happy to take it. My favourite headline of the time was from the *Financial Mail:* American bulls go potty in the chintz china shop. A new magazine hit the stands in England that same summer: *Collect it!* with a Julia teapot on the front cover and the first of a number of stories on chintz. In September, Paul Atterbury, better known for his books on Moorcroft and Cornish Ware, wrote "Coming into Bloom" for *Homes & Antiques*. Early in 1998 it seemed as though you couldn't pick up an American decorating magazine without seeing chintz. *Victoria* described Sheryl Lowe's "Romance with Chintzware" in February, *Traditional Home* showcased Cathy Lasry's collection in "Chintz is the Dish of the Day" in May, and in the summer *Better Homes & Gardens* featured Joanne Welsh's 'everblooming chintz'. I even shared a stage with Eric Knowles from the BBC Antiques Road Show— he talked about Lalique Glass and I talked about chintzware!

In all honesty, I never expected to be writing a third edition for this chintz book. As many of the readers of the first and second edition already know, Linda Eberle and I met in 1992 via the telephone. After a first meeting at Newark Antique Show in England, and my talk at the first chintz convention in California, we agreed to collaborate on a book on chintz. Linda was the ultimate collector and assembled a huge assortment of interesting patterns and shapes from a variety of English chintz makers. While she was out buying, I was sitting in the library looking through old trade catalogues and *Pottery Gazettes*, trying to figure out how and where chintz had been produced and distributed around the world. We took several unforgettable trips to England together in our search for chintz and information.

After the 1997 convention, Linda decided that she had collected all the chintz anyone could possibly want and she left the field open to other collectors. Jane Fehrenbacher and Carolyn Fox took over the American Chintz Collector newsletter and worked closely with Ken and Diana Glibbery of the English International Royal Winton Collectors Club — the clubs have recently amalgamated under the English banner. I continued to do my research on twentieth century collectables including chintz. In the summer of 1995 I wrote my first article about chintz for a Canadian decorating magazine *Canadian House & Home*. The article led directly to the monthly hot collectables column I have written for them for the past four years. I now work with the Royal Ontario Museum to stage an annual Collecting the Twentieth Century weekend and we have recently developed our own web site www.collecting20thcentury.com.

In June 1998, Bill Cross of The Charlton Press asked if I was interested in working on a third edition because the second edition was fast selling out. I said I would let them know after I attended the Keele University summer course in Stoke-on-Trent. The two weeks I spent in the Potteries convinced me that there was more than enough new material to justify a third book. As usual when I arrived in Hanley, I called Ivy Mayer, the former secretary to the Export Director at Grimwades and we met for our annual pub dinner. I told her I had been invited by Michael Southall to go to Royal Winton and make my own **Welbeck** teapot. I begged her to come along for moral support and she happily agreed.

I know that many collectors expect transfers to meet perfectly with no visible seams or faults of any kind. I have always rather liked the little flaws and found they gave the china a personality. I hope that, if someone should buy my teapot 100 years from now, they will find all the missed spots and obvious joins charming rather than evidence of sloppy work. I assure you I spent hours labouring over my teapot and I had Ivy's encouragement and the help of the head decorator, Glenda Bennett, and it still isn't perfect.

At the Collect it! Fair at Newark in August I simply couldn't believe the displays of new chintz. I met Christine Cope of the Old Chintz Company and she very kindly introduced me to Mr. and Mrs. Hadida, the owners of the James Kent factory. Clare Hadida offered a tour of the factory. Ivy, Christine and I had a personally conducted tour all through the factory including the mould room where we saw the original moulds for a number of early chintz shapes. We watched the decorators carefully covering every inch of every pot with transfer and Ivy whispered to me that this was too labour intensive and would greatly increase the unit cost. I explained to her that chintz was now directed at a different market than in the 1930s and the buyers would pay more for this attention to detail.

When we got back to Clare Hadida's office, we were introduced to Miss Ruth Kent and her niece Mary Aynsley. Miss Kent is a truly formidable woman and managed to reduce all of us to schoolgirls in a matter of moments. She told Clare Hadida she would never make a potter if she didn't get to the factory earlier in the day. When I showed Miss Kent a Herbert Mills of Hamilton, Ontario catalogue I had bought recently, she told me that he had been one of her best customers for chintz and talked about the strength of the Canadian market. Mrs. Hadida suggested I come back and go through the old files in her office. All the James Kent shape pages we have reproduced in this third edition came from catalogue pages I found there, which Mrs. Hadida has kindly allowed me to use.

I would never have been able to write this third edition without the help of a long list of people. First and foremost I want to thank my husband Douglas Scott who suggested I leave my job at the university more than ten years ago to pursue my dream of doing research and writing. He has continued to be supportive even when I have gone off to England for a few days and not returned for almost a month. My daughter Victoria came home when her husband was posted to Saudi Arabia for a year. As well as bringing our grandson with her, she brought her extensive computer skills. I have the head of The Charlton Press, Bill Cross himself, to thank for the editing of this third edition.

Although Steve and Jennifer Phillips are relatively new friends — they appeared at the airport in Dallas, Texas in September 1998 holding up a Julia plate so I would be able to identify them — I would not have been able to finish this book without their help. Steve contacted the US Patent Office and he was able to trace the registration of Royal Winton patterns **Cheadle** and **Evesham**, patented on March 25, 1952, and designated numbers 166,273 and 166,274. Steve discovered that these patents had a term of 14 years in the United States and that the inventor was listed as James Plant of Eccleshall, England. Steve is webmaster of chintznet — I may not have met Steve in person until last year but I certainly felt as though I knew him from hours on the telephone and dozens of helpful messages. He encouraged me to put together some information he then turned into a mini web site and encouraged all the visitors to his site to send me any material I was missing. Chintznet is a free chat line and every time I posted asking for help, the subscribers rushed to offer help and encouragement. I can't imagine how I did the other editions without this new electronic world.

Collectors and dealers from almost everywhere in the world have rallied around to help — as you can see by the list of contributors on the first page of the book. As you Shelley experts know, we needed some help with the Shelley backstamps. Curt Leiser, of the National Shelley China Club sent me as many backstamps as he could along with suggestions for improving the Shelley section and a picture of the elusive **Black Chintz**. I know that Shelley collectors will find this section of the book woefully inadequate. The subject of Shelley shapes and variations in chintz is a book in itself, and I understand that Kelly Moran is writing that book. For those of you who want more information in the meantime, I suggest you contact the National Shelley Club: Curt and Lynne Leiser have written several excellent articles on Shelley chintzes for the newsletter.

I felt I needed some new shapes and once again Fritz Mueller was incredible. He was in the midst of renovating his kitchen when I was in Vancouver. He allowed me to work my way through the construction site and carry any pieces I wanted outside where he built a temporary photographic backdrop on the trunk of his car. Closer to home, Bill Hogan gathered a shelf of unusual shapes for me to photograph in St. Catharines, Ontario and Britt Smith and Phil Neilsen, here in Toronto, called me every time something interesting turned up. Phil, as well as being a chintz collector, is an Agfa representative and supplied me with boxes of Agfa film. Dealer Mary Odette found me the Herbert Mills china catalogue. As usual, Bob Ostrowski in Idaho was more than happy to help. He sent a huge envelope of photographs and spent hours and hours sharing his knowledge with me. Toni Cardwell of New Zealand, didn't manage to come up with another catalogue this year, but she did trace the registration of **Evesham** in New Zealand and discovered that it was registered there on March 12, 1952, registration number 6484. Toni also sent excellent photographs of some interesting new patterns.

I can't possibly list every member of the Chintz Collectors Clubs both American and English who sent me photographs and backstamps for possible inclusion in this edition. Some collectors and dealers, however, went to quite extraordinary lengths to be of help. I needed a particular backstamp and a package arrived from Californian Char Jorgenson. She said she wasn't a photographer so she sent the plates themselves. Some weeks later she bought an 1950s advertisement for Royal Winton **Cheadle** on eBay, and then sent it to me to reproduce in the book. Andrew Mattijssen from Holland sent photographs of Dutch chintz from the Société Céramique and showed me that a number of English chintz patterns were also used on the continent. Cheryl Fullerton from Queensland, Australia taught herself photography in order to help; some of the most interesting new shapes in the Royal Winton section come directly from her. Ruth Whittaker, Texas, and Mary Finegan, North Carolina, took the time to send me information on a number of Johnson Brothers chintz patterns. Carolyn Evers, from Oregon, photographed the many additions to her amazing collection of **Old Cottage Chintz** to add to the shape section of the book. Karen Stopper was always on the lookout for new and interesting pieces and sent me an envelope full of photographs to add to this edition.

In the end, I decided to write the third edition after three weeks of research in England and the time spent with English collectors and dealers. As a result of a motorway crash, Ken and Diana Glibbery spent five hours in the car fighting their way north to the Collect it! Fair so that we could spend a couple of hours discussing plans for their International Chintz Convention in Stoke-on-Trent. Since then, Diana has spent countless hours working through all the chintz patterns and shapes and giving me advice on the differences between the English and the North American collector. Show promoter, antique dealer, Carltonware collector and chef, Dennis Harwood, and his partner John, gave me a bed, fed me poached salmon and raspberry tart, and drove me to the N.E.C. in Birmingham so I could see this famous fair for the first time. Michael Poole and Peter Saville, antique dealers and old friends who live near Stoke-on-Trent, invited me for our traditional dinner and potteries gossip session. Len Griffin, in the midst of writing the centenary book on Clarice Cliff, and his partner Michael Slaney, took the evening off work and gave me room and board as well as their usual good advice on effective research techniques. Kathy Niblett, Senior Assistant Keeper of Ceramics at the Potteries Museum, has offered me encouragement since I first met her many years ago. This trip, she allowed me access to the Crown Ducal pattern books and was able to shed light on the Brexton backstamp. Walter and Liz Moorcroft invited me to spend the night with them and Walter regaled me with a hundred stories about life in the Potteries.

When I left the potteries and headed into London, Jocelyn Lukins, author of more than a dozen books on Royal Doulton, once again gave me the top floor of her house in Shepherds Bush and access to her extensive research library. Joy Humphreys, long time chintz dealer at Camden Passage, took a rare day off work and we wandered through the Victoria & Albert Museum together while she offered suggestions and encouragement. Beverley and Beth Adams pulled out yet more interesting pieces of chintz for me to photograph and took me for our annual Thai dinner on Edgeware Road. Mark Wilkinson and Michael Jeffery of Christie's South Kensington, gave me any transparencies I needed and showed me anything unusual which had found its way to Christie's. My cousin Wendy Watson and her husband Peter still live about ten minutes from the Ardingly Fair Grounds. Wendy and I wandered the fields for another year in search of treasure.

I have continued my search for new information about chintz but the search doesn't get any easier. Obviously, the section on new shapes for James Kent is my most exciting discovery for this edition. While I was taking the course at Keele University, I was able to make use of the university library and found some good information on Elijah Cotton. I have incorporated any other new pieces of information I found or I have been sent in the past two years to the factory or to the individual pattern descriptions.

I have added a completely new section to the book on the new and reproduction chintz. I know that this is a subject that has caused some concern for collectors. I read an article on design trends in the January 1953 *Pottery & Glass Record*; the author concluded his discussion by pointing out that a pottery producer sinks or swims according to the amount of pottery he sells. When I was poking about in Clare Hadida's office I found a letter dated July 1980 asking if James Kent still made **Du Barry**. The young woman suggested that **Du Barry** had the freshness of the countryside and the simple life that people today yearn for and that the pattern would go over extremely well. Late last year Royal Doulton were forced to let over 1200 workers go. Royal Winton and James Kent are two of the only factories in the Potteries who are hiring — Royal Winton have bought a new factory on Greenedock Street and they have tripled their workforce in two years. Having said all this, I am concerned for the new collector who is buying both off the Internet and in shops. Too many are paying old chintz prices for new chintz. I hope this section will help to clear up some of the confusion. I am also including this section so that forty years from now, if there are collectors buying the chintz which is being produced today, they will not have as difficult a research task as we have all had. They will be able to look at this section and know which pieces were produced in 1999 and identify backstamps like Clementine Rusk and Magnolia Antiques.

The section on new chintz was put together with the help of a number of people. Michael Southall of Royal Winton was willing to help and advise. Victoria magazine allowed me to reproduce the images of their **Welbeck** pieces. Gail Claridge sent photographs of the House of Claridge lines. Clare Hadida gave me copies of the flyers for the **Du Barry** lines produced in the mid-1980s and photographs of their new chintzes. Clementine Rusk and Magnolia Antiques in California let me know about their exclusive pieces and special backstamps. Compton & Woodhouse sent information on The Chintz Plate Collection.

I had to make choices as to new patterns to include or exclude and I used various criteria. I was sent a great number of photographs of very rare chintz patterns the owner would have liked to see in this edition. Unfortunately, when there are only one or two examples of a pattern it is difficult to establish a market and it is of little interest to most collectors. I looked for patterns which seemed to me to be representative of a type or which are commonly found and often asked about. In this way, I added a couple of Empire patterns, the Myott pattern **Bermuda**, the Barker Brothers pattern **Fantasy** plus the unnamed Barker Brothers pattern most popular with collectors, one new Lord Nelson pattern and a number of Royal Winton patterns. I have not included the dozens of factories that produced one or two chintz patterns among their other lines. There are collectors for Japanese chintz and Czechoslovakian Erphila chintz as well as American chintzes like Lefton. Bone china chintz is a subject all by itself. I hope that one of the collectors of bone china chintz will undertake the necessary research. I have included a discussion on Royal Winton bone china in the Grimwades section since this was an experiment of interest to Royal Winton collectors.

A number of collectors wrote, phoned or e-mailed to say how much they enjoyed and benefited from the Advice for Collectors. With the advent of the Internet and eBay, I have gathered a number of tales of Internet woe and I have added these to this section along with more traditional, but equally disastrous, transactions which collectors and dealers have shared with me.

Over the years, people have expressed surprise when they find out I am neither a chintz collector nor a chintz dealer but a researcher. They wonder how it is possible for me to write a book on the subject. I tell them about all the readers and the collectors and the letters and photographs they send me. Please take a look at the long list of people who contributed photographs, backstamps and other pieces of information which were used in this edition. I would never have been able to produce a third edition with so much new information without their help. On my own, I have managed to find a number of factory descriptions, advertisements and catalogues over the years and assembled a partial picture of the history of chintz through the twentieth century. For the rest, I have relied on you to help with your small and large collections of chintz and your passion for knowing more about each piece. I hope that you will continue to write to me and to send me any new information you have gathered. Thank you all for your help and encouragement. I apologize in advance for any omissions and errors.

Susan Scott

INTRODUCTION

THE HISTORY OF CHINTZ

The history of chintz goes back hundreds of years, although the chintz so eagerly sought today is very much a twentieth-century industrial product. Chintz — the Indian word was *chintes* — goes back to the fantastical fabrics imported into England from the India of the late seventeenth century. Richly hued flowers and brightly plumed mythical birds decorated both the persons and the houses of the early 1700s to such an extent that it threatened domestic weavers. Even before 1800 chintz had come to mean homey, cozy, overstuffed furniture and a certain English country house look. An advertisement in *The Pottery Gazette* as late as 1957 describes "the homely rustle of chintz, the warm welcoming design of flowered pattern."

Inevitably the china manufacturers created hand-painted tableware which captured the feel of Indian chintz. The development of the process of transfer printing was very important in the popularizing of chintz ceramics. By the 1820s there were a number of Staffordshire factories producing chintz that was meant for everyday use. This chintz is recognizable by the very Victorian shapes to which it was applied and by the loose patterning and subtle colouring.

Around 1912 Royal Doulton produced several versions of an all-over pattern called **Persian,** which remained in production until the second world war and was used mainly on cabinet pieces. However, chintzware was not really produced to any extent by any of the carriage-trade pottery firms. The firms catering to the middle classes and to the masses were the firms that came to personify chintz. In 1918 A. G. Richardson developed their first chintz — a pattern so far identified only as A500 — but followed with **Rose and Motifs** and **Delhi** in the same year. Most of these early Crown Ducal chintzes were used for vases and trinket boxes, not for dinnerware. In dating chintzware to the 1920s, it is useful to study the patterns produced by Richardsons, since they seem to exemplify that exotic 1920s look. They were particularly popular in America, and a long article in *The Pottery, Glass & Brass Salesman* extols Richardsons work:

. . . there is always a steady demand for the chintz patterns . . . these come in many variations of colour background, and the subdued brilliance of the realistic flowers and plumaged birds makes an ever-delightful note. Festival decoration with its intertwined lanterns hanging over blithely frolicsome scenes seems to have the ability to capture the fancy of many who like its vivacity. Crown Ducal ware is a beautiful piece of industrial accomplishment with none of the slight faults of immaturity.

It is useful to place this tableware against a broader historical background. The 1920s were the Jazz Age, the time of the exotic and art deco. Yet the world had barely survived the war to end all wars and the Russian Revolution. The January 1927 advertisement for the new Crown Ducal chintzes describes them as "bordering on the sensational . . . novel indeed and radically different, but not bolshevik." Chintzes somehow managed to be both different but cozy, exotic but not revolutionary. Books on twentieth-century design never contain references to chintz. They were intended for seaside cottages and bungalow furnishings, not avant garde houses in New York.

From 1918 through the first half of the 1920s, most of the Crown Ducal chintz pieces were vases and console sets (candle sticks and bowls), as well as toilet sets. A 1929 report pointed out that ten years before, the Crown Ducal Works in England had produced only a few vases of various shapes and some odd pieces of decorative earthenware. *"Today a tremendous volume business in dinnerware is theirs — and they serve the American market chiefly, for this ware appeals immensely to the value-loving and thrifty native housewife, in whom more for the money awakens instant response. The early examples of CD ware consisting of chintz all-over pattern vases and similar items gained great favor with all who saw them. . ."* A steady stream of requests for individual breakfast sets to match, for tea sets and salad services flowed into the offices of Maddock & Miller, exclusive agents for Crown Ducal. In 1925 the manufacture of dinner services began the first specimens were of the popular chintz effects which are still in steady demand especially for subsidiary sets. The Americans calculated that a Crown Ducal dinner service would cost about $100, while a comparable bone china service would be over $500. After a strange gap of almost ten years, Crown Ducal produced a series of chintzes in the 1930s such as **Primrose**, **Priscilla** and **Pansy** but these have never achieved the popularity with collectors of the earlier patterns.

Other firms that were producing chintz very like the 1920s Crown Ducal were Samuel Ford & Company, Wood & Sons, and A. J. Wilkinson Ltd. all located in Burslem. All these firms were geographically very close together and exhibited at the same trade shows. Soon after one firm produced something marketable, the others followed very quickly. For most of them, however, these all-over patterns were simply one out of the many lines they produced. In order to have an exclusive pattern, a company would have to buy the complete run, which required a sizable capital outlay. Having a "controlled" pattern was expensive not just in money but in space; it meant buying the whole run from the lithographic firm and keeping it on premises. The *Pottery Gazette* noted in May 1924 *"It is almost needless to add that the pattern is a controlled one, for Grimwades, Ltd., as a matter of fact, take care to see that all their lithographed patterns are reserved."* Although Barker Brothers went on in the 1930s-1950s to produce many unnamed chintz patterns, interestingly, in the mid-1920s their chintz pattern **Fantasy** was a real innovation and was much discussed in the *Pottery Gazette*. **Fantasy** was exclusive to Barker Brothers and the name was included in the backstamp. A number of other factories simply went to the lithographer and selected one of the stock patterns out of their books. Patterns like James Kents **Mille Fleur** were clearly not controlled patterns; A. G. Richardson had the same pattern in their books as Crown Ducal Pattern Number 5007 and Lord Nelson named this pattern **Marigold**. The Société Céramique also used this pattern as well as several other uncontrolled English lithos to produce chintz in Holland. A. J. Wilkinson introduced a new pattern **Mayflower** in 1925 for which they were commended by the *Pottery Gazette*. Grimwades used the identical pattern on a cube teapot clearly dating around the same time. Interestingly, the teapot was also marked **Mayflower**, the only instance I have found of two factories using, not only the same litho, but the same pattern name as well. The Grimwades pattern **Rose Du Barry** has been found as James Kents **Chelsea Rose** and Shelleys **Briar Rose**, and a piece of James Kent's **Silverdale** turned up with a Royal Winton backstamp. These factories were all close, and many of the workers were related or acquainted. When factories were sold or went bankrupt, the stacks of lithos would have been sold as well and this may account for some of the controlled patterns appearing occasionally on the work of other factories. Inevitably, strange pieces will have been produced.

Grimwades rarely used stock patterns. The company became known for their colourful chintz ware. Their chintz lines were a major part of their business and they tended to use exclusive patterns designed in their own shop. Throughout this early period Grimwades Ltd. was producing a wide range of products; the company was noted for their ewers and basins amongst other lines. At this time their chintzes were closer to the Victorian versions than to the Crown Ducal fantastical and seem somewhat old-fashioned in comparison (see Grimwades **Merton**, **Carnation**, and **Fernese** for comparison with other mid 1920s chintz patterns). Gradually their patterns changed, and in 1928 Grimwades introduced their first modern chintz, **Marguerite**, which was an instant success. The pattern was available on an amazing assortment of articles; it has even been found on a ceramic hot-water bottle.

As the decade ended and the world-wide depression deepened, the production of decorative pieces was replaced more and more with useful items at reasonable prices more suited to the hard economic times. Clearly there were still decorative items made but the prices had to be low. Grimwades is first mentioned in *The Pottery, Glass & Brass Salesman* in March 1933. Ebeling & Reuss, china and glass importers, is praised for importing fancy chintz earthenware baskets, vases, flatware and even short sets. Buyers are urged to look at the cake plates which they should be able to retail for $1.00 or possibly $1.25. The July 1932 *Gazette* discussed the reorganization of Grimwades lines during recent months "occasioned no doubt by the fact that certain lines which were at one time very largely manufactured by Grimwades such as ornamentals and toiletware are less in demand than formerly and therefore these have had to be substituted by other creations more in keeping with the demand of the times." In addition, the improvements that had been made in sanitation spelled the end of the broad production of toiletwares for all but a limited market. Tolie Coales, the daughter of the Canadian representative for Grimwades, recalled her father having ewers and basins shipped directly to the Canadian Maritime provinces. He took orders and then sold off the samples since there was little or no market for them in the rest of Canada. In an interview in *The Gift Buyer*, May 1953, George Coales recalled his first trip to Western Canada — it was 1910 and he took almost half a ton of baggage and his excess baggage charges were greater than the original fare. He traveled with his sample cases by train from coast to coast of Canada for more than forty years and was always surprised by the success of his chintz lines.

The first British Industries Fair was held in 1915, and each year firms mounted displays of their newest lines and hoped to capture the attention of the buying public, as well as trade publications. Ceramics designers were forced to come up with hundreds of new patterns every year to keep up with their competitors and attract publicity. The Grimwades pattern **Summertime** dates to 1932 and is numbered 775, and the pattern **Clyde** is numbered 5637 and probably dates to 1939. Grimwades therefore came up with something close to a thousand patterns a year throughout the 1930s. Obviously most of these were not chintz patterns but it is not surprising that in their constant search for new patterns, Grimwades took patterns such as **Welbeck** (2204) and redid them in different colourways like **Hazel** (2208) and **Spring** (2506). It is said that the first chintz pattern **Marguerite** was copied from a cushion cover embroidered by the wife of Leonard Grimwade, the owner of the factory. Other patterns came from clothing worn by staff, from pictures in books, from anywhere and everywhere. They were known throughout the 1930s and indeed through the 1950s as the acknowledged pre-eminent house for chintz patterns.

Publicity was eagerly sought by all the Staffordshire firms. In the early 1930s Elijah Cotton supplied dealers who carried a sufficient range of Lord Nelson Ware with a five-foot-tall ceramic Nelson monument like the one in Trafalgar Square, made up of plates, sandwich trays and egg cups drilled and bolted together. Even today you occasionally run across drilled Nelson Ware chintz plates in the street markets around Stoke-on-Trent.

Not only did the factories turn out new patterns on a weekly basis; they attempted to create new and interesting shapes regularly. In 1922 Crown Ducal were lauded in the American press for their chintz "trays and cups" which have come to be known as tennis or hostess sets. Later that year they introduced the chintz patterns with solid colour borders to generate new interest. In 1923 it was their 12-inch lily bowls with matte black interiors which won approval. By the late 1920s it was Grimwades that were leading the way in innovative chintz designs and shapes. In 1933 it is Grimwades who are noted in the American trade journals for their plates with plain embossed borders and chintz centers (these plates are known to American collectors as Wedgwood plates). The 1932 *Pottery and Glass Record* noted that Grimwades "latest design among sets is the small tray with a toast rack, sugar, cream and little teapot, all fitted into grooves but detachable. . . this being called the Bed-side set. It is also supplied with an irregular oblong shape and including a little groove for butter " It was not until 1938 that Crown Ducal presented their newly designed bedside set described by the *Pottery Gazette* as "of very good value and acceptable design."

Grimwades introduced the square Ascot shape and the deco Norman shape in 1932. In 1935 the Athena shape was introduced and described in the *Gazette* as "hexagonal sided in rectangular form with a fancy handle." The 1936 Grimwades Australian Export Catalogue (we have again reproduced some of the interesting shape pages) is invaluable in showing which shapes were available in the mid-1930s. In 1940 the whole Rosebud line was introduced to great acclaim, and although initially produced in a solid colour with hand-painted handles and finials, it was not long before chintz was applied to the whole line. Lily and Petunia followed soon after. One of the most popular of the post-war shapes was the Albans with its clean lines and acorn finial. Interestingly the stacking teapot, which is so incredibly popular in North America, never appears to have been mentioned in the British press and has rarely been seen by British dealers. One of the first mentions of the stacker was in an advertisement in the Canadian Birks catalogue for 1941, where a plain pink, blue and green three-in-one Breakfast set is advertised for sale for $2.00. In the same catalogue a Countess Bedside set is offered for $3.50.

By 1940 the British government had imposed restrictions on the decoration and production of pottery and these remained in force for the home market until 1952. As a result, patterns such as **Morning Glory** and **May Festival** often appear in England without hand painting and are presumably pre-1952. By the time the war ended, the Canadian representative alone had two years of back orders, which the factory simply could not supply. Shipments went around the world as fast as they could be packed, but often there were mix-ups and pieces intended for Canada landed in New Zealand or elsewhere. Sheryl Vogt, the founder of the Australian Royal Winton Collectors Club, heard from a New Zealand dealer that "the US buyers would not accept old or outmoded designs so the newest ware was kept for the Americans and the government insisted on 75% of production being exported, up to 1952 . . . so as much old stock as could be mustered from warehouses was sent out to Australia and New Zealand up until that time. This has turned out to be most fortunate as we still have a good range of pre-war ware from what was essentially a small family pottery. "

The wartime production of plain white utility ware created a craving for colour and warmth, which resulted in a tremendous upsurge in the sales of chintzware both at home and abroad throughout the 1950s. Considering the direction of the design movement during this decade, this is quite surprising. Firms like Midwinter Ltd. produced a tremendous amount of chintzware from just after the war until the 1970s, yet a recent book on the company devotes one line to chintz. James Kent Ltd., under the able management of Ruth Kent, exported containers full of **Du Barry**, **Apple Blossom** and **Rosalynde** to North America through the 1950s and the 1960s. Export was so important that Miss Kent, who was the Sales Director after the war, was sent to Canada in 1951 to attempt to understand the Canadian needs; after crossing Canada, she went on to Australia.

The Canadian market was of tremendous importance to all the Staffordshire Potteries. In 1957 the Wedgwood Review reported that Canada with a population of 17 million bought nearly double the amount of British pottery bought by 170 million Americans. The United States had a 30% protective tariff and 65% of their pottery imports came from Japan while only 15% came from Britain. Americans came to Canada when they wanted to buy English china and pottery. In the 1950s most Canadian china catalogues were directed at the American market and explained to the Americans how much they were entitled to take home duty free after a 48 hour stay. The Montreal correspondent for *Pottery & Glass* reported in 1948 that Canadian shops were preparing for the May invasion of American tourists. **"For** weeks these shops have been trying to build up stocks to meet this invasion, for American women, who usually arrive in automobiles, are the biggest customers for British makes of china and glass, and do not appear to care how much they pay."

In *The Gift Buyer* from 1949 to 1953 there were a whole series of advertisements for new Royal Winton chintz patterns. In fact, in a 1953 interview, George Coales was quoted as saying that he was delighted that Grimwades had been able *"to issue fifteen new chintz patterns in the last year."* Clearly chintz enjoyed a resurgence at least through the early part of the 1950s. There were suddenly advertisements for **Cottonwood** by Langdale Pottery Company, for **Wild Rose Chintz** by Winterton Pottery, for **Springtime** by John Shaw & Sons Ltd. and for **Summer Flowers** by Myott Son & Company. The prices remained quite low. For example, a Barker Brothers Royal Tudor Ware cake plate and server was advertised in the *Montreal Gazette* in May of 1954 for $2.35, while a Royal Winton chintz stacking teapot is noted in the Christmas 1951 *Canadian House & Home* for $2.50. An American collector recently bought a Summertime covered box with the original paper sticker from the store, Zollinger-Harnod Co., Allentown, Pennsylvania priced at $3.00 (Marked down from $3.80). A Canadian dealer found a **Julia** breakfast set with the $7.95 price tag still attached from a Quebec gift shop.

Although many of the patterns that we now know were produced after the war are similar to the pre-war patterns, such as **Marion**, **Nantwich** and **Cheadle**, there are others that are very much in the 1950s mold, such as **June Festival**, **Spring Glory** and **Peony**. Suddenly, from being new and fresh, all-over floral prints came to be described very differently in the 1950 *Crockery & Glass Journal*: "Dinner sets with small rosebuds or other tiny all over motifs crawling have lost stature as the stock-in-trade of foreign-made wares. In their stead are larger floral motifs . . . sophisticated stylized versions." Just as the 1920s chintzes have a certain look, so do the 1950s versions. The flowers are much larger and further apart and the ground colours tend to be black, navy and burgundy.

Desperate to find markets, the factories not only changed the chintz patterns, they changed the body on which chintz was produced. Although there were examples of bone china chintz before World War II, this does seem to have been mainly a post-war phenomenon. A number of factories including Royal Standard, Spencer, Stevenson & Co., Royal Albert, Royal Stafford and Colclough China Ltd. produced bone china tea wares. Grimwades also looked to bone china to increase their sales. Ivy Mayer gave me three unmarked bone china plates — **Nantwich**, **Victorian Rose**, and **Old Cottage Chintz** — which she took home when the factory moved in 1964. She remembered that Grimwades had tested various patterns on bone china blanks to see how they looked. Although Shelley and Susie Cooper actually phased out the production of earthenware in favour of bone china, for Grimwades this experiment does not appear to have been successful. Collectors have reported finding bone china cups and saucers or tennis sets in **Summertime**, **Florence**, **Marion**, **Cotswold**, **Sweet Pea**, **Hazel**, **Shrewsbury**, and **O.C.C.**, but not in any great quantity. Whether bone or earthenware, large flower or tightly knit clusters of flowers, chintz could not be made to enhance the look of Scandinavian blond wood furniture and the amoeba shapes of the modern dishes. Gradually the potteries phased out their chintz lines altogether and moved on to a completely different style.

Grimwades was bought by the Howard Group in 1964 and moved their operation to Norfolk Street. At the time of the takeover, Canada was the largest single overseas market with Australia and New Zealand not far behind. Ivy Mayer says that whenever she thinks of chintz she thinks of Canada, and when she thinks of Rosebud she thinks of Australia. After the move there was little room in the new location for the production of chintzware. Ivy does remember, however, a room with shelves full of sheets of chintz lithographs and she says good customers could still order chintz. If the sheets were available, the factory would fill the orders. I found two invoices from Grimwades to J.L. Bradshaw Ltd. in Stratford, Canada, one dated March 24, 1969, and the other June 5, 1969. The one invoice is for 215 two tier Tid Bit sets in **Cheadle**, **Victorian Rose** and **Old Cottage Chintz**. Everything else on the invoice appears to be in later non-chintz patterns, such as **Thistle** 1594. The backstamp used by Royal Winton after 1964 is easily recognizable and the earthenware has a whiter cast than before (See the section on backstamps).

Although MIKASA turned out a complete line of James Kent **Du Barry** in the late 1980s, Staffordshire potteries ignored the returning popularity of chintz until recently. Crownford China Company Ltd., with the trade name Queens China manufactured a fine bone china they called **English Chintz.** Years ago when we went to watch the lithographs being applied, we were told that most workers find the transfers too difficult and prefer not to work with chintz. Spouts and handles were left plain white like many of the old Lord Nelson pots. Since 1995 the production of new chintz has exploded. Both Royal Winton and James Kent have reproduced a number of their old shapes and patterns (See the section on new chintz).

THE HUMAN FACE OF CHINTZ

There were no records that we could find to tell us more about chintz ware. We advertised in the *Evening Sentinel* in Stoke-on-Trent. Several letters came in response. One was from Florrie Dennis who worked for Royal Winton from the age of fourteen. "I worked for two weeks and didn't receive any pay until the end of the third week which was five shillings and nine pence a week" They were told "we must always decorate a piece of ware how we would like to buy it . . . perfect."

Florrie wrote a long letter describing the process of applying the lithograph to the pottery. It will be easier to understand her remarks if you think of wall papering around windows and difficult corners and try to imagine how hard it must have been to do toast racks and lamps. Large sheets of patterned paper were kept in a separate room and the girls had to go and get pieces and cut them into the appropriate size for the ware they were decorating.

"We had a pot of size which we then brushed on the piece of ware with a camel haired brush which we had to buy for one shilling old money so of course used to clean them every night. We applied the size onto the piece of ware then wafted it until nice and tacky. In front of us was placed a pattern of whatever piece of ware you were going to

practise on. We had to fetch our litho from a little decorating shop. We applied the litho onto the piece of pottery looking closely at the pattern in front of you then we were shown a geyser at the bottom of the shop and given a chamber pot to carry very hot water to the bench and a piece of waste rag and a hard sponge and a soft sponge and a piece of hard yellow soap. When we had applied the litho sprays to the piece of ware we then dipped the hard sponge into the hot water then rubbed the sprays of litho on the ware then a little harder then of course it was very wet then taking the soft sponge which we have rubbed onto the hard soap began to sponge off the wet paper which by now had fastened the floral sprays onto the ware. Then taking the piece of soft cloth gently dabbed the piece of ware to be passed as perfect...the most popular pattern was **Summertime** which consisted of all summer flowers . . . also we did a chintz called **Black Hazel** and a lot of tea ware which was called ajax ware (this was a shape range). We were not allowed to cut into flowers and used a razor blade to decorate round the handles and teapot spouts and cup and cream handles. All the patterns we used were all set out and each had a number." ...after six months you were expected to go on piece work to earn your wages. The prices then were very low. I worked in my dinner hour many days. When we went to see Florrie she told us much more about her life. She left school at fourteen on a Friday and she started at Royal Winton on the Monday. She started in 1928 and the first pattern she worked on was **Marguerite** the first real all over chintz at Winton. Out of her wages, she gave all but a shilling to her father. One week she worked every lunch hour and made an extra shilling which she hid in the toe of her shoe. When she went to bed she forgot about it and it hit the floor when she took her shoe off. Even at eighty she can remember vividly the beating her father gave her that night.

The decorating manager was a man called Mr. Parry and he could be very unkind to the young girls who worked for him. Florrie told us you always got more for your fittings but only if they were perfect (fittings were pieces like teapots and coffee pots). You had to do the pieces that were assigned to you. She still remembers girls sitting crying over their benches because they could not manage to do the spouts of the teapots or coffee pots and at the end of the day might have nothing to show for their efforts. They didn't get paid as a result and could be beaten when they came home empty handed. She remembers staying late to help girls with their spouts and handles. "I was only small and can remember how difficult it was to handle putting the border on the inside and outside of the large wash basins ..."

In 1995 we again asked for help in the *Evening Sentinel* and two more Grimwades workers responded. Jean Heath, nee Edwards, agreed to have me come out and talk to her. She had wonderful stories of the kindness of the staff at Grimwades. When she went to work there she was thirteen years old and her birthday was at Christmas. She can still remember the cake and the gifts that the Grimwades workers gave her. Her sister worked there all her life as a gilder and soon before she left she was asked to work on a white and silver tea set. She was told it was a special order and extra care was needed. This was the tea set presented to her upon her retirement from Grimwades. Jean still had a letter she received in 1946 from The English China Shop Ltd., Importers of Fine English China in Vancouver, British

Columbia. When she packed a Royal Winton coffee set she put a letter in the coffee pot. The reply is worth quoting: "The coffee set is now on its way to the United States. I sold it to some American tourists and they were really delighted with it. The Americans come up to Canada just to buy our nice English ware which they can't get down there." It may be fifty years later but the Americans are still coming up over the border in search of Royal Winton!

The other letter was from Mrs. H. Cooper who wrote to say that our plea for help brought back memories of when she worked on the "Potbanks." She was 85 years old but she still remembered being a lithographer "doing the **Balmoral** chintz and sizing and cutting out of the intricate pattern for the pieces of earthenware, especially the toastracks which were the bane of my life." She said that she could remember taking four sheets of pattern with the white border (like wallpaper edges) and sticking them together in order to be able to get more pieces out of each sheet. "You had to be careful and cut around the flower."

Grimwades were considered the pre-eminent producers of chintzware and when you look at the products from the various factories you will begin to understand why. Elijah Cotton usually did not attempt to cover the handles and spouts with the chintz and were therefore able to sell their product at a lower price. Interestingly, a few Lord Nelson stacking teapots have turned up with spout and handles covered in chintz so perhaps an ex-Grimwades employee went to the Cotton factory and did the same work for them.

It was — and is — "hard work for small wages." When you read these letters and talk to these elderly ladies, you get a vivid picture of how young these workers were and how difficult the work was. When you are enjoying your special **Welbeck** coffee pot, think of the fourteen year old who decorated it, and if it isn't perfectly done think of her sitting on her three-legged stool weeping as she tries to achieve perfection with materials that were far from perfect. They did it so well that thousands around the world still seek out and enjoy the "cheap and cheerful" product of their labors.

ADVICE FOR COLLECTORS

One of the questions Americans in particular often ask is "What about buying chintz as an investment?" Please don't. Buy chintz because you love the look. Buy it because you are trying to put together a shelf of interesting patterns in your kitchen. Buy it because you have always wanted to collect something and chintz really appeals to you. But don't buy it as an investment. Art and antiques and collectibles can go up or down in price according to the vagaries of fashion and the whim of the collecting public. You would be much wiser to put your retirement money into blue chip stocks and your fun money into chintz.

I have heard all kinds of fresh stories of triumphs and disasters in the buying of chintz especially on the Internet. I have left in most of my earlier advice since it is still valid but I have added a section at the end dealing very specifically with the Internet and the eBay auction site for those of you who are using this method of finding chintz.

Again this year, the biggest single complaint I have heard is the number of pieces sold as perfect which are restored. A major Florida collector told me that almost half her collection was starting to show discoloration where restoration had been performed. In each case, she had been sold so-called perfect pieces. When a vase sells for $10 it is not worth spending $30 to restore but when it sells for $325 . . . as the price of chintz goes up and up, there are obviously going to be more restored pieces on the market. Look very closely at the spouts of teapots and coffee pots, since they are the most vulnerable to chips. Always check finials to make sure they haven't been reattached. Look at the undecorated parts of the piece and if it is crazed all over except for one smooth corner, this may be an indication of a restoration. Try to look at a piece in bright sunlight, since many repairs become visible in this light. Go to a science store and buy a magnifying glass and don't be embarrassed to use it. As long as the piece is marked restored and the price has been adjusted accordingly, if you want the piece buy it by all means — especially if it is for display and you don't have that particular shape or pattern. Do be careful in washing a restored piece. Several collectors discovered a restoration through over-zealous cleaning.

The depth of colour in various patterns and even the shading can greatly affect the price. There are several Winton patterns, in particular **Sweet Pea** and **Julia**, and James Kent **Florita** where pieces can vary tremendously in the depth of colour. Ask how strong the colours are to make sure you will not be disappointed, if and when a faded vase arrives.

Both **Summertime** and **Old Cottage Chintz** were made from the early 1930s until well into the 1960s. The lithographs changed over the intervening thirty years. The pinks and reds in **Summertime** and the pinks and blues in **OCC** are quite different, and if you are trying to make up sets it is important to find out which decade you are talking about.

If you are buying **Summertime**, **Somerset**, **Cranstone** or one of the other patterns which was produced with more than just the usual gold trim, be sure to ask what colour the trim is. Sheryl Vogt helped a friend buy some **Summertime** and they were both very surprised when it arrived with green trim. If you are matching teasets or dinner plates, this can be quite important.

If the pattern colour matches don't worry about each backstamp on a breakfast set or even cup and saucer being identical. The factories would never throw anything out so odd backstamps turn up all the time. Australian Sheryl Vogt told me about a woman who was looking for parts to complete a chintz breakfast set. She and her mother had bought the original parts in an Australian department store on a seconds table. Who knows how long the chintz had been in the store?

Royal Winton cheese dishes and cheese keeps still cause difficulty. Both the 1930s Australian and the 1950s Canadian trade catalogues list the rectangular covered dish as an Ascot cheese dish and the square covered dish as an Ascot butter dish. Americans think of both these dishes as butter dishes and when they imagine cheese dishes they are thinking of the large slope-sided cheese keeps like the Rex and the Dane (refer to the shape section).

One of the most common complaints is still the size of the teapot or coffee pot — what was expected and what arrived. There are many ways of measuring size. Sometimes when you read an advertisement, such as Ebeling & Reuss for James Kent, and see that a teapot 30 is more expensive than a teapot 36 you may be confused. According to Dora Shaw, the number refers to the number of pots loaded into each pannier. The panniers were loaded on to horses that carried the ware down to the barges for shipping out. Obviously, the larger the number the smaller the piece. It is only in the past few years that this system has been abandoned for decimalization. When you are offered a two-cup, or four-cup, or six-cup teapot or coffee pot, be sure that you are clear what that means. Usually a two-cup teapot means two six-ounce cups of tea and four-cup means four six-ounce cups; if you are expecting a normal eight-ounce cup measurement you will be disappointed.

Another common complaint is trays which are meant to house various bits and come either incomplete or incorrect. If you are offered a divided tray, make sure it is a divided tray and not simply a tray with indentations for eggcups and salt and pepper which are not in evidence. A long-time collector was offered a complete breakfast set, but after some discussion discovered that although there was a teapot, toast rack, and cup, there was a salt and pepper in the place of the cream and sugar! A 1938 advertisement in a Toronto newspaper offered a breakfast set for sale with a teapot, cream and sugar, toast rack and **jam pot** although the illustration clearly shows the standard cup. A report in 1946 of a display at a Toronto store recommended the breakfast tray with toast rack, teapot, cup, **marmalade jar** and petit cream jug. It is not surprising that we also get confused. Mistakes are easily made. It is wise to ask very detailed questions if you are buying from another country and you want to be sure of what you are getting.

If you are offered a cruet set, make sure that the mustard has a lid if it ought to have one and that you are sent one pepper and one salt not two of either one.

Sometimes when you are at a show and in a hurry, you will buy what you think is a great bargain and discover that you got what you paid for. Some patterns are very similar and sadly sometimes tops and bottoms do not really go together once you get them into the light of day. The most common mismatch is the various cruet sets. One woman had a **Sunshine** salt and pepper and the rest of her set was **Summertime**. In fifty years she had never noticed that they were two different patterns.

Always ask for the measurements of whatever piece you are buying. If you ever see a plate listed as four-inch nominal, you are talking about a six-inch actual size plate. None of our experts in the potteries were able to give us an answer as to why plates and dishes are listed in trade catalogues in nominal sizes when the actual size is two inches bigger. Royal Winton plates were made in sizes from four-inch actual to ten-inch. It seems to be much easier to find nine-inch plates than ten-inch plates so the ten-inch usually sells for a premium. Plates also seem to vary in size because of shrinkage and the age of the moulds. I have measured a number of 9-inch plates and found that they are rarely exactly nine inches.

Trays came in all shapes and sizes. Cake plates came with and without cutout handles since the cutout handles cracked more often, the price is usually a little higher. Jugs came in sizes ranging from three to nine inches and every conceivable shape, so make sure of the dimensions and the shape. The prices in this guide are for the more common

shapes such as the Royal Winton Globe or Countess. You would expect to pay more for a rarer shape like Duval or Athena.

There a great variety of different cream and sugar shapes in Royal Winton especially but in all the other makers as well. The Winton Ascot, the Globe and the Countess cream and sugar came with two versions of the sugar bowl, so if it matters to you, be sure that you are getting the shape you want. The Ascot, the Albans and the Raleigh cups and saucers came in a larger size as well so if you are trying to match other pieces be sure to ask for the measurements.

Midwinter, James Kent and Howard Potteries Royal Winton coffee pots, teapots, cream and sugars and cups and saucers sometimes come with a plain white foot. Some people do not like the look of the white rim; remember to ask.

The most fragile colour in chintz is the blue, and various reactions can cause them to fade quite badly. Relish dishes that have been used for something acidic such as pickles may be very faded where the juices bleached out the colours. When you are buying a bowl look carefully at the edges and the bottom. Sometimes you won't notice with a pattern like **Welbeck** until you look closely and then you will realize that the blue is gone from the bottom of the bowl.

If you buy a teapot and it has a fine white dust inside when you rub your finger over it, it may have been bleached. Whenever something is put in bleach (which I do **not** recommend), it must be neutralized in water for an equal length of time or the chemical reaction will continue indefinitely and could destroy the piece.

People often ask which cup should be on the breakfast sets because they are concerned about having the right one. Ivy Mayer, the secretary of Royal Wintons export director, told us that the breakfast sets were always sold with the buyer's "cup of choice", so any cup could be considered correct since who knows what a Philadelphia importer chose forty years ago. The exception to this is the breakfast sets in **Lily, Rosebud** and **Petunia**, where normally you would expect everything on the tray to match.

Sauce boats and jam pots normally come with an under plate, and you should expect to pay less if it is missing. Some of the Royal Winton and the Midwinter jam pots came with chrome lids, some with ceramic. The ceramic lid is inset and the chrome fits over the pot with a protruding rim. Look carefully to make sure that you have the right lid. The price I quote in the guide is for a tall Rheims jam pot with a metal lid. Many collectors prefer the all-ceramic jam pots, so the price is higher

If you are buying a bowl or compote ask if the pattern is on both the inside and the outside of the piece. The tray under the salt and pepper sometimes has pattern on the outside of the tray, sometimes just on the top. Some salt and pepper collectors care. Some baskets and bowls have a thin strip of pattern on the inside and others don't. Ivy Mayer showed us a Canoe dish with the pattern only on the inside and gilding on the outside and told us it was an experiment to reduce costs after the war. There is always a premium for pieces completely covered with the pattern.

Many of the 1930s chintzes were used for what Americans call Wedgwood plates. The pattern covers the centre of the plate and the rim is white and embossed.

The plates came in several sizes — round and square plates in nine and 12 inches. The 1950s versions had no embossing and were available with solid colour bands in maroon, green or yellow in eight and ten inch square plates. Although some collectors don't like these plates, they seem to be growing in popularity.

The 1950s Royal Winton cups with the pattern on the inside of the cup and the center of the saucer are rare in England, Australia and New Zealand. They were advertised in the 1953 Canadian catalogue and turn up in North America quite often. Make sure that the pattern inside the cup matches the pattern in the center of the saucer — this hint comes from a personal experience of Linda's.

Sometimes new collectors become very concerned about the crazing on many of the pieces, especially Royal Winton. This is not fine bone china but earthenware, and often the glaze will become crazed over a number of years If you are a new collector pick up a piece of chintz and give it what people call the ping test. If there is a hairline and not just crazing, there will be a dull thud, rather than a ping. Unless a hairline crack has appeared, slight crazing should not greatly effect the value. As chintz is shipped around the world from climate to climate one wonders if this will effect the crazing. An Australian collector recommends that you keep a dish of water in the china cabinet to prevent further crazing. Even if you are paying more for your chintz these days than for Royal Worcester, do not forget that it was cheap and cheerful when it started life. The ill-fitting lid is not necessarily the wrong lid — it may never have fit properly.

Sometimes the lithographs are very badly applied, especially with some of the James Kent and Lord Nelson Ware. The joins are supposed to be invisible and some of the Royal Winton pieces are remarkably well done. If this is important to you, look carefully, especially around awkward corners. Some people like the homemade quality of the badly done pieces. My Lord Nelson **Rosetime** bud vase looks as though a young girl, thinking about her date on a Friday night, just threw the litho onto the vase — nothing matches, but it has its own peculiar charm.

The advent of eBay and other Internet auction sites has allowed the collector and the very occasional dealer to deal directly. Although this results in the appearance of wonderful pieces that would not otherwise be available, it does mean that you must ask detailed questions before bidding. I have heard that pieces arrived with chips, cracks and faded blues and the seller really hadn't noticed. Most people don't know how to go over china carefully noting faults; in fairness, it is very easy to miss with chintz.

I have seen all kinds of new chintz for sale on the Internet via individual sites and via eBay. Be aware of the backstamps for the new chintz and be careful of the pieces produced for the giftware line before Royal Winton added 1995 as part of the backstamp. If the circular Royal Winton backstamp has a black circle around it, it is new. Some of the earliest Winton reproduction do not have the black circle (see section or new chintz.) Although long time collectors are not easily deceived with the new chintz, new collectors are not as knowledgeable and should read the section on new chintz carefully and pay attention to the backstamps.

Although some collectors like Royal Winton bone china, they usually prefer the semi porcelain and would not pay as much for the bone as for the earthenware. Royal Winton seems to have produced mainly cups and saucers in bone china although I have seen cream and sugar sets. Several experienced collectors told me they had bought Royal Winton cups and saucers on the Internet and discovered they were bone china when they arrived. Most pieces are marked bone china but not all. If the dealer can't tell you, ask about their return policy.

Descriptions on the eBay auction site can be very misleading. Be very careful to read between the lines and to ask questions before you bid. Collectors love bud vases. I saw a **Julia** pepper pot with a silver plate rim missing its top described as a possible bud vase on eBay recently. Needless to say, it sold for much more than it would have if described as an incomplete pepper pot.

Even though you may be looking at a picture on your computer screen, ask questions about dimensions or you may be disappointed. One collector bought a cup and saucer thinking it was teacup size; it was a demi-tasse. There were no measurements given and there was no way of telling from the image.

Even when the size is given, be sure you understand what it means. Jugs are a real problem for collectors. What is the difference between a creamer and a jug? Royal Winton countess shape jugs sold in three sizes, for example, 4 inches, 4½ inches, and 5 inches. The countess creamer is 3½ inches in height and the breakfast set Countess creamer is obviously smaller still. I recently saw a Julia countess creamer described as a jug (the measurements were given accurately but no reference was made to its being a cream jug). The next week there was a Julia Ascot cream and sugar on a tray and the three pieces sold for less money that the cream jug the week before.

I have included photographs of both tea stands or trivets and the bottom of a muffin dish or butter dish in the shape section so that you will be able to tell the difference. Some Royal Winton muffin dishes came with silver plate tops and I have seen several of these described and sold as trivets. If you look at the trivet you will see that it is raised about ¼ inch; the muffin base is flat.

Now that dealers have access to a world market, prices tend to be in American dollars and local collectors have a difficult time competing for pieces. One collector thought she had bought a piece of chintz for an agreed price. Before she could pick it up, the dealer had sold it to an American dealer who had called in the interim. I am not sure what the moral of this story is except to say that if you are offered something wonderful and you want it, do not hesitate and pick it up as quickly as you can.

Canadians are buying from New Zealanders, Australians are selling to Americans, South Africans are shipping to England and every country has a different set of postage and customs requirements. If you are buying something from another country, be clear on what the charges will be. One English collector I know bought something on eBay from America. By the time he had paid duty, insurance and shipping, his total was almost double.

If you are shipping something expensive to someone you have never dealt with before, you may want to take a picture of the piece or attach a difficult-to-remove tag. One English dealer shipped a teapot to an American and was told that the pot came missing its lid. She knew that she had shipped the lid but felt obligated to refund the money and take back the lidless teapot. Another dealer shipped a perfect platter. He was told that when it arrived, it had a large scratch down the centre. He took the platter back and refunded the money. He is confident that the platter he shipped is not the platter that came back. He now takes photos of the pieces he ships. These are very rare occurrences but if you have any doubts, you may want to take precautions.

What about the dealer who ships you something you are not happy with and refuses to refund your money? When you are bidding, check very carefully to see what the seller says about the return policy, and what happens in the event of loss or breakage. If this is not stated, ask, and then keep the e-mail reply in the event of a problem.

No matter how much chintz you have looked at, it is still easy to make mistakes. If you look at the Albans Julia coffee pot on page 198 of the second edition of this book you will realize that the lid is not right — it is the lid for a Chelsea jam pot. I must have looked at that picture a hundred times without noticing that glaring error.

HOW TO USE THIS PRICE GUIDE

PRICES

There were incredible changes in the chintz world between the publication of the first and second editions of the chintz guide. In the two years since, the changes have been even more dramatic. The advent of new chintz has certainly had an impact on prices especially of the reproduced patterns. I have tried to track the changes in prices but, as all of you know, this is a very difficult task. Prices differ not only from country to country but from one part of the country to another and even from one dealer to the next. Some patterns have gone up in England and down in the United States. Some shapes are more collectible in one country than another. Cream and sugars don't sell particularly well in North America, for example, but they are popular in England and even more so in Australia and New Zealand. The price I have quoted in the Winton section is for Ascot cream and sugar sets. Other shapes are more popular and will usually cost more.

I now get e-mails as well as letters and phone calls to ask about different sizes and shapes. As you know, the chintz producing companies covered an incredible variety of shapes and sizes with chintz. I have given the price for three sizes of Royal Winton Globe shaped jugs but there are jugs in Countess, Athena, Duval, Fife, Albans, Wycombe, Ventnor, Raleigh, Dutch, Cambridge, Rosebud, Lily and on and on. Some of these jugs like Duval are harder to find and therefore cost more. The prices I have included in the Lord Nelson section for stacking teapots are for the usual ones with the white spouts and handles. If you are lucky enough to find one which is completely covered, you can expect to pay $150-200 more.

I haven't changed the shape lists because I can only give a selection of the pieces that are most commonly found by the collector. I still get questions about the prices of items like Royal Winton lamps, baskets, wall pockets, spoons, salad sets, and music boxes. I have included even more pictures of some of these rare items in the shape section but I still haven't attempted to put prices on pieces that only turn up once in a long time. It truly is a question of what one person is asking and another person is willing to pay and there is no consistency in price to make a price list of any value.

The majority of collectors are still American, and prices still tend to be higher there than in the rest of the world. The spread of Internet use and the phenomenal growth of eBay and other Internet auction sites resulted in almost a world price in American dollars. Many dealers sell via the Internet directly into the American market and this has made chintz very difficult to find for the collector — especially in Canada but also in Australia and New Zealand. English prices in some cases now exceed American prices, particularly for Royal Winton chintzes. Canadian prices have gone up since the second edition since most Canadian dealers are selling to American collectors.

Christies South Kensington was the first major auction house to recognize the interest in chintz since 1997 their August sale has contained a chintz only section. At the chintz convention in Orlando in 1997 and then at the chintz convention in Pasadena a year later, the collector chintz auctions achieved some very high prices. On May 2, 1998 Copake Auctions of Copake, New York sold over 350 lots of chintz — the collection of Canadian collector and dealer Ann Sachar. The May 1, 1999 Copake auction had over 1000 pieces of chintz in their annual all-chintz auction. In this new technological world, bidders competed not only from the floor but via phone, fax and E-mail. Auctions can confuse the collector since prices achieved at a particular auction for a particular piece may never be achieved again. The Kew stacking teapot at the first Copake Auction was estimated at $750-1000 — two determined bidders finally stopped at $3400. If I used this price in the guide none of you would believe me. On eBay one week a Julia plate will sell for over $300; two weeks later it may not reach reserve.

Elijah Cotton, James Kent and Crown Ducal, as well as some of the lesser-known manufacturers have continued to be priced lower than Royal Winton. The gap has narrowed however as more and more new collectors have come into the market and just want a piece of chintz, whoever made it. Other collectors want only Royal Winton and only certain shapes and patterns. Bud vases continue to be popular in the US but egg cups and toast racks seem to be sought worldwide. English collectors want sets of bowls or plates and are less willing to pay much for single items. American collectors often want examples of different patterns and love single plates they can hang on their walls.

I still haven't included bone china other than Shelley — except to identify which Royal Winton patterns have been found in bone china. When you think of the semi porcelain selling for so much less than bone china originally, it is ironic that today bone china chintz sells for less than its earthenware equivalent.

As any of you who have used a price guide know, they are always subject to fierce debate. I can only repeat, as Linda and I did in the first and second edition, that in the case of something like chintzware, where the collecting field is very new and prices have risen both quickly and dramatically, the debate is very heated indeed. A price guide is exactly that: a guide to recent prices paid for the pieces described. Chintz collecting is still a new enough field that many dealers and collectors are unsure what to charge and what to pay. Some dealers have no idea what chintz is but they have heard that it is collectible so you find an unpopular pattern in an undesirable shape for big dollars. Another dealer may have two pieces of chintz, a Julia bud vase and a Marguerite cup and saucer and they will be the same price. What I have tried to do as accurately as possible is to show the relative differences between the patterns, which sell for the least, which for the most, and which shapes have gone up, which down.

Charltons once again asked long time dealers and collectors around the world to go through the second edition and mark the changes in the prices they had observed. A number of them spent many hours going through the book and their advice has been invaluable in putting together this third edition. Chintz articles have appeared in major decorating magazines around the world. People still manage to pick up bits of chintz for next to nothing at garage sales and even antique shows. One man called to say he had found a bowl and two candle sticks in Crown Ducal **Blue Chintz** for $150 and he wondered whether to buy them for his mother. I urged him to run, not walk, back to the shop and I assured him his mother would be ecstatic. A new collector picked up a **Nantwich** cloverleaf cruet at a garage sale for $2.50 a few months ago and e-mailed to ask if I considered this a bargain. Char Jorgenson reported from England earlier this year that her friend Leanne bought 6 **Julia** demi-tasses at an antique show in England for the equivalent of $132US and then bought an Albans-shaped **Royalty** teapot from the same dealer for about $66US! A week later I had a call from a woman in Georgia. She wanted to add to the set of chintz dishes she had bought for $125 at a garage sale a year earlier. When I asked what she had bought, it turned out to be **fourteen 5-piece place settings of Royal Winton Evesham with platters and vegetable dishes.** I explained it would cost more than she had paid for everything to buy another dinner plate and that she might want to sell a couple of place settings to buy additional serving pieces. Somewhere between the prices paid at a garage sale in Georgia and an up-market antique show in Southern California, I have tried to find a guide for the price of chintz.

Do remember that if you have a set of chintz and you want to sell it, the price you get will very much depend on the venue. The prices in this guide are average prices paid by a collector not by a dealer. If you want to advertise and find the ultimate collector you may be able to get the same price but it will take time and effort. If you are selling to a dealer, you may only get 40-50% of the book price since that dealer has overheads, carrying costs, and so on, but you will sell quickly. If you want to sell on the Internet you will reach the collector and you may get more money. You will have to arrange for a digital image, handle the sale whether on eBay or another auction site, and package and ship the items you have sold. There are advantages and disadvantages to everything and you have to decide how much monetary value your time has.

In the final analysis Oscar Wilde's trenchant comment about pricing is as true today as it was last year: A cynic is a man who knows the price of everything and the value of nothing.

In this book I share with you what I know about chintz, and about the prices of chintz. I also try to talk about the value of chintz as a pleasing collectible, as a part of our shared history and as a product of the ingenuity of the men and women who worked in the potteries in hard times.

NUMBERING SYSTEM

The system we have in place enables every piece of chintz to have an exclusive letter and number.

PATTERN NAME CODES

The letter codes represent the pattern; for example GT is **Green Tulip.** In the third edition I have added two Royal Winton patterns **Exotic Bird** and **Blue Tulip.** To avoid confusion, I used the same names as Muriel Miller (with her permission of course). I added one 1920s pattern (found unmarked or with a Shelley and or Grimwades backstamp) and I have called it **Grapes and Roses** for obvious reasons. I also added **Rose Brocade** (I found the name in a Canadian advertisement) and **Primrose** — some collectors have called this pattern Cosmos but the description of **Primrose** in the *Pottery Gazette* seems to fit this pattern exactly. As I explained in the first and second edition, A.G. Richardson presented special problems, since there were well over a dozen patterns and we had names for only **Primula** and **Marigold** when we started working on this project. With Gerrard Shaw's guidance, I found copies of forty years of the *Pottery Glass & Brass Salesman* and discovered advertisements for a number of the Crown Ducal patterns, including pattern names. I was able to identify **Ascot, Blue Chintz, Festival, Florida** and **Ivory Chintz.** Gerrard was able to give me **Canton** and **Rose & Motifs** from his research in England. In order to make the collectors' life easier, Linda and I decided to create appropriate names for the other five patterns until we could find the actual factory names: **Grey Fruit, Ivory Fruit, Mauve Chintz, Pink Chintz,** and **Purple Chintz.** For the second edition, after letters, calls and photographs from collectors we added **Delhi, Pansy, Peony, Priscilla** to our Ducal pattern list. We created a separate page for **Blue Chintz without Bird** which we called **Spring Blossom** because several people pointed out that they are valued differently by collectors of the pattern. I haven't found names for the five unknown patterns yet but I continue to look.

I still don't have a name for Wade **Butterfly Chintz** or Myott **Spring Flower** so I have left them as is until factory names can be found. I was sent dozens of photographs of unknown chintz patterns and I chose a few which were representative of styles of chintz or interesting companies. I hope once again that collectors will continue to send me information so that I can gradually fill in the missing names.

PATTERN CODES

Barker Brothers Ltd.

Letter Code	Pattern Name
Bab1	Unnamed
Bab2	Unnamed
Bab3	Unnamed
Bab4	Unnamed
Bab5	Unnamed
Fa	Fantasy

Brexton

Letter Code	Pattern Name
Bx1	Unnamed
Bx2	Unnamed

Elijah Cotton Ltd. (Lord Nelson Ware)

Letter Code	Pattern Name
AC	Anemone Chintz
BB	Black Beauty
BR	Briar Rose
CL	Country Lane
FBC	*Flow Blue Chintz*
GT	Green Tulip
He	Heather
Mag	Marigold
Ma	Marina
P	Pansy
Ro	Rosetime
RB	Royal Brocade
Sk	Skylark

Empire Porcelain Co. Ltd.

Letter Code	Pattern Name
BM	Black Marguerite
GW	Golden Wattle
LT	Lilac Time
WL	Water Lily
WLT	White Lilac Time

Ford & Sons

Letter Code	Pattern Name
FS	Unnamed

Grimwades Ltd. (Royal Winton)

Letter Code	Pattern Name
A	Anemone
Ba	Balmoral
Be	Bedale
Bee	Beeston
BT	*Blue Tulip*
Car	Carnation
Chd	Cheadle
Chl	Chelsea
Chz	Chintz
Cl	Clevedon
Cly	Clyde
Co	Cotswold

Letter Code	Pattern Name
Cr	Cranstone
Cro	Crocus
Crom	Cromer
De	Delphinium Chintz
Do	Dorset
EB	*Exotic Bird*
El	Eleanor
ER	English Rose
Esl	Estelle
Est	Esther
Ev	Evesham
Fer	Fernese
FiB	Fireglow Black
FiW	Fireglow White
FF	Floral Feast
FG	Floral Garden
Fl	Florence
GR	*Grape and Roses*
H	Hazel
JL	Joyce-Lynn
J	Julia
JF	June Festival
JR	June Roses
Ke	Kew
Ki	Kinver
Maj	Majestic
Mag	Marguerite
Mar	Marion
May	Mayfair
Mer	Merton
MF	May Festival
MG	Morning Glory
N	Nantwich
Of	Offley
OC	Old Cottage Chintz
O	Orient
Pa	Paisley
Pe	Pekin
Pel	Pelham (Sampler)
Peo	Peony
PRI	Primrose
QA	Queen Anne
Q	Quilt
Ri	Richmond
RoB	Rose Brocade
RD	Rose Du Barry
Roy	Royalty
Ru	Rutland
Sh	Shrewsbury
So	Somerset
Sp	Spring
SG	Spring Glory
Spt	Springtime
St	Stratford
Su	Summertime
Sun	Sunshine
SN	Sweet Nancy
SP	Sweet Pea

Letter Code	Pattern Name
T	Tartans
Tr	Triumph
V	Victorian
VR	Victorian Rose
W	Welbeck
WF	Wild Flowers
Wi	Winifred

Johnson Brothers Ltd.

Letter Code	Pattern Name
RC	Rose Chintz

James Kent, Ltd.

Letter Code	Pattern Name
AB	Apple Blossom
CP	Crazy Paving
D	Du Barry
F	Florita
Ha	Harmony
Hy	(white background) Hydrangea
HyB	(black background) Hydrangea
L	Lichfield
Mg	Marigold
MF	Mille Fleurs
Pr	Primula
Ra	Rapture
Roc	Rochelle
Ro	Rosalynde
S	Silverdale
Tp	Tapestry

Midwinter

Letter Code	Pattern Name
Br	Brama
C	Coral
LD	Lorna Doone

Myott Son & Co.

Letter Code	Pattern Name
Ber	Bermuda
SF	*Spring Flower*
SuF	Summer Flower

A.G. Richardson Ltd. (Crown Ducal)

Letter Code	Pattern Name
As	Ascot
BC	Blue Chintz
Ca	Canton
Dh	Delhi
Fe	Festival
Fd	Florida
GF	*Grey Fruit*
IC	Ivory Chintz
IF	*Ivory Fruit*
MgR	Marigold

Letter Code	Pattern Name
MC	*Mauve Chintz*
PaR	Pansy
Py	Peony
PC	*Pink Chintz*
PrR	Primula
Ps	Priscilla
PuC	*Purple Chintz*
RM	Rose & Motifs
SB	*Spring Blossom*

Ridgway Potteries Ltd.

Letter Code	Pattern Name
RP	Unnamed

Royal Doulton Ltd.

Letter Code	Pattern Name
Per	Persian

Shelley Potteries Ltd.

Letter Code	Pattern Name
BlC	Black Chintz
BD	Blue Daisy
Clo	Cloisonne
Cs	Countryside
GD	Green Daisy
MS	Marguerite
Mat	Maytime
Me	Melody
PiSG	Pink Summer Glory
Pri	Primrose
RG	Rock Garden
SuG	Summer Glory
TR	Tapestry Rose

Wade & Company

Letter Code	Pattern Name
Bu	*Butterfly Chintz*
Pai	Paisley
Th	Thistle Chintz

Wedgwood & Co. Ltd.

Letter Code	Pattern Name
WC1	Unnamed
WC2	Unnamed

A. J. Wilkinson Ltd.

Letter Code	Pattern Name
Maf	Mayflower
MM	*Modern Mayflower*

Wood & Sons Ltd.

Letter Code	Pattern Name
WS	Unnamed

SHAPE NUMBERS

The number codes represent the shapes and are the same across all the factories for the same item; a round seven-inch plate, for example, is 104 whether it is Lord Nelson Ware or A.G. Richardson. We have left gaps in the numbering system to accommodate the variety of chintz pieces that will inevitably come to light.

Number	Shape
01	Ashtray, small
02	Ashtray, large
04	Bonbon dish
05	Bonbon dish, tab handles
09	Bowl, 5"
10	Bowl, 6"
14	Bowl, 8" soup
15	Bowl, 9"
17	Bowl, lily 12" (matte black interior)
22	Bowl, octagonal, 7"
24	Bowl, octagonal, 8"
23	Breakfast set
28	Butter dish
30	Butter pat
35	Cake plate, open handles
36	Cake plate, tab handles
37	Cake plate, 8" square pedestal
40	Cake stand, 2 tier
41	Cake stand, 3 tier
42	Cake plate, with server
43	Cake stand, chrome handle
44	Cake stand, chrome base
45	Canoe-shaped dish
50	Cheese keep
52	Coaster
53	Coffee pot, 3 cup
55	Coffee pot, 6 cup
60	Compote, footed
65	Condiment set on tray
70	Cream and sugar
71	Cream and sugar on tray
75	Demi-tasse
77	Egg cup, footed
80	Hot water jug
85	Jam pot with liner
90	Jug, 4" round
91	Jug, 4 1/2" round

Number	Shape
92	Jug, 5" round
95	Jug, 5" straight-sided
96	Jug, 7" straight-sided
97	Nut dish
102	Plate, 6 round
103	Plate, 6 1/2" round
104	Plate, 7" round
105	Plate, 8" round
106	Plate, 9" round
107	Plate, 10 round
201	Plate, 4" square
202	Plate, 5" square
203	Plate, 6" square
204	Plate, 7" square
205	Plate, 8" square
206	Plate, 9" square
207	Plate, 10" square
301	Plate, 4" triangular
402	Plate, octagonal, 5"
406	Plate, octagonal, 9"
407	Plate, octagonal, 10"
112	Relish dish, small
115	Salad bowl, chrome rim
117	Salt and pepper
118	Salt and pepper on tray
120	Sandwich tray, 10" x 6"
121	Sandwich tray, 12" x 7"
122	Sandwich tray, 13"x 6
125	Sauce boat and liner
130	Teacup and saucer
131	Teacup and saucer, oleander shape
132	Teacup and saucer, Ripon shape
135	Teapot, 2 cup
136	Teapot, 4 cup
137	Teapot, 6 cup
140	Teapot, stacking
145	Tennis set
150	Toast rack, 4 slice
151	Toast rack, 2 slice
155	Trivet
160	Vase, bud
163	Vase, spill, 8"
162	Vase, trumpet 6"
165	Vase, 9"
169	Sugar shaker
170	Biscuit barrel
180	Lamp base

DUBARRY

The homey rustle of Chintz, the warm welcoming design of a flowered pattern is the keynote of Homemakers the world over. From the Pottery of James Kent & Son, England, this pattern "DuBarry" has been translated into terms of a tableware decoration, and is proving to be a very popular pattern.

For prices see inside back cover.

VINTAGE CHINTZ

BARKER BROTHERS LTD.
BREXTON
ELIJAH COTTON LTD. (LORD NELSON)
EMPIRE PORCELAIN COMPANY LTD.
FORD & SONS
GRIMWADES LTD. (ROYAL WINTON)
JAMES KENT, LTD.
JOHNSON BROTHERS LTD.
W. R. MIDWINTER LTD.
MYOTT SON & COMPANY
A. J. RICHARDSON & CO. LTD. (CROWN DUCAL)
RIDGEWAY POTTERIES LTD.
ROYAL DOULTON LTD.
SHELLEY POTTERIES LTD.
WADE CERAMICS LTD.
WEDGWOOD & COMPANY LTD.
A. J. WILKINSON, LTD.
WOOD & SONS LTD.

BARKER BROTHERS LTD.

In the Meir Works at Longton, the Barker Brothers factory became noted for its ability to copy the best new ideas on the market quickly and efficiently. Although originally the company produced both china and earthenware, in 1925 they decided to concentrate on semi-porcelain, which is a high-quality earthenware. John Guildford created patterns for Barker Brothers that were remarkably like those of Clarice Cliff. Their hand-painted pieces looked very like those of Poole Pottery. Like Myott Son & Co. and Wade, they produced several chintz patterns in the 1920s and the 1930s, along with all the other product lines they created. The pattern Fantasy was introduced in the mid-1920s and created favourable comment in the Pottery Gazette. Interestingly, the later chintz patterns do not appear to have been given names.

They were still producing chintz patterns in the 1950s and they still advertised chintzware in Canadian publications as late as 1957. The trade name Tudor Ware or Royal Tudor Ware was incorporated into several versions of the Barker Brothers backstamp from about 1937. The quality is probably closer to Lord Nelson ware than to Grimwades. The most common Barker Brothers piece is the cake plate and matching server. In an 1954 Canadian newspaper a chintz plate and server were featured in an Eatons of Canada advertisement for $2.35.

The company was acquired by Alfred Clough in 1961 and in turn they were bought up by Coloroll Housewares Group in 1987.

FANTASY

The April 1931 Pottery Gazette reported that this firm "may be said to have been amongst the leaders as regards courageous colour treatments in tablewares, for they went much further than many of their contemporaries in the trade when, some years ago now, they instituted such patterns as their well-known **Fantasy** an all-over cretonne treatment with which pattern most dealers will be thoroughly familiar. "

Cat. No.	Shape	U.S. $	Can. $	U.K. £
BaB1-42	Cake plate, with server	150.00	180.00	90.00

Cat. No.	Shape	U.S. $	Can. $	U.K. £
BaB1-70	Cream and sugar	80.00	100.00	50.00

UNKNOWN 1

This is one of the more common Barker Brothers Royal Tudor Ware patterns. In May 1954 a cake plate and server were featured in the Montreal Gazette newspaper advertisement for $2.35.

Cat. No.	Shape	U.S. $	Can. $	U.K. £
BaB1-42	Cake plate, with server	175.00	210.00	120.00

Cat. No.	Shape	U.S. $	Can. $	U.K. £
BaB1-70	Cream and sugar	100.00	120.00	65.00

UNKNOWN 2

This is one of the earlier Barker Brothers Royal Tudor Ware patterns.

Cat. No.	Shape	U.S. $	Can. $	U.K. £
BaB2-42	Cake plate, with server	100.00	120.00	60.00

Cat. No.	Shape	U.S. $	Can. $	U.K. £
BaB2-70	Cream and sugar	60.00	75.00	40.00

UNKNOWN 3

This Barker Brothers pattern appears more often in England than North America.

Cat. No.	Shape	U.S. $	Can. $	U.K. £
BaB3-42	Cake plate, with server	165.00	200.00	110.00

Cat. No.	Shape	U.S. $	Can. $	U.K. £
BaB3-70	Cream and sugar	100.00	120.00	60.00

UNKNOWN 4

This is one of the more common Barker Brothers patterns in North America.

Cat. No.	Shape	U.S. $	Can. $	U.K. £
BaB4-42	Cake plate, with server	100.00	120.00	60.00

Cat. No.	Shape	U.S. $	Can. $	U.K. £
BaB4-70	Cream and sugar	60.00	75.00	40.00

UNKNOWN 5

This is one of the more common Barker Brothers patterns found in North America. It is probably the most popular of the Barker Brothers patterns.

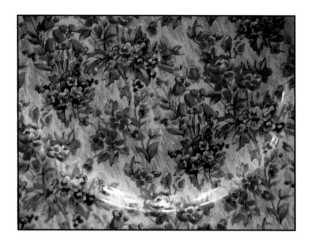

Cat. No.	Shape	U.S. $	Can. $	U.K. £
BaB5-42	Cake plate, with server	250.00	300.00	175.00

Cat. No.	Shape	U.S. $	Can. $	U.K. £
BaB5-70	Cream and sugar	125.00	150.00	85.00

GRIMWADES LTD. :: STOKE-ON-TRENT

(Incorporating Rubian Art Pottery & Atlas China)

Royal Winton
"Regina"

No. 1980.

A newly modelled series of Table articles in strong relief depicting the Regina Lily foliage and flowers. The ground is Old Ivory with veining pencilled in darker shade and flowers in a pleasing tone of Soft Pink.

All Hand-painted.

Also the same series :—

No. 2055. with flowers in a delicate Blue.

No. 2054. with flowers in Cardinal Red—a striking combination for those who prefer vivid colouring.

Prices for all colourings as under.

Item No.		Price
1.	Marmalade and Stand	21/- per doz.
2.	Eggset, 4 cups	21/- ,, ,,
3.	Mayonnaise and Stand	16/- ,, ,,
	,, Ladle	3/- ,, ,,
4.	Condiment Set (Salt & Pepper on Tray)	15/- ,, ,,
5.	Cruet, 3 pieces on Tray	21/- ,, ,,
6.	Toast-Rack, 3 bar	12/6 ,, ,,
	Also 5 bar	16/- ,, ,,
7.	Cheese	33/- ,, ,,
8.	Egg-Cruet Set, 5 pieces	21/- ,, ,,
9.	Triple Tray	36/- ,, ,,
10.	Sweet, 7"	12/- ,, ,,

Item No.		Price
11.	Teapot, 42 ozs. capacity	33/- per doz.
12.	Covered Butter	21/- ,, ,,
13.	Twin Tray	18/- ,, ,,
14.	Sugar, Bridge size, 4" diameter ... } 20/- per doz. pairs	
15.	Cream, ,, ,, 5 ozs. capacity	
16.	Cup and Saucer, Tea size	12/- per doz.
	Tea Plate, 6¼" diameter	6/6 ,, ,,
17.	Covered Jug, 20 ozs. capacity ...	24/- ,, ,,
18.	Square Salad Bowl, 7½" diameter ...	48/- ,, ,,
	Salad Servers	12/- per doz. pairs
19.	Jug, S/S, 20 ozs. capacity 15/- per doz. } or	
	M/S, 28 ,, ,, 18/- ,, } 4/6	
	L/S, 38 ,, ,, 21/- ,, } Set of 3 pcs.	

Can also supply :—

Sugar Sifter	15/- per doz.
Mint Boat and Stand	12/- ,, ,,
Shallow Fruit, 8" diameter	24/- ,, ,,
Round Salad Bowl, 9½" diameter ...	48/- ,, ,,
Dessert Plate 8½" diameter	14/- ,, ,,
Cake Comport, 8¾" diameter, 2¼" high ...	39/- ,, ,,

Cake Plate, Handled, 10¼" diameter	24/- per doz.
Watercress and Stand, 8" diameter	39/- ,, ,,
Small Cake Plate, 8" diameter	14/- ,, ,,
Deep Fruit, 8½" diameter	33/- ,, ,,
Flower Jug, 8½" high	30/- ,, ,,

-win & Co. (Hanley), Ltd., Printers.

BREXTON

I have been trying to find more information about Brexton for some years. I contacted Kathy Niblett, the Assistant Keeper of Ceramics at the Potteries Museum and Art Gallery in Stoke-on-Trent and she reminded me that Brexton is the name of a company, based in Birmingham, which makes picnic baskets both wicker and the suitcase type. The baskets normally contain dishes and cutlery and Kathy suggested that they may have ordered crockery both for the baskets and for general sale with their own trade mark. Since the identical lamp base has turned up with an impressed mark Brentleigh Ware Staffordshire England, it is likely that Brexton ordered these chintz pieces from Howard Pottery (trade name Brentleigh) and had them marked Brexton, Made in England.

UNKNOWN 1

Cat. No.	Shape	U.S. $	Can. $	U.K. £
Bx1-130	Teacup and saucer	75.00	90.00	50.00

Cat. No.	Shape	U.S. $	Can. $	U.K. £
Bx1-180	Lamp base	450.00	540.00	150.00

UNKNOWN 2

Brexton made a number of different lamp shapes using this chintz pattern but many collectors do not like the lime green trim which always appears to a greater or lesser extent. This pattern has recently turned up on interesting pieces a covered box and a jampot and liner with a scalloped white Wedgwood border and a Royal Norfolk backstamp (Norfolk Pottery Ltd. 1958-1970s). Since both Howard Pottery (Trademark Brentleigh ware) and Norfolk Pottery (Trademark Royal Norfolk) were members of the Howard Pottery Group, it is not surprising that they both used the same pattern.

Cat. No.	Shape	U.S. $	Can. $	U.K. £
Bx2-130	Teacup and saucer	75.00	90.00	50.00

Cat. No.	Shape	U.S. $	Can. $	U.K. £
Bx2-180	Lamp base	450.00	540.00	150.00

TRIPLE TRAY 9"x9" TEA CADDY. AIRTIGHT COVER 5"x4" BUTTER DISH 5" CONDIMENT SET 5½"

Springtime Chintz

CHINESE BOWL

2-TIER CAKE STAND

SALAD BOWL. CHROMIUM RIM

HONEY POT. CHROMIUM COVER

BISCUIT JAR
AIRTIGHT COVER

SUGAR DREDGER

ROUND SWEET TRAY 5"

OVAL SWEET TRAY 4½"x5½"

SQUARE SWEET TRAY 5"

OPEN PRESERVE DISH 5½"

ABRA TRAY 6½"x9½"

THESE PIECES CAN BE SUPPLIED IN OTHER ATTRACTIVE AND COLOURFUL DECORATIONS.

LONDON SHOWROOMS
Hales, Hancock & Godwin, Ltd., 31, Ely
Place, Holborn, E.C.1. Phone: Holborn 6106

AUSTRALIAN AGENT
Mr. R. M. Hall, 185/87, Queen Street,
Melbourne, C.I, Australia.

W·R·MIDWINTER·LTD
E A R T H E N W A R E   S P E C I A L I S T S

ALBION   AND   HADDERIDGE   POTTERIES   BURSLEM   STOKE-ON-TRENT

D

ELIJAH COTTON LTD.
(LORD NELSON)

The firm advertised themselves as being established since 1758, but it was not until 1889 that they were known as Nelson Pottery in Hanley. To date little has been written about Elijah Cotton. They were better than many of the lower echelon firms at self-promotion. They created a ceramic model of the Nelson Monument in Trafalgar Square probably copied from the Clarice Cliff Bizooka using sandwich trays, tea plates and eggcups from their product lines. As was widely reported in the press at the time, they made these models available to any retailer who bought the required amount of product.

When the Nelson and Wellington Potteries amalgamated in the 1920s, the firm expanded from being mainly a jug producer to making a full range of domestic earthenware. As early as 1924 the *Pottery Gazette* said of Elijah Cotton "they specialize in the production of a brand of pottery that is eminently suitable for ordinary everyday needs. It is a type of earthenware that will always be in strong demand because it is everywhere wanted and wanted all the time." In 1925 the *Gazette* reported that Cotton could legitimately claim to rank as "a house of jug specialists." Although they expanded beyond jugs, the *Gazette*, as late as 1933, reported that "it would almost seem as though Elijah Cotton produce jugs in sufficient numbers to keep the whole world supplied, so large and so varied is their output of such articles." Although the shape name is not impressed into the jugs, Elijah Cotton named each jug shape — Dart, Leda, Cecil, Holborn and Bute. Most chintz patterns appear on the tankard shape BUTE, introduced in 1925 and the wide-bellied shape BELL, introduced in 1933 and modeled in three sizes.

Elijah Cotton continued to enjoy good press throughout the 1920s. The September 1927 *Pottery Gazette* included a long description of new lines. "For a big variety of sound, practical semi-porcelain, calculated to appeal with strong force to any dealer whose activities are centred round the middle class trade, the dealer can turn with confidence to Elijah Cotton, Ltd., who appear to have made a scientific study of the pottery requirements of middle class folk…they are an intensely practical house; they do not waste their energies upon a multiplicity of lines of mere aesthetic interest. Their main concern is the production of lines that are likely to remain in strong demand amongst ordinary householders."

Elijah Cotton certainly never had a light hand when it came to either the product or the decoration. During the 1930s the designs were heavily applied to chunky-shaped earthenware by paintresses working by eye and not by printed or sketched outlines. This was a utilitarian pottery and little or no time was spent on the production of bric-a-brac. The *Pottery Gazette* reported in 1931 that they produced a range in domestic ware from plain white glaze upwards. They were big producers of kitchen and hospital plain white and their advertisements from the 1950s feature plain white jugs in a wide variety of shapes. Their chintzes were rarely applied to handles or spouts, since these required special skill. **As a result, stacking teapots which are completely covered with pattern tend to sell for $150-200 above the same patterns with plain white handle and spout.** Often the work is sloppy enough that it is unlikely that another factory would have allowed it to pass.

The *Pottery Gazette* reported that Nelson patterns #1580, 1581 and 1582 were introduced at the British Industries Fair in 1931 and #1801 and 1825 at the BIF in 1933. This would suggest that the earliest Nelson chintz patterns — **Marigold** (2122) **Pansy** (2207), and **Anemone** (2446) — were probably introduced in 1934 or 1935. The *Gazette* pointed to "some very gay lithographs in the sample range which appeared to fall in admirably with the modern vogue." Since Cotton were quick to study trends, they would surely have noted Royal Winton's success with chintz patterns and been interested in following suit. These first three patterns were not exclusive to Cotton so they were probably testing the market and watching the other factories before committing to the expense of a controlled pattern. Although **Marina** was reported a bestseller for Elijah Cotton in 1939, there is certainly never a mention of any member of the royal family taking home a teaset in Nelson chintz. Parsons Steiner were the exclusive distributors for Elijah Cotton in Canada and their advertisements in January 1955 offered a wide range of exclusive chintz designs "Old as the hills — as fresh as a daisy." Interestingly, it is Cotton who, in 1955, came out with **Kaleidoscope**, an all-over, multi-colour snow crystal design more in keeping with the 50s style.

The Old Chintz Company bought the Lord Nelson backstamp and will be reproducing patterns including Rosetime in 1999 or 2000.

ANEMONE

The pattern number is 2446. This chintz pattern was not a controlled pattern and was used by other companies such as Winterton Ltd. and John Shaw & Sons Burlington Ware — who called the pattern **Springtime**.

Backstamp not available
at
press time

Cat. No.	Shape	U.S. $	Can. $	U.K. £
AC-04	Bonbon dish	40.00	50.00	25.00
AC-28	Butter dish	125.00	150.00	75.00
AC-35	Cake plate, open handles	165.00	200.00	85.00
AC-36	Cake plate, tab handles	125.00	150.00	60.00
AC-41	Cake stand, 3 tier	135.00	165.00	95.00
AC-50	Cheese keep	200.00	240.00	115.00
AC-55	Coffee pot, 6 cup	750.00	865.00	255.00
AC-65	Condiment set on tray	200.00	240.00	125.00
AC-70	Cream and sugar	125.00	150.00	75.00
AC-71	Cream and sugar on tray	195.00	235.00	95.00
AC-85	Jam pot with liner	175.00	210.00	85.00
AC-92	Jug, 5" round	300.00	360.00	125.00
AC-96	Jug, 7" straight-sided	375.00	450.00	150.00

Cat. No.	Shape	U.S. $	Can. $	U.K. £
AC-301	Plate, 4" triangular	45.00	55.00	30.00
AC-104	Plate, 7"	65.00	80.00	40.00
AC-105	Plate, 8"	95.00	115.00	60.00
AC-112	Relish dish	150.00	180.00	95.00
AC-117	Salt and pepper	95.00	115.00	55.00
AC-118	Salt and pepper on tray	165.00	200.00	95.00
AC-122	Sandwich tray, 13" x 6"	110.00	135.00	65.00
AC-125	Sauce boat and liner	125.00	150.00	85.00
AC-130	Teacup and saucer	85.00	105.00	45.00
AC-137	Teapot, 6 cup	700.00	800.00	295.00
AC-140	Teapot, stacking	950.00	1,100.00	395.00
AC-145	Tennis set	95.00	115.00	65.00
AC-160	Vase, bud	135.00	165.00	75.00

BLACK BEAUTY

This is the only Nelson pattern with a black background and is considered the most desirable by many collectors. Advertised in the Canadian *Gift Buyer* in November 1955, it was still being "stocked by wholesalers across Canada."

Cat. No.	Shape	U.S. $	Can. $	U.K. £	Cat. No.	Shape	U.S. $	Can. $	U.K. £
BB-04	Bonbon dish	75.00	90.00	55.00	BB-301	Plate, 4" triangular	50.00	60.00	35.00
BB-28	Butter dish	225.00	270.00	135.00	BB-104	Plate, 7"	85.00	105.00	50.00
BB-35	Cake plate, open handles	200.00	240.00	125.00	BB-105	Plate, 8"	125.00	150.00	75.00
BB-36	Cake plate, tab handles	175.00	210.00	105.00	BB-112	Relish dish	250.00	300.00	160.00
BB-41	Cake stand, 3 tier	200.00	240.00	140.00	BB-117	Salt and pepper	125.00	150.00	85.00
BB-50	Cheese keep	250.00	300.00	210.00	BB-118	Salt and pepper on tray	195.00	235.00	135.00
BB-55	Coffee pot, 6 cup	900.00	1,035.00	475.00	BB-122	Sandwich tray, 13" x 6"	150.00	180.00	95.00
BB-65	Condiment set on tray	250.00	300.00	160.00	BB-125	Sauce boat and liner	165.00	200.00	125.00
BB-70	Cream and sugar	135.00	165.00	85.00	BB-130	Teacup and saucer	100.00	120.00	65.00
BB-71	Cream and sugar on tray	200.00	240.00	135.00	BB-137	Teapot, 6 cup	750.00	865.00	475.00
BB-85	Jam pot with liner	195.00	235.00	135.00	BB-140	Teapot, stacking	900.00	1,035.00	595.00
BB-92	Jug, 5" round	400.00	480.00	160.00	BB-145	Tennis set	135.00	165.00	85.00
BB-96	Jug, 7" straight-sided	550.00	635.00	195.00	BB-160	Vase, bud	150.00	180.00	110.00

BRIAR ROSE

This pattern has not proven particularly popular with American collectors.

Cat. No.	Shape	U.S. $	Can. $	U.K. £
BR-04	Bonbon dish	45.00	55.00	30.00
BR-28	Butter dish	140.00	170.00	95.00
BR-35	Cake plate, open handles	135.00	165.00	85.00
BR-36	Cake plate, tab handles	125.00	150.00	75.00
BR-41	Cake stand, 3 tier	125.00	150.00	100.00
BR-50	Cheese keep	175.00	210.00	125.00
BR-55	Coffee pot, 6 cup	525.00	600.00	300.00
BR-65	Condiment set on tray	165.00	200.00	120.00
BR-70	Cream and sugar	100.00	120.00	80.00
BR-71	Cream and sugar on tray	150.00	180.00	95.00
BR-85	Jam pot with liner	125.00	150.00	95.00
BR-92	Jug, 5" round	225.00	270.00	115.00
BR-96	Jug, 7" straight-sided	300.00	360.00	140.00

Cat. No.	Shape	U.S. $	Can. $	U.K. £
BR-301	Plate, 4" triangular	40.00	50.00	35.00
BR-104	Plate, 7"	60.00	75.00	45.00
BR-105	Plate, 8"	85.00	105.00	60.00
BR-112	Relish dish	150.00	180.00	135.00
BR-117	Salt and pepper	75.00	90.00	45.00
BR-118	Salt and pepper on tray	150.00	180.00	105.00
BR-122	Sandwich tray, 13" x 6"	100.00	120.00	65.00
BR-125	Sauce boat and liner	125.00	150.00	90.00
BR-130	Teacup and saucer	85.00	105.00	55.00
BR-137	Teapot, 6 cup	475.00	570.00	375.00
BR-140	Teapot, stacking	650.00	750.00	395.00
BR-145	Tennis set	100.00	120.00	65.00
BR-160	Vase, bud	115.00	140.00	85.00

COUNTRY LANE

This pattern is more common in Australia and New Zealand than it is in North America.

Cat. No.	Shape	U.S. $	Can. $	U.K. £
CL-04	Bonbon dish	35.00	45.00	25.00
CL-28	Butter dish	105.00	125.00	75.00
CL-35	Cake plate, open handles	90.00	110.00	65.00
CL-36	Cake plate, tab handles	90.00	110.00	65.00
CL-41	Cake stand, 3 tier	115.00	140.00	75.00
CL-50	Cheese keep	150.00	180.00	100.00
CL-55	Coffee pot, 6 cup	400.00	480.00	250.00
CL-65	Condiment set on tray	115.00	140.00	85.00
CL-70	Cream and sugar	65.00	80.00	45.00
CL-71	Cream and sugar on tray	105.00	130.00	75.00
CL-85	Jam pot with liner	75.00	90.00	50.00
CL-92	Jug, 5" round	150.00	180.00	90.00
CL-96	Jug, 7" straight-sided	180.00	215.00	100.00

Cat. No.	Shape	U.S. $	Can. $	U.K. £
CL-301	Plate, 4" triangular	25.00	30.00	20.00
CL-104	Plate, 7"	35.00	45.00	25.00
CL-105	Plate, 8"	45.00	55.00	40.00
CL-112	Relish dish	125.00	150.00	75.00
CL-117	Salt and pepper	65.00	80.00	40.00
CL-118	Salt and pepper on tray	115.00	140.00	75.00
CL-122	Sandwich tray, 13" x 6"	65.00	80.00	45.00
CL-125	Sauce boat and liner	90.00	110.00	75.00
CL-130	Teacup and saucer	45.00	55.00	30.00
CL-137	Teapot, 6 cup	375.00	450.00	250.00
CL-140	Teapot, stacking	475.00	570.00	325.00
CL-145	Tennis set	65.00	80.00	50.00
CL-160	Vase, bud	95.00	115.00	70.00

FLOW BLUE CHINTZ

This pattern turns up in North America, particularly Canada. The pattern number 2524 suggests this pattern was introduced in 1935 or 1936.

Cat. No.	Shape	U.S. $	Can. $	U.K. £
FBC-04	Bonbon dish	35.00	45.00	25.00
FBC-28	Butter dish	105.00	125.00	75.00
FBC-35	Cake plate, open handles	90.00	110.00	65.00
FBC-36	Cake plate, tab handles	90.00	110.00	65.00
FBC-41	Cake stand, 3 tier	115.00	140.00	75.00
FBC-50	Cheese keep	150.00	180.00	100.00
FBC-55	Coffee pot, 6 cup	400.00	480.00	250.00
FBC-65	Condiment set on tray	115.00	140.00	85.00
FBC-70	Cream and sugar	65.00	80.00	45.00
FBC-71	Cream and sugar on tray	105.00	125.00	75.00
FBC-85	Jam pot with liner	75.00	90.00	50.00
FBC-92	Jug, 5" round	150.00	180.00	90.00
FBC-96	Jug, 7" straight-sided	180.00	215.00	100.00

Cat. No.	Shape	U.S. $	Can. $	U.K. £
FBC-301	Plate, 4" triangular	25.00	30.00	20.00
FBC-104	Plate, 7"	35.00	45.00	25.00
FBC-105	Plate, 8"	45.00	55.00	40.00
FBC-112	Relish dish	125.00	150.00	75.00
FBC-117	Salt and pepper	65.00	80.00	40.00
FBC-118	Salt and pepper on tray	115.00	140.00	75.00
FBC-122	Sandwich tray, 13" x 6"	65.00	80.00	45.00
FBC-125	Sauce boat and liner	90.00	110.00	75.00
FBC-130	Teacup and saucer	45.00	55.00	30.00
FBC-137	Teapot, 6 cup	375.00	450.00	250.00
FBC-140	Teapot, stacking	475.00	570.00	275.00
FBC-145	Tennis set	65.00	80.00	50.00
FBC-160	Vase, bud	80.00	100.00	40.00

GREEN TULIP

This pattern is rare in North America but found more often in New Zealand and Australia. It has recently become as popular as **Black Beauty** in North America.

Cat. No.	Shape	U.S. $	Can. $	U.K. £
GT-04	Bonbon dish	75.00	90.00	45.00
GT-28	Butter dish	225.00	270.00	135.00
GT-35	Cake plate, open handles	200.00	140.00	125.00
GT-36	Cake plate, tab handles	175.00	210.00	100.00
GT-41	Cake stand, 3 tier	225.00	270.00	135.00
GT-50	Cheese keep	325.00	390.00	200.00
GT-55	Coffee pot, 6 cup	900.00	1,035.00	450.00
GT-65	Condiment set on tray	250.00	300.00	150.00
GT-70	Cream and sugar	150.00	180.00	85.00
GT-71	Cream and sugar on tray	250.00	300.00	125.00
GT-85	Jam pot with liner	200.00	240.00	100.00
GT-92	Jug, 5" round	475.00	570.00	150.00
GT-96	Jug, 7" straight-sided	575.00	665.00	165.00

Cat. No.	Shape	U.S. $	Can. $	U.K. £
GT-301	Plate, 4" triangular	50.00	60.00	35.00
GT-104	Plate, 7"	85.00	105.00	55.00
GT-105	Plate, 8"	125.00	150.00	75.00
GT-112	Relish dish	275.00	330.00	165.00
GT-117	Salt and pepper	100.00	120.00	65.00
GT-118	Salt and pepper on tray	200.00	240.00	125.00
GT-122	Sandwich tray, 13" x 6"	175.00	210.00	85.00
GT-125	Sauce boat and liner	175.00	210.00	100.00
GT-130	Teacup and saucer	120.00	145.00	65.00
GT-137	Teapot, 6 cup	825.00	950.00	450.00
GT-140	Teapot, stacking	1000.00	1,150.00	450.00
GT-145	Tennis set	135.00	165.00	85.00
GT-160	Vase, bud	175.00	210.00	75.00

HEATHER

The pattern number is 2750.

Cat. No.	Shape	U.S. $	Can. $	U.K. £
He-04	Bonbon dish	45.00	55.00	35.00
He-28	Butter dish	150.00	180.00	95.00
He-35	Cake plate, open handles	160.00	195.00	80.00
He-36	Cake plate, tab handles	125.00	150.00	75.00
He-41	Cake stand, 3 tier	150.00	180.00	90.00
He-50	Cheese keep	200.00	240.00	125.00
He-55	Coffee pot, 6 cup	650.00	750.00	300.00
He-65	Condiment set on tray	165.00	200.00	110.00
He-70	Cream and sugar	100.00	120.00	75.00
He-71	Cream and sugar on tray	150.00	180.00	95.00
He-85	Jam pot with liner	175.00	210.00	75.00
He-92	Jug, 5" round	275.00	330.00	125.00
He-96	Jug, 7" straight-sided	325.00	390.00	140.00

Cat. No.	Shape	U.S. $	Can. $	U.K. £
He-301	Plate, 4" triangular	40.00	50.00	25.00
He-104	Plate, 7"	65.00	80.00	40.00
He-105	Plate, 8"	85.00	105.00	55.00
He-112	Relish dish	200.00	240.00	115.00
He-117	Salt and pepper	75.00	90.00	45.00
He-118	Salt and pepper on tray	150.00	180.00	85.00
He-122	Sandwich tray, 13" x 6"	100.00	120.00	65.00
He-125	Sauce boat and liner	125.00	150.00	75.00
He-130	Teacup and saucer	85.00	105.00	50.00
He-137	Teapot, 6 cup	550.00	635.00	325.00
He-140	Teapot, stacking	650.00	750.00	325.00
He-145	Tennis set	100.00	120.00	60.00
He-160	Vase, bud	150.00	180.00	60.00

MARIGOLD

The pattern number for Elijah Cotton is 2122. This pattern was produced as **Mille Fleurs** by James Kent and pattern number 5007 by A. G. Richardson. The Czechoslovakians and the Dutch also produced this pattern.

Cat. No.	Shape	U.S. $	Can. $	U.K. £
MaG-04	Bonbon dish	45.00	55.00	40.00
MaG-28	Butter dish	130.00	160.00	80.00
MaG-35	Cake plate, open handles	150.00	180.00	75.00
MaG-36	Cake plate, tab handles	125.00	150.00	65.00
MaG-41	Cake stand, 3 tier	160.00	195.00	85.00
MaG-50	Cheese keep	200.00	240.00	125.00
MaG-55	Coffee pot, 6 cup	550.00	635.00	275.00
MaG-65	Condiment set on tray	185.00	225.00	100.00
MaG-70	Cream and sugar	115.00	140.00	60.00
MaG-71	Cream and sugar on tray	165.00	200.00	95.00
MaG-85	Jam pot with liner	135.00	165.00	65.00
MaG-92	Jug, 5" round	275.00	330.00	125.00
MaG-96	Jug, 7" straight-sided	325.00	390.00	135.00

Cat. No.	Shape	U.S. $	Can. $	U.K. £
MaG-301	Plate, 4" triangular	30.00	40.00	20.00
MaG-104	Plate, 7"	50.00	60.00	30.00
MaG-105	Plate, 8"	75.00	90.00	45.00
MaG-112	Relish dish	165.00	200.00	125.00
MaG-117	Salt and pepper	85.00	105.00	55.00
MaG-118	Salt and pepper on tray	135.00	165.00	95.00
MaG-122	Sandwich tray, 13"x 6"	95.00	115.00	50.00
MaG-125	Sauce boat and liner	135.00	165.00	75.00
MaG-130	Teacup and saucer	85.00	105.00	55.00
MaG-137	Teapot, 6 cup	525.00	605.00	325.00
MaG-140	Teapot, stacking	650.00	750.00	325.00
MaG-145	Tennis set	95.00	115.00	65.00
MaG-160	Vase, bud	145.00	175.00	65.00

MARINA

This chintz pattern was a best seller for Nelson ware in 1939. The pattern itself was registered in 1937, English registration number 821468. This pattern was also produced by Royal Albert in bone china.

Cat. No.	Shape	U.S. $	Can. $	U.K. £
Ma-04	Bonbon dish	45.00	55.00	30.00
Ma-28	Butter dish	150.00	180.00	85.00
Ma-35	Cake plate, open handles	165.00	200.00	75.00
Ma-36	Cake plate, tab handles	135.00	165.00	75.00
Ma-41	Cake stand, 3 tier	125.00	150.00	90.00
Ma-50	Cheese keep	185.00	225.00	125.00
Ma-55	Coffee pot, 6 cup	550.00	635.00	300.00
Ma-65	Condiment set on tray	165.00	200.00	100.00
Ma-70	Cream and sugar	100.00	120.00	65.00
Ma-71	Cream and sugar on tray	150.00	180.00	85.00
Ma-85	Jam pot with liner	135.00	165.00	75.00
Ma-92	Jug, 5" round	275.00	330.00	115.00
Ma-96	Jug, 7" straight-sided	325.00	390.00	125.00

Cat. No.	Shape	U.S. $	Can. $	U.K. £
Ma-301	Plate, 4" triangular	40.00	50.00	25.00
Ma-104	Plate, 7"	65.00	80.00	35.00
Ma-105	Plate, 8"	85.00	105.00	50.00
Ma-112	Relish dish	165.00	210.00	125.00
Ma-117	Salt and pepper	75.00	90.00	45.00
Ma-118	Salt and pepper on tray	125.00	150.00	85.00
Ma-122	Sandwich tray, 13" x 6"	100.00	120.00	65.00
Ma-125	Sauce boat and liner	125.00	150.00	75.00
Ma-130	Teacup and saucer	85.00	105.00	40.00
Ma-137	Teapot, 6 cup	500.00	600.00	325.00
Ma-140	Teapot, stacking	650.00	750.00	325.00
Ma-145	Tennis set	100.00	120.00	65.00
Ma-160	Vase, bud	145.00	175.00	60.00

PANSY

This was not a controlled pattern and was produced by other Staffordshire factories as well as by the Japanese. Ford & Sons used this litho as one of their unnamed patterns on earthenware in the 1930s. Shelley also produced this pattern in earthenware before World War II. After the war Shelley used this pansy litho on bone china as did Royal Albert. Interestingly, Crown Clarence Pottery were still advertising this as an earthenware pattern — pattern No. T12 — as late as July 1954. "The potter who designs colourfully contributes to the gaiety of life. Moreover, he shows sales sense, for no woman can resist colour. Particularly when it is used as tastefully as in this Crown Clarence ware which buyers please note has the additional attraction of a favourable price."

Cat. No.	Shape	U.S. $	Can. $	U.K. £
P-04	Bonbon dish	65.00	80.00	45.00
P-28	Butter dish	125.00	150.00	75.00
P-35	Cake plate, open handles	175.00	210.00	75.00
P-36	Cake plate, tab handles	150.00	180.00	65.00
P-41	Cake stand, 3 tier	125.00	150.00	95.00
P-50	Cheese keep	195.00	235.00	140.00
P-55	Coffee pot, 6 cup	675.00	780.00	275.00
P-65	Condiment set on tray	190.00	230.00	110.00
P-70	Cream and sugar	125.00	150.00	65.00
P-71	Cream and sugar on tray	175.00	210.00	85.00
P-85	Jam pot with liner	175.00	210.00	60.00
P-92	Jug, 5" round	275.00	330.00	125.00
P-96	Jug, 7" straight-sided	325.00	390.00	150.00

Cat. No.	Shape	U.S. $	Can. $	U.K. £
P-301	Plate, 4" triangular	30.00	40.00	25.00
P-104	Plate, 7"	60.00	75.00	40.00
P-105	Plate, 8"	95.00	115.00	65.00
P-112	Relish dish	175.00	210.00	135.00
P-117	Salt and pepper	85.00	105.00	55.00
P-118	Salt and pepper on tray	145.00	175.00	95.00
P-122	Sandwich tray, 13" x 6"	120.00	145.00	50.00
P-125	Sauce boat and liner	145.00	175.00	95.00
P-130	Teacup and saucer	95.00	115.00	55.00
P-137	Teapot, 6 cup	575.00	665.00	350.00
P-140	Teapot, stacking	900.00	1,035.00	450.00
P-145	Tennis set	115.00	140.00	65.00
P-160	Vase, bud	165.00	200.00	75.00

ROSETIME

The English registration number for **Rosetime** was 829287, and the pattern was registered sometime in 1938. This pattern was produced by Royal Albert in bone china.

Cat. No.	Shape	U.S. $	Can. $	U.K. £
Ro-04	Bonbon dish	50.00	60.00	40.00
Ro-28	Butter dish	150.00	180.00	110.00
Ro-35	Cake plate, open handles	200.00	240.00	100.00
Ro-36	Cake plate, tab handles	175.00	210.00	85.00
Ro-41	Cake stand, 3 tier	150.00	180.00	100.00
Ro-50	Cheese keep	200.00	140.00	150.00
Ro-55	Coffee pot, 6 cup	825.00	950.00	350.00
Ro-65	Condiment set on tray	225.00	270.00	125.00
Ro-70	Cream and sugar	150.00	180.00	65.00
Ro-71	Cream and sugar on tray	225.00	270.00	100.00
Ro-85	Jam pot with liner	165.00	200.00	85.00
Ro-92	Jug, 5" round	325.00	390.00	125.00
Ro-96	Jug, 7" straight-sided	400.00	480.00	135.00

Cat. No.	Shape	U.S. $	Can. $	U.K. £
Ro-301	Plate, 4" triangular	45.00	55.00	30.00
Ro-104	Plate, 7"	65.00	80.00	40.00
Ro-105	Plate, 8"	95.00	115.00	50.00
Ro-112	Relish dish	195.00	235.00	135.00
Ro-117	Salt and pepper	110.00	135.00	50.00
Ro-118	Salt and pepper on tray	180.00	215.00	100.00
Ro-122	Sandwich tray, 13" x 6"	125.00	150.00	65.00
Ro-125	Sauce boat and liner	165.00	200.00	85.00
Ro-130	Teacup and saucer	100.00	120.00	55.00
Ro-137	Teapot, 6 cup	700.00	805.00	400.00
Ro-140	Teapot, stacking	950.00	1,100.00	450.00
Ro-145	Tennis set	135.00	165.00	75.00
Ro-160	Vase, bud	165.00	200.00	75.00

ROYAL BROCADE

This pattern was also produced by Royal Albert in bone china.

Cat. No.	Shape	U.S. $	Can. $	U.K. £
RB-04	Bonbon dish	35.00	45.00	25.00
RB-28	Butter dish	110.00	135.00	75.00
RB-35	Cake plate, open handles	90.00	110.00	65.00
RB-36	Cake plate, tab handles	90.00	110.00	65.00
RB-41	Cake stand, 3 tier	95.00	115.00	75.00
RB-50	Cheese keep	125.00	150.00	100.00
RB-55	Coffee pot, 6 cup	375.00	450.00	250.00
RB-65	Condiment set on tray	125.00	150.00	85.00
RB-70	Cream and sugar	65.00	80.00	45.00
RB-71	Cream and sugar on tray	105.00	125.00	75.00
RB-85	Jam pot with liner	75.00	90.00	50.00
RB-92	Jug, 5" round	150.00	180.00	90.00
RB-96	Jug, 7" straight-sided	180.00	215.00	100.00

Cat. No.	Shape	U.S. $	Can. $	U.K. £
RB-301	Plate, 4" triangular	25.00	30.00	25.00
RB-104	Plate, 7"	35.00	45.00	30.00
RB-105	Plate, 8"	45.00	55.00	50.00
RB-112	Relish dish	95.00	115.00	75.00
RB-117	Salt and pepper	65.00	80.00	45.00
RB-118	Salt and pepper on tray	115.00	140.00	75.00
RB-122	Sandwich tray, 13" x 6"	65.00	80.00	45.00
RB-125	Sauce boat and liner	90.00	110.00	75.00
RB-130	Teacup and saucer	45.00	55.00	40.00
RB-137	Teapot, 6 cup	375.00	450.00	250.00
RB-140	Teapot, stacking	450.00	540.00	275.00
RB-145	Tennis set	65.00	80.00	50.00
RB-160	Vase, bud	95.00	115.00	55.00

SKYLARK

This pattern is not common in North America. But, unlike other rare Lord Nelson patterns, **Skylark** is not popular with American collectors.

Cat. No.	Shape	U.S. $	Can. $	U.K. £
Sk-04	Bonbon dish	40.00	50.00	25.00
Sk-28	Butter dish	125.00	150.00	70.00
Sk-35	Cake plate, open handles	155.00	190.00	60.00
Sk-36	Cake plate, tab handles	135.00	165.00	60.00
Sk-41	Cake stand, 3 tier	115.00	140.00	70.00
Sk-50	Cheese keep	155.00	190.00	95.00
Sk-55	Coffee pot, 6 cup	500.00	600.00	240.00
Sk-65	Condiment set on tray	165.00	200.00	80.00
Sk-70	Cream and sugar	100.00	120.00	45.00
Sk-71	Cream and sugar on tray	165.00	200.00	70.00
Sk-85	Jam pot with liner	125.00	150.00	50.00
Sk-92	Jug, 5" round	250.00	300.00	85.00
Sk-96	Jug, 7" straight-sided	300.00	360.00	100.00

Cat. No.	Shape	U.S. $	Can. $	U.K. £
Sk-301	Plate, 4" triangular	40.00	50.00	25.00
Sk-104	Plate, 7"	50.00	60.00	40.00
Sk-105	Plate, 8"	75.00	90.00	50.00
Sk-112	Relish dish	125.00	150.00	115.00
Sk-117	Salt and pepper	95.00	115.00	55.00
Sk-118	Salt and pepper on tray	150.00	180.00	85.00
Sk-122	Sandwich tray, 13" x 6"	75.00	90.00	45.00
Sk-125	Sauce boat and liner	110.00	135.00	75.00
Sk-130	Teacup and saucer	85.00	105.00	45.00
Sk-137	Teapot, 6 cup	475.00	325.00	240.00
Sk-140	Teapot, stacking	800.00	570.00	275.00
Sk-145	Tennis set	95.00	115.00	65.00
Sk-160	Vase, bud	135.00	165.00	65.00

EMPIRE PORCELAIN COMPANY LTD.

This company was established at the Empire Works in Stoke around 1896 and continued in business until 1967. Although they called themselves the Empire Porcelain Company they produced mainly fine earthenware, including a number of chintzes. One of their 1930s chintz patterns **Lilac Time** was very popular and was produced in more than one colourway.

They were big exporters of china in the 1950s and they had overseas agents in Argentina, Southern Rhodesia, Sweden and Trinidad. The trade name Empire Ware or Shelton Ivory is often found within the backstamp. Backstamps from the late 1940s and 1950s usually incorporate numbers for the month and year of manufacture.

BLACK MARGUERITE

   This pattern was widely produced by a number of Staffordshire companies. The Empire version dates to the 1950s and usually has wide gold banding around the foot, spout and black handle. Empire also produced this pattern with a white background but it turns up very rarely.

Cat. No.	Shape	U.S. $	Can. $	U.K. £
BM-55	Coffee pot, 6 cup	300.00	360.00	165.00
BM-70	Cream and sugar	65.00	80.00	50.00
BM-75	Demi-tasse	50.00	60.00	35.00

Cat. No.	Shape	U.S. $	Can. $	U.K. £
BM-104	Plate, 7"	30.00	40.00	25.00
BM-130	Teacup and saucer	60.00	75.00	40.00
BM-137	Teapot, 6 cup	300.00	360.00	150.00

GOLDEN WATTLE

This pattern seems to appear more often in England than North America.

Cat. No.	Shape	U.S. $	Can. $	U.K. £
GW-55	Coffee pot, 6 cup	350.00	420.00	175.00
GW-70	Cream and sugar	75.00	90.00	50.00
GW-75	Demi-tasse	50.00	60.00	30.00

Cat. No.	Shape	U.S. $	Can. $	U.K. £
GW-104	Plate, 7"	30.00	40.00	25.00
GW-130	Teacup and saucer	60.00	75.00	35.00
GW-137	Teapot, 6 cup	325.00	390.00	175.00

LILAC TIME

This pattern was produced in two colourways, green and ivory, the green being the most common and the more highly desired. (See **White Lilac Time** page 34)

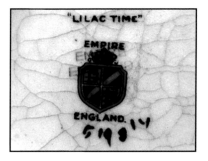

Cat. No.	Shape	U.S. $	Can. $	U.K. £
LT-55	Coffee pot, 6 cup	675.00	780.00	285.00
LT-70	Cream and sugar	125.00	150.00	70.00
LT-75	Demi-tasse	90.00	110.00	50.00

Cat. No.	Shape	U.S. $	Can. $	U.K. £
LT-104	Plate, 7"	70.00	85.00	30.00
LT-130	Teacup and saucer	100.00	120.00	50.00
LT-137	Teapot, 6 cup	650.00	750.00	350.00

WATER LILY

This pattern seems to appear more often in England than North America.

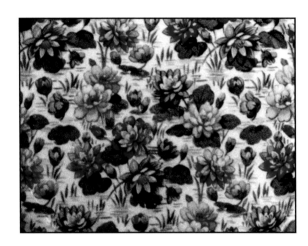

Cat. No.	Shape	U.S. $	Can. $	U.K. £
WL-55	Coffee pot, 6 cup	350.00	420.00	150.00
WL-70	Cream and sugar	60.00	75.00	45.00
WL-75	Demi-tasse	50.00	60.00	35.00

Cat. No.	Shape	U.S. $	Can. $	U.K. £
WL-104	Plate, 7"	50.00	60.00	25.00
WL-130	Teacup and saucer	60.00	75.00	35.00
WL-137	Teapot, 6 cup	325.00	390.00	175.00

WHITE LILAC TIME

This pattern was produced in two colourways, green and ivory, the green being the most common and the more highly desired. (See **Lilac Time** page 32)

Cat. No.	Shape	U.S. $	Can. $	U.K. £
LTW-55	Coffee pot, 6 cup	550.00	635.00	250.00
LTW-70	Cream and sugar	80.00	100.00	50.00
LTW-75	Demi-tasse	70.00	85.00	40.00

Cat. No.	Shape	U.S. $	Can. $	U.K. £
LTW-104	Plate, 7"	40.00	50.00	25.00
LTW-130	Teacup and saucer	75.00	90.00	35.00
LTW-137	Teapot, 6 cup	500.00	600.00	275.00

FORD & SONS

From 1893 until 1938 this company was known as Ford & Sons and the backstamp was minimal: F & S or F & SONS LTD, or F & SONS BURSLEM. They produced several of the exotic bird and flower chintzes during the 1920s and perhaps earlier. They do not appear to have produced any exclusive all-over floral chintzes in the 1930s although they did use several uncontrolled chintzes (see Lord Nelson **Pansy** and Grimwades **Rose Du Barry**). Although the company name did not change to Ford & Sons (Crownford) Ltd. until 1938, the most common backstamp through the 1930s incorporated the trade name Crownford Ware.

UNKNOWN

This was not a controlled pattern. It is sometimes found with a Bridgwood & Sons backstamp and it is sometimes unmarked.

Cat. No.	Shape	U.S. $	Can. $	U.K. £
FS-36	Cake plate, tab handles	150.00	180.00	85.00
FS-95	Jug, 7" straight-sided	300.00	360.00	150.00

Cat. No.	Shape	U.S. $	Can. $	U.K. £
FS-130	Teacup and saucer	85.00	105.00	50.00

GRIMWADES LTD.
(ROYAL WINTON)

In 1885 Leonard Lumsden Grimwade founded a pottery with his brother at the Winton Pottery, Stoke-on-Trent. Although the brothers started with a shed, they grew very quickly and by 1900, after the takeover of the Stoke Pottery, Grimwade Brothers had become Grimwades Limited. Atlas China was acquired in 1906, which enabled the Grimwades to produce quality teasets. Tolie Coales, daughter of the Grimwades representative in Canada, still has beautiful teaware which was hand-painted by the art director at Atlas and sent to her mother as a gift.

Export became a very important part of the Grimwades business. Around the turn of the century G.O. Coales came out to Canada. He became a china buyer for Carsley, a Montreal department store and he became the first retailer in Canada to buy from Grimwades. In 1903 Leonard Grimwade persuaded George to become the Grimwades representative for Canada. "Thanks to his undeviating efforts, Royal Winton became known from coast to coast . . . In days when Canada was still a pioneer country, he probed into sparsely settled areas, using the crude transportation methods of the time." His first trips were to Toronto, Quebec and St. Johns, Newfoundland and it was not until 1910 that he ventured into Western Canada. After that, every January he would leave central Canada and head to the Maritime Provinces. In February he would head west. During the summer he would repeat the journey. In an interview in 1953, Mr. Coales talked of his early plans for Grimwades. His aim was to make the name Grimwades so well known in the retail trade that the salesmen of wholesale houses would be asked for the ware and would start to keep it in stock. The plan was to give distributors control of the patterns they carried, hoping they would work harder on lines that were exclusive to them. The pattern **Rose du Barry** was advertised by Henry Morgans of Montreal in 1938 and has been found with no name, with the name **Chelsea Rose** and with **Rose du Barry**. The backstamp on **Rose du Barry** always has Henry Morgan & Co. Ltd.; perhaps the name **Rose du Barry** was exclusively given to Morgans by Mr. Coales as part of this plan. The advertisements in the 1950s *Gift Buyer* make it clear that his plan was successful by this point. **English Rose** and **Kew** were exclusive to Dingle, Davidson, **May Festival** and **June Festival** belonged to Michaelsons, **Morning Glory** to Enterprise Sales, **Balmoral** to Nerlich & Company, **Nantwich** and **Orient** to Cassidys — all in Toronto; **Spring Glory, Pekin** and **Marion** to Anglo-Canadian Mercantile Co. in Montreal. By the time George Coales retired he had crossed the Atlantic more than sixty times and Grimwades was known throughout Canada.

Much less is known about the export of Grimwades to the United States. Clearly there was no George Coales crisscrossing the country with trunk loads of chintz. However, from an article and an advertisement found in the American trade magazine *Crockery & Glass Journal* (May 1933), it is apparent that the firm of Wright, Tyndale & van Roden, Inc., a luxury store in Philadelphia, were given exclusive rights to at least three patterns in 1933 — **Summertime, Somerset** and **Floral Feast** and these patterns were backstamped COPYRIGHT Wright, Tyndale & van Roden, Inc. ENGLAND. In 1930 the *Crockery & Glass* published an editorial entitled "Unauthorized Borrowing" discussing the issue of commercial piracy of patterns and shapes. A. G. Richardson took out an advertisement around the same time warning their customers of the pirating of some of their patterns and shapes. The Wright Tyndale backstamp was an attempt to discourage American copyists. Their ad which was aimed at retailers says "each Copyrighted for your protection — all patterns exclusive with us." This relationship must have continued for a number of years. Other Royal Winton patterns with the Wright Tyndale backstamp include **Queen Anne, Hazel, Cranstone, Old Cottage Chintz,** and the 1950s pattern **Fireglow**. It is interesting to discover these marked pieces in New Zealand, Australia, England, and South Africa. Whether pieces were shipped out with the wrong backstamp or they have gradually moved around the world through collectors and antique dealers is open to question. The article in the *Journal* after the introduction of the first patterns is worth quoting: "Assured of a warm welcome are Wright Tyndale & van Roden's three new designs in their English Chintz ware . . . all these, needless to say, are excellently executed on the lovely clean-bodied Royal Winton Ivory . . . I liked particularly well a quaintly square open sugar and creamer on a tray that will retail around $1.50 . . . the fat and inviting tea pot . . . and a large buffet or sandwich plate 11 ½ inches in diameter to retail for about $1.95 . . . Good compositions are, to my mind, a tea set for four that you may retail around $10.00 . . . and an individual tray set that will retail around $8.50. I think I should also mention that these three new patterns are copyrighted."

Grimwades Ltd. produced any number of chintzes earlier in the century, but it was not until 1928 with the production of the first "modern" chintz pattern, **Marguerite**, that Grimwades found the line which would become their particular specialty. **Marguerite** chintz was described in the November *Gazette* as "a treatment employing a very pleasing ground tint in natural colours and a theme expressive of the charm of the countryside, the shapes being new and unquestionably appealing." It is said to have come from a design worked by Leonard Grimwade's wife on a cushion. Over the next few years several chintz designs were introduced but in 1932 **Summertime** chintz brought even greater popularity for the firm. The *Gazette* waxed lyrical: "It is a sort of fantasia compounded of roses, daisies, violets, harebells and similar summertime flowers." Although we have been told that **Summertime** is not common in Australia, it was shipped in huge quantities to North America and even today dinner services for 12 turn up with some regularity. The pattern was applied to everything including, clocks, sick feeders for hospitals and even a souvenir plate with Niagara Falls lithographed in the centre.

Throughout the 1930s vast quantities of chintzware were produced and a number of new patterns were introduced at the British Industries Fair every year. Ivy Mayer, secretary to the export director Fred Seabridge for thirty years, remembers seeing big red pattern books with each pattern recorded by number. The books have long since disappeared, and dating the patterns has become an exercise in piecing together various bits of information. Every year when new ceramic lines were introduced at the B.I.F., trade publications including *Pottery Gazette* and *Glass Trade Review* might mention particularly popular patterns or patterns which were bought by members of the Royal family, who were staunch supporters of British industry.

It is important to remember that **all** patterns were recorded in order in the pattern books and not simply chintz patterns. There are, therefore, large gaps between the various chintz pattern numbers since many numbers were allocated to the non-chintz patterns produced by Grimwades. We know that the first modern all-over-floral was **Marguerite** and that the pattern was introduced in 1928 with the number 9432 (The *Gazette* refers to pattern number 9467 which is **Marguerite** with blue trim). **Old Cottage Chintz** 9632 and **Delphinium Chintz** 9889 have a slightly old-fashioned appearance and are often featured on the older shapes. Similarly **Springtime** usually appears on older shapes and has been found with the pattern number 10017. Suddenly the number drops to 775 with **Summertime,** which we know from the *Gazette* appeared in 1932. It is logical to assume that Grimwades, like so many other factories, decided the pattern numbers were getting too long to record and started again in the low hundreds with their pattern numbering. **Floral Feast** (1394) and **Somerset** (1420) were exported to America along with **Summertime** in the spring of 1933. **Clevedon** and **Kinver** were mentioned in January 1934 as new patterns intended for the spring of 1934 and the pattern numbers we have found for them are 1844 (**Clevedon**) and 2254 (**Kinver**).

With the pattern numbers that collectors from around the world contributed, we were able to compile a list of patterns in the order in which they appeared in the pattern book. I have added pattern numbers for patterns with different trim **June Roses** with gold trim has the pattern number 1924, with silver trim 1945, and with green trim 2036. It is not surprising that so many pattern numbers were used each year when you realize that each trim had a different number. There are several anomalies with the patterns in the late 1930s. Unfortunately, in 1939 the last recorded pattern is **Sweet Nancy** at 5828 and the next is **Julia** at 109. Originally we assumed that this might have been pre- and post war, but **Crocus** is mentioned in the 1939 *Gazette* as a new pattern, and the number recorded for white **Crocus** is 111. A piece of what we thought was **Black Crocus** has been found with the backstamp **Triumph** so we have renamed the pattern. The Canadian trade magazine *Gift Buyer* has been of great help in figuring out when patterns were introduced. The navy background pattern we thought was **June Festival** is, in fact, **May Festival** (135) and was advertised in Canada in May, 1952, then **June Festival** (137), the same pattern with a burgundy background. **May Festival** (139) with the black background came out about the same time. If we assume that something odd happened to the numbering and the patterns around World War II, we can still figure out roughly which patterns came out from 1950 onwards. **Kew, Dorset** and **Joyce-Lynn** were all advertised in Canada in 1950. In a May

1953 interview with George Coales, he is said to be have been delighted that Grimwades issued **fifteen new patterns in the last year.** The new patterns probably start with **Nantwich** and continue to **Victorian Rose** or **Chelsea**. With copies of chintz patterns from Japan becoming a serious problem, copyright became a worldwide issue in the late 1930s. Just as Wright Tyndale added COPYRIGHT to their backstamp to discourage American copyists, Royal Winton started to register many of their designs in the late 1930s to deter the Japanese copies. An article in the *Pottery Gazette* on September 1, 1937 is entitled Japanese copy British Designs. The shapes and decorations were exact copies of British wares but the prices were much lower. The Australian Association of British Manufacturers convinced the Australian Registrar to reduce the price of registering designs and assisted British manufacturers to register their wares in Australia. This continued to be a problem after the war and many of the new Royal Winton chintz patterns were registered in Canada, the United States, New Zealand and Australia. Both **Cheadle** and **Mayfair** were registered in 1951 and **Stratford** and **Florence** were registered in 1953.

Clearly there were two golden ages of chintz for the Royal Winton factory — the early 1930s and the early 1950s. The Grimwades chintzes caught the public attention in 1932 with **Summertime** and this continued for some years. The second world war meant that most of the factories were reduced to making white ware and orders continued to pile up until 1945. A report in May of 1949 in The *Gift Buyer* laments that there is still no sign of new patterns from this pottery...none will be issued until present orders are filled . . . new lines already planned by the art department will be speedily brought out. Presumably these are patterns like **Kew** and **Joyce-Lynn** which had been designed but were awaiting release. After the furious designing of fifteen chintz patterns within the year 1952-1953, it would appear that demand gradually fell and no more chintz patterns came out of the design shop.

By the time Howard Potteries took over Grimwades Ltd. in 1964, chintzware was not important to the factory. Norfolk Street had little room for chintz production, according to Ivy Mayer, but special orders were still produced for long-standing customers such as John Bradshaw of Stratford, Canada. Grimwades history from 1964 to the present is typical of so many of the factories which had competed successfully in a different time but found the second half of the twentieth century crippling. Although the company passed through several hands, Royal Winton continued. From the collapse of the Coloroll Group in 1990, the company went from crisis to crisis. Five owners in five years all but finished the firm. Bullers (Staffordshire) Ltd. bought the firm from the liquidators in mid-1995 but subsequently sold it to Taylor Tunnicliffe who moved production from Shelton to Chadwick Street, Longton. Royal Winton started to reproduce their earlier chintz patterns in 1996 starting with a **Florence** vase in a limited edition of 2000. They produced several limited editions for The Old Chintz Company in **Florence, Julia and Summertime**. The interest from the buying public persuaded them to start producing tableware as well as giftware. Production has been so great that they have been hiring new people and recently bought a new factory (see the section on new chintz for more information on current reproductions and possible additions).

DATING ROYAL WINTON: TASK FOR A DETECTIVE

There are a number of different routes one could use to try and determine when a particular piece was made but, truthfully, it will still be in large part speculation. *The Pottery Gazette and Glass Trade Review* published an annual Directory and Diary listing the backstamps used by the various firms in that given year. After going through more than fifty years of these directories I was surprised to find that the backstamp I thought of as deco was still listed in the 1970 review. There are at least a couple of pointers, however. The Grimwades Royal Winton Ivory England backstamp is listed in 1936 but

then appears to die out as does the backstamp with the globe and a ribbon Grimwades across it. In 1943 the directory lists the A.B.C. Pottery firms and according to this list Grimwades

was a Group III factory and required to mark their wares under glaze with the letter A. You can be sure, therefore, if your piece has a backstamp with the letter A incorporated

into it, it will have been produced after 1943. The 1970 directory still lists a script backstamp incorporating the letter A which makes it difficult to narrow it down much further.

If your backstamp includes an English registration number, you can look it up in the Table of Registration Numbers c1884-1987. For example the Cheadle lighter pictured in the Royal Winton shape section has REG.DESIGN 888067 which dates to 1958. Some patented shapes were in use for many years, however, so this only gives you the date of registration and does not necessarily tell you when the piece was made.

Similarly, you can also use advertisements to help date your pieces. (PRESENTA) MUSICAL NOVELTIES took out an advertisement for their wares in October 1957. They were wholesaling non-chintz Royal Winton tankards and caskets with Thorens Musical movements "Easy to sell on sight and sound." They bought the ceramic boxes from Winton and the movements from Thorens and sold the music boxes to retailers. This would explain why most chintz music boxes are in the post-war pattern **Marion.**

You now have a list of the pattern numbers and an idea of when these patterns were introduced which will also serve to narrow down the date. We can be reasonably confident that **English Rose**, for example, was a 1950s pattern judging by the pattern number, the registration date and the advertisements in the Canadian publications. The style of the pattern can also be an indicator since it is difficult to imagine **Morning Glory** or **Orient** dating to anything but the 1950s.

Another way of estimating whether your piece is pre-or post-war is to look at where the pattern has been applied. The factory was forced to economize after the war and salt and peppers no longer had pattern around the outside of the underplate. Baskets had pattern only outside, no more borders along the inside edge. Rosebud jam pots with ceramic lids were probably produced only briefly. We know that the Rosebud shape was introduced in 1940 and we have been told that after the war silver plated lids were found to be more economic.

Shapes can be quite a useful way of narrowing down the dates. Shapes like the Duval jug, the Elite teapot, and the Crown bowl, date to the 1920s and they usually appear with early patterns like **Old Cottage Chintz, Beeston** and **Somerset.** Athena and Ascot were shapes designed in the mid-1930s. Wedgwood plates are mentioned in 1933 and are found with 1930s patterns. The 1950s version of this plate had solid coloured borders instead of embossing. When Athena is missing the little piece off the handle, it is post-war Athena yet another attempt to cut production costs in tough times. The first mention of Albans, however, is a picture of a Queen Anne teapot in the March 1945 *Pottery Gazette.* If your pot is in the Albans shape you can be reasonably confident that it is also post-war. Unless you are putting together a dinner service in **Summertime** or **Old Cottage Chintz**, you may not be very concerned about when your piece was made. It is interesting from a mystery or a research point of view but for the most part it is irrelevant in determining value — except for the very late pieces done at Howard Pottery which do not have the same Ivory body and lack the warmth of the earlier chintzes.

Although I prepared this preliminary list of the Royal Winton patterns in the order in which they appeared, many of the numbers were difficult to decipher and I am still missing pattern numbers for the following patterns: **Peony, Rose du Barry, Rose Brocade** and **Winifred**. I hope readers will be able to help me with these in time for the next edition.

ROYAL WINTON BACKSTAMPS 1910- 1999

1910 - 1930

1920s

c.1926

c.1928

1930s +

1930s

c.1930s

Pre 1936

Pre 1936

c.1938

Post 1943

c.1948

c.1950

c.1950 +

c.1958

Howard Potteries, post 1964

Giftware; 1997 — February 1998

Giftware; February 1998 - 1999

Limited Editions 1997 - 1998

ROYAL WINTON SPECIAL BACKSTAMPS

Clementine Rusk 1998	Magnolia Antiques 1999	Collect It 1998	Old Chintz Company 1998

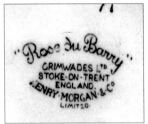

Backstamps made for Wright Tyndale and Van Roden Inc. of Philadelphia 1930s

Variations of backstamps made for Jay-Willfred Co. Ltd. United States from the late 1940s — 1950s

Made for Henry Morgan and Co. Ltd., Canada c.1938

Musical novelties produced for English firm 'Presenta' 1950s

Variations of backstamps made for the American importer John H Roth & Co. 1930s — c.1956

DESIGN DATE	PATTERN NAME	PATTERN NUMBER
c1925	Paisley (green)	8152
1925	Fernese	8786
1928	Paisley (blue)	154
1928	Marguerite	9432
	Marguerite (blue trim)	9467
	Old Cottage	9632
	Delphinium Chintz	9889
	Blue Tulip	9927
	Exotic Bird	10011
	Springtime	10017
1932	Summertime	775
	Cranstone (gold trim)	1154
	Floral Feast	1394
	Somerset (gold trim)	1420
	Rutland	1470
	Somerset (blue trim)	1611
	Bedale	1703
	Clevedon	1844
	Cranstone (burgundy trim)	1877
	June Roses (gold trim)	1924
	June Roses (silver trim)	1945
	June Roses (green trim)	2036
	Cromer	2078
	Pelham	2201
	Beeston	2203
1934	Welbeck	2204
	Hazel	2208
	Kinver	2254
	Floral Feast (blue trim)	2255
	Cranstone (green trim)	2256
	Spring	2506
	Fireglow (original)	2510
	Chintz	2836
	Queen Anne	2995
	Sweet Pea	3030
	Royalty	3079
	Wild Flowers	3149
	Victorian	3164
	Majestic	3311
	Sunshine	4030
1938	Richmond	4249

DESIGN DATE	PATTERN NAME	PATTERN NUMBER
	Tartans	4514
	Quilt	4515
	Floral Garden	4547
1938	Fernese	4771
	Bedale (green trim)	4969
	Anemone	4806
	Clyde (green)	5315
	Clyde (brown)	5637
	Sweet Nancy	5828
	Primrose (yellow)	5995
	Primrose (pink)	5999
	Primrose (green)	6001
	Julia	109
c1939	Crocus	111
	Triumph	112
	May Festival (navy)	135
	June Festival	137
	May Festival (black)	139
	Kew	240
C1949	Dorset	274
	Joyce-Lynn	275
	Nantwich	291
	Dorset	294
c1950	Cheadle	311
	Pekin	320
	Marion	324
	Balmora	1374
	Eleanor	375
	English Rose	381
	Morning Glory	384
	Mayfair	392
	Spring Glory	402
c1952	Evesham	404
	Cotswold	408
	Shrewsbury	418
	Estelle	423
	Victorian Rose	440
	Chelsea	455
	Orient	471
	Florence	472
	Esther	473
1953	Stratford	493
	Fireglow (black)	533

ANEMONE

The pattern number is 4801 and it was available with a light blue, navy blue and black background. The light blue and the black sell for less than the navy blue. Some of the large flowers are hand-painted on top of the transfer.

Cat. No.	Shape	U.S. $	Can. $	U.K. £
A-04	Bonbon dish	40.00	50.00	30.00
A-09	Bowl, 5"	25.00	30.00	20.00
A-14	Bowl, 8" soup	40.00	50.00	30.00
A-23	Breakfast set	550.00	635.00	375.00
A-28	Butter dish	125.00	150.00	75.00
A-30	Butter pat	35.00	45.00	25.00
A-35	Cake plate, open handles	125.00	150.00	75.00
A-37	Cake plate, 8" sq. pedestal	125.00	150.00	85.00
A-40	Cake stand, 2 tier	125.00	150.00	85.00
A-45	Canoe-shaped dish	165.00	200.00	115.00
A-50	Cheese keep	150.00	180.00	100.00
A-52	Coaster	30.00	40.00	25.00
A-55	Coffee pot	450.00	540.00	325.00
A-60	Compote, footed	100.00	120.00	75.00
A-65	Condiment set on tray	135.00	165.00	85.00
A-70	Cream and sugar	75.00	90.00	50.00
A-71	Cream and sugar on tray	135.00	165.00	85.00
A-75	Demi-tasse	50.00	60.00	35.00
A-77	Egg cup, footed	70.00	85.00	40.00
A-80	Hot water jug	200.00	240.00	125.00
A-85	Jam pot with liner	100.00	120.00	65.00
A-90	Jug, 4"	165.00	200.00	115.00
A-91	Jug, 4 1/2"	175.00	210.00	135.00
A-92	Jug, 5"	200.00	240.00	150.00

Cat. No.	Shape	U.S. $	Can. $	U.K. £
A-97	Nut dish	35.00	45.00	25.00
A-201	Plate, 4" sq.	25.00	30.00	20.00
A-202	Plate, 5" sq.	30.00	40.00	25.00
A-203	Plate, 6" sq.	35.00	45.00	25.00
A-204	Plate, 7" sq.	40.00	50.00	30.00
A-205	Plate, 8" sq.	50.00	60.00	35.00
A-206	Plate, 9" sq.	65.00	80.00	45.00
A-207	Plate, 10" sq .	75.00	90.00	50.00
A-112	Relish dish, small	100.00	120.00	65.00
A-115	Salad bowl, chrome rim	100.00	120.00	65.00
A-117	Salt and pepper	50.00	60.00	40.00
A-118	Salt and pepper on tray	125.00	150.00	75.00
A-120	Sandwich tray, 10" x 6"	75.00	90.00	50.00
A-121	Sandwich tray, 12" x 7"	100.00	120.00	65.00
A-125	Sauce boat and liner	100.00	120.00	65.00
A-130	Teacup and saucer	65.00	80.00	35.00
A-135	Teapot, 2 cup	275.00	330.00	175.00
A-136	Teapot, 4 cup	325.00	390.00	225.00
A-137	Teapot, 6 cup	425.00	510.00	300.00
A-140	Teapot, stacking	650.00	750.00	325.00
A-145	Tennis set	75.00	90.00	50.00
A-150	Toast rack, 4 slice	165.00	200.00	125.00
A-151	Toast rack, 2 slice	135.00	165.00	85.00
A-155	Trivet	75.00	90.00	50.00
A-160	Vase, bud	115.00	140.00	60.00

BALMORAL

The pattern number is 374, and it was controlled in Canada in 1951 by Nerlich & Company. The wholesale price for the Ascot cream and sugar was $1.90 and the undertrays sold for $17.22 a dozen.

Cat. No.	Shape	U.S. $	Can. $	U.K. £
Ba-04	Bonbon dish	60.00	75.00	55.00
Ba-09	Bowl, 5"	45.00	55.00	45.00
Ba-14	Bowl, 8" soup	75.00	90.00	60.00
Ba-23	Breakfast set	1,200.00	1,320.00	500.00
Ba-28	Butter dish	150.00	180.00	150.00
Ba-30	Butter pat	50.00	60.00	45.00
Ba-35	Cake plate, open handles	175.00	210.00	110.00
Ba-37	Cake plate, 8" sq. pedestal	175.00	210.00	110.00
Ba-40	Cake stand, 2 tier	150.00	180.00	100.00
Ba-45	Canoe-shaped dish	200.00	240.00	175.00
Ba-50	Cheese keep	225.00	270.00	175.00
Ba-52	Coaster	90.00	110.00	45.00
Ba-55	Coffee pot	975.00	1,125.00	575.00
Ba-60	Compote, footed	150.00	180.00	125.00
Ba-65	Condiment set on tray	225.00	270.00	150.00
Ba-70	Cream and sugar	150.00	180.00	85.00
Ba-71	Cream and sugar on tray	225.00	270.00	175.00
Ba-75	Demi-tasse	100.00	120.00	60.00
Ba-77	Egg cup, footed	110.00	135.00	65.00
Ba-80	Hot water jug	400.00	480.00	250.00
Ba-85	Jam pot with liner	175.00	210.00	125.00
Ba-90	Jug, 4"	375.00	450.00	140.00
Ba-91	Jug, 4 1/2"	425.00	510.00	165.00
Ba-92	Jug, 5"	475.00	570.00	195.00

Cat. No.	Shape	U.S. $	Can. $	U.K. £
Ba-97	Nut dish	50.00	60.00	40.00
Ba-201	Plate, 4" sq.	45.00	55.00	35.00
Ba-202	Plate, 5" sq.	50.00	60.00	40.00
Ba-203	Plate, 6" sq.	60.00	75.00	45.00
Ba-204	Plate, 7" sq.	75.00	90.00	55.00
Ba-205	Plate, 8" sq.	115.00	140.00	75.00
Ba-206	Plate, 9" sq.	135.00	165.00	95.00
Ba-207	Plate, 10" sq.	150.00	180.00	120.00
Ba-112	Relish dish, small	150.00	180.00	125.00
Ba-115	Salad bowl, chrome rim	325.00	390.00	200.00
Ba-117	Salt and pepper	110.00	135.00	60.00
Ba-118	Salt and pepper on tray	185.00	225.00	120.00
Ba-120	Sandwich tray, 10" x 6"	100.00	120.00	75.00
Ba-121	Sandwich tray, 12" x 7"	125.00	150.00	125.00
Ba-125	Sauce boat and liner	150.00	180.00	125.00
Ba-130	Teacup and saucer	100.00	120.00	60.00
Ba-135	Teapot, 2 cup	425.00	510.00	225.00
Ba-136	Teapot, 4 cup	650.00	750.00	350.00
Ba-137	Teapot, 6 cup	850.00	980.00	425.00
Ba-140	Teapot, stacking	1,050.00	1,155.00	550.00
Ba-145	Tennis set	115.00	140.00	75.00
Ba-150	Toast rack, 4 slice	325.00	390.00	175.00
Ba-151	Toast rack, 2 slice	250.00	300.00	125.00
Ba-155	Trivet	125.00	150.00	75.00
Ba-160	Vase, bud	175.00	210.00	75.00

BEDALE

The pattern number is 1703, and it is an alternate colourway to **Summertime** 775. When it has a green trim, the pattern number is 4969. This is one of the patterns copied by the Japanese.

Cat. No.	Shape	U.S. $	Can. $	U.K. £
Be-04	Bonbon dish	50.00	60.00	40.00
Be-09	Bowl, 5"	40.00	50.00	35.00
Be-14	Bowl, 8" soup	65.00	80.00	50.00
Be-23	Breakfast set	1,000.00	1,150.00	525.00
Be-28	Butter dish	140.00	170.00	125.00
Be-30	Butter pat	40.00	50.00	35.00
Be-35	Cake plate, open handles	175.00	210.00	125.00
Be-37	Cake plate, 8" sq. pedestal	175.00	210.00	125.00
Be-40	Cake stand, 2 tier	125.00	150.00	100.00
Be-45	Canoe-shaped dish	175.00	210.00	135.00
Be-50	Cheese keep	175.00	210.00	150.00
Be-52	Coaster	85.00	105.00	40.00
Be-55	Coffee pot	675.00	780.00	550.00
Be-60	Compote, footed	125.00	150.00	85.00
Be-65	Condiment set on tray	185.00	225.00	120.00
Be-70	Cream and sugar	145.00	175.00	75.00
Be-71	Cream and sugar on tray	195.00	235.00	135.00
Be-75	Demi-tasse	90.00	110.00	50.00
Be-77	Egg cup, footed	105.00	125.00	50.00
Be-80	Hot water jug	400.00	480.00	225.00
Be-85	Jam pot with liner	150.00	180.00	125.00
Be-90	Jug, 4"	325.00	390.00	150.00
Be-91	Jug, 4 1/2"	375.00	450.00	175.00
Be-92	Jug, 5 "	400.00	480.00	200.00

Cat. No.	Shape	U.S. $	Can. $	U.K. £
Be-97	Nut dish	40.00	50.00	35.00
Be-201	Plate, 4" sq.	45.00	55.00	35.00
Be-202	Plate, 5" sq.	50.00	60.00	40.00
Be-203	Plate, 6" sq.	55.00	70.00	45.00
Be-204	Plate, 7" sq.	65.00	80.00	50.00
Be-205	Plate, 8" sq.	85.00	105.00	60.00
Be-206	Plate, 9" sq.	105.00	130.00	65.00
Be-207	Plate, 10" sq.	125.00	150.00	85.00
Be-112	Relish dish, small	125.00	150.00	125.00
Be-115	Salad bowl, chrome rim	325.00	390.00	165.00
Be-117	Salt and pepper	100.00	120.00	55.00
Be-118	Salt and pepper on tray	175.00	210.00	95.00
Be-120	Sandwich tray, 10" x 6"	100.00	120.00	85.00
Be-121	Sandwich tray, 12" x 7"	125.00	150.00	95.00
Be-125	Sauce boat and liner	125.00	150.00	90.00
Be-130	Teacup and saucer	95.00	115.00	55.00
Be-135	Teapot, 2 cup	300.00	360.00	200.00
Be-136	Teapot, 4 cup	450.00	540.00	325.00
Be-137	Teapot, 6 cup	550.00	635.00	375.00
Be-140	Teapot, stacking	950.00	1,095.00	525.00
Be-145	Tennis set	110.00	135.00	70.00
Be-150	Toast rack, 4 slice	295.00	355.00	175.00
Be-151	Toast rack, 2 slice	225.00	270.00	125.00
Be-155	Trivet	115.00	140.00	70.00
Be-160	Vase, bud	165.00	200.00	85.00

BEESTON

The pattern number is 2203. This pattern was copied by the Japanese. Beeston is probably the earliest black background pattern and it has become increasingly sought after in the past year.

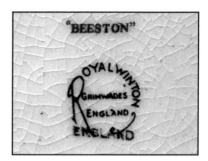

Cat. No.	Shape	U.S. $	Can. $	U.K. £
Bee-04	Bonbon dish	85.00	105.00	60.00
Bee-09	Bowl, 5"	55.00	70.00	45.00
Bee-14	Bowl, 8" soup	95.00	115.00	70.00
Bee-23	Breakfast set	1,450.00	1,595.00	700.00
Bee-28	Butter dish	245.00	295.00	175.00
Bee-30	Butter pat	75.00	90.00	55.00
Bee-35	Cake plate, open handles	295.00	355.00	175.00
Bee-37	Cake plate, 8" sq. pedestal	245.00	295.00	175.00
Bee-40	Cake stand, 2 tier	210.00	255.00	175.00
Bee-45	Canoe-shaped dish	300.00	360.00	200.00
Bee-50	Cheese keep	300.00	360.00	225.00
Bee-52	Coaster	125.00	150.00	45.00
Bee-55	Coffee pot	1,350.00	1,485.00	700.00
Bee-60	Compote, footed	225.00	270.00	150.00
Bee-65	Condiment set on tray	325.00	390.00	215.00
Bee-70	Cream and sugar	185.00	225.00	125.00
Bee-71	Cream and sugar on tray	300.00	360.00	205.00
Bee-75	Demi-tasse	135.00	165.00	85.00
Bee-77	Egg cup, footed	130.00	160.00	60.00
Bee-80	Hot water jug	575.00	665.00	300.00
Bee-85	Jam pot with liner	225.00	270.00	175.00
Bee-90	Jug, 4"	450.00	540.00	275.00
Bee-91	Jug, 4 1/2"	500.00	600.00	300.00
Bee-92	Jug, 5"	550.00	635.00	325.00

Cat. No.	Shape	U.S. $	Can. $	U.K. £
Bee-97	Nut dish	75.00	90.00	50.00
Bee-201	Plate, 4" sq.	55.00	70.00	45.00
Bee-202	Plate, 5" sq.	65.00	80.00	55.00
Bee-203	Plate, 6" sq.	75.00	90.00	60.00
Bee-204	Plate, 7" sq.	110.00	135.00	75.00
Bee-205	Plate, 8" sq.	145.00	175.00	85.00
Bee-206	Plate, 9" sq.	160.00	195.00	120.00
Bee-207	Plate, 10" sq.	175.00	210.00	135.00
Bee-112	Relish dish, small	220.00	265.00	175.00
Bee-115	Salad bowl, chrome rim	395.00	475.00	195.00
Bee-117	Salt and pepper	125.00	150.00	75.00
Bee-118	Salt and pepper on tray	210.00	255.00	150.00
Bee-120	Sandwich tray, 10" x 6"	165.00	200.00	125.00
Bee-121	Sandwich tray, 12" x 7"	195.00	235.00	145.00
Bee-125	Sauce boat and liner	185.00	225.00	120.00
Bee-130	Teacup and saucer	135.00	165.00	75.00
Bee-135	Teapot, 2 cup	650.00	750.00	400.00
Bee-136	Teapot, 4 cup	900.00	1,035.00	550.00
Bee-137	Teapot, 6 cup	1,100.00	1,210.00	600.00
Bee-140	Teapot, stacking	1,600.00	1,760.00	650.00
Bee-145	Tennis set	135.00	165.00	120.00
Bee-150	Toast rack, 4 slice	375.00	450.00	205.00
Bee-151	Toast rack, 2 slice	300.00	360.00	150.00
Bee-155	Trivet	150.00	180.00	100.00
Bee-160	Vase, bud	195.00	235.00	100.00

"BLUE TULIP"

The pattern number for **Blue Tulip** is 9927 which would date it to 1931, after **Delphinium Chintz** and before **Springtime**. This pattern has never been very popular with chintz collectors, but is easily found in both North America and England.

Cat. No.	Shape	U.S. $	Can. $	U.K. £
BT-04	Bonbon dish	25.00	30.00	25.00
BT-09	Bowl, 5"	25.00	30.00	25.00
BT-14	Bowl, 8" soup	35.00	45.00	30.00
BT-23	Breakfast set	350.00	420.00	325.00
BT-28	Butter dish	90.00	110.00	65.00
BT-30	Butter pat	25.00	30.00	20.00
BT-35	Cake plate, open handles	90.00	110.00	75.00
BT-37	Cake plate, 8" sq. pedestal	90.00	110.00	65.00
BT-40	Cake stand, 2 tier	90.00	110.00	65.00
BT-45	Canoe-shaped dish	120.00	145.00	85.00
BT-50	Cheese keep	115.00	140.00	100.00
BT-52	Coaster	25.00	30.00	20.00
BT-55	Coffee pot	375.00	450.00	250.00
BT-60	Compote, footed	65.00	80.00	50.00
BT-65	Condiment set on tray	90.00	110.00	65.00
BT-70	Cream and sugar	55.00	70.00	45.00
BT-71	Cream and sugar on tray	90.00	110.00	65.00
BT-75	Demi-tasse	35.00	45.00	30.00
BT-77	Egg cup, footed	35.00	45.00	25.00
BT-80	Hot water jug	165.00	200.00	125.00
BT-85	Jam pot with liner	75.00	90.00	60.00
BT-90	Jug, 4"	135.00	165.00	65.00
BT-91	Jug, 4 1/2"	150.00	180.00	75.00
BT-92	Jug, 5"	165.00	200.00	95.00

Cat. No.	Shape	U.S. $	Can. $	U.K. £
BT-97	Nut dish	25.00	30.00	20.00
BT-201	Plate, 4" sq.	30.00	40.00	25.00
BT-202	Plate, 5" sq.	35.00	45.00	25.00
BT-203	Plate, 6" sq.	40.00	50.00	30.00
BT-204	Plate, 7" sq.	45.00	55.00	35.00
BT-205	Plate, 8" sq.	55.00	70.00	45.00
BT-206	Plate, 9" sq.	65.00	80.00	50.00
BT-207	Plate, 10" sq.	75.00	90.00	55.00
BT-112	Relish dish, small	75.00	90.00	60.00
BT-115	Salad bowl, chrome rim	145.00	175.00	65.00
BT-117	Salt and pepper	45.00	55.00	40.00
BT-118	Salt and pepper on tray	100.00	120.00	80.00
BT-120	Sandwich tray, 10" x 6"	45.00	55.00	45.00
BT-121	Sandwich tray, 12" x 7"	65.00	80.00	50.00
BT-125	Sauce boat and liner	65.00	80.00	45.00
BT-130	Teacup and saucer	35.00	45.00	30.00
BT-135	Teapot, 2 cup	150.00	180.00	125.00
BT-136	Teapot, 4 cup	225.00	270.00	175.00
BT-137	Teapot, 6 cup	300.00	360.00	225.00
BT-140	Teapot, stacking	400.00	480.00	275.00
BT-145	Tennis set	45.00	55.00	40.00
BT-150	Toast rack, 4 slice	150.00	180.00	125.00
BT-151	Toast rack, 2 slice	90.00	110.00	65.00
BT-155	Trivet	45.00	55.00	40.00
BT-160	Vase, bud	65.00	80.00	45.00

CARNATION

This pattern is mentioned in March 1933 in *The Pottery, Glass & Brass Salesman;* "reference can be made to a cake plate done in a choice of two all-over chintz decorations for which many doubtless will be able to get $1.25... **Carnation** is very well executed and a veritable riot of color." Interestingly, this pattern was sold in Australia with the name backstamp **Ostria**. This pattern does not appear to have been used on many of the Royal Winton shapes.

Cat. No.	Shape	U.S. $	Can. $	U.K. £
Car-35	Cake plate, open handles	100.00	120.00	60.00
Car-115	Salad bowl, chrome rim	200.00	240.00	85.00
Car-130	Teacup and saucer	50.00	60.00	35.00

Cat. No.	Shape	U.S. $	Can. $	U.K. £
Car-203	Plate, 6" sq.	40.00	50.00	30.00
Car-206	Plate, 9" sq.	75.00	90.00	40.00

CHEADLE

The pattern number is 311 and the pattern dates to 1950. This pattern was featured in an Ebeling & Reuss Company advertisement in September 1950. Retailers were offered 4 cup Albans teapots for $30.00 a dozen and 6 cup teapots for $36.00 a dozen. Interestingly, there was both a covered and an open sugar. The cream and covered sugar was $9.00 more per dozen which may explain why so few turn up. Cheadle is a pattern which is becoming more popular particularly in Australia. The pattern comes in two colourways with the other pattern having more pink and a white flower.

Cat. No.	Shape	U.S. $	Can. $	U.K. £
Chd-04	Bonbon dish	60.00	75.00	55.00
Chd-09	Bowl, 5"	45.00	55.00	40.00
Chd-14	Bowl, 8" soup	70.00	85.00	60.00
Chd-23	Breakfast set	1,250.00	1,375.00	550.00
Chd-28	Butter dish	175.00	210.00	150.00
Chd-30	Butter pat	50.00	60.00	45.00
Chd-35	Cake plate, open handles	235.00	285.00	175.00
Chd-37	Cake plate, 8" sq. pedestal	200.00	240.00	175.00
Chd-40	Cake stand, 2 tier	175.00	210.00	150.00
Chd-45	Canoe-shaped dish	225.00	270.00	195.00
Chd-50	Cheese keep	240.00	290.00	175.00
Chd-52	Coaster	110.00	135.00	55.00
Chd-55	Coffee pot	1,050.00	1,155.00	500.00
Chd-60	Compote, footed	150.00	180.00	125.00
Chd-65	Condiment set on tray	275.00	330.00	150.00
Chd-70	Cream and sugar	175.00	210.00	85.00
Chd-71	Cream and sugar on tray	250.00	300.00	150.00
Chd-75	Demi-tasse	115.00	140.00	60.00
Chd-77	Egg cup, footed	125.00	150.00	55.00
Chd-80	Hot water jug	450.00	540.00	250.00
Chd-85	Jam pot with liner	150.00	180.00	125.00
Chd-90	Jug, 4"	400.00	480.00	200.00
Chd-91	Jug, 4 1/2"	450.00	540.00	225.00
Chd-92	Jug, 5"	500.00	600.00	250.00

Cat. No.	Shape	U.S. $	Can. $	U.K. £
Chd-97	Nut dish	50.00	60.00	40.00
Chd-201	Plate, 4" sq.	55.00	70.00	40.00
Chd-202	Plate, 5" sq.	65.00	80.00	45.00
Chd-203	Plate, 6" sq.	75.00	90.00	50.00
Chd-204	Plate, 7" sq.	95.00	115.00	60.00
Chd-205	Plate, 8" sq.	130.00	160.00	75.00
Chd-206	Plate, 9" sq.	150.00	180.00	95.00
Chd-207	Plate, 10" sq.	165.00	200.00	110.00
Chd-112	Relish dish, small	150.00	180.00	125.00
Chd-115	Salad bowl, chrome rim	375.00	450.00	175.00
Chd-117	Salt and pepper	125.00	150.00	75.00
Chd-118	Salt and pepper on tray	200.00	240.00	120.00
Chd-120	Sandwich tray, 10" x 6"	115.00	140.00	75.00
Chd-121	Sandwich tray, 12" x 7"	135.00	165.00	85.00
Chd-125	Sauce boat and liner	165.00	200.00	120.00
Chd-130	Teacup and saucer	125.00	150.00	60.00
Chd-135	Teapot, 2 cup	475.00	570.00	300.00
Chd-136	Teapot, 4 cup	675.00	780.00	425.00
Chd-137	Teapot, 6 cup	900.00	1,035.00	475.00
Chd-140	Teapot, stacking	1,200.00	1,320.00	625.00
Chd-145	Tennis set	135.00	165.00	75.00
Chd-150	Toast rack, 4 slice	365.00	440.00	150.00
Chd-151	Toast rack, 2 slice	285.00	345.00	120.00
Chd-155	Trivet	140.00	170.00	75.00
Chd-160	Vase, bud	185.00	225.00	85.00

CHELSEA

The pattern number is 455 and the name has been seen on an invoice as late as 1969. The pattern was registered in Canada in 1952. This pattern has become popular with American and English collectors although it is difficult to find.

Cat. No.	Shape	U.S. $	Can. $	U.K. £
Chl-04	Bonbon dish	75.00	90.00	60.00
Chl-09	Bowl, 5"	50.00	60.00	45.00
Chl-14	Bowl, 8" soup	75.00	90.00	65.00
Chl-23	Breakfast set	1,300.00	1,430.00	750.00
Chl-28	Butter dish	200.00	240.00	165.00
Chl-30	Butter pat	60.00	75.00	55.00
Chl-35	Cake plate, open handles	265.00	320.00	175.00
Chl-37	Cake plate, 8" sq. pedestal	225.00	270.00	195.00
Chl-40	Cake stand, 2 tier	200.00	240.00	175.00
Chl-45	Canoe-shaped dish	250.00	300.00	250.00
Chl-50	Cheese keep	250.00	300.00	250.00
Chl-52	Coaster	110.00	135.00	60.00
Chl-55	Coffee pot	1,200.00	1,320.00	750.00
Chl-60	Compote, footed	175.00	210.00	160.00
Chl-65	Condiment set on tray	300.00	360.00	225.00
Chl-70	Cream and sugar	200.00	240.00	125.00
Chl-71	Cream and sugar on tray	275.00	330.00	205.00
Chl-75	Demi-tasse	125.00	150.00	80.00
Chl-77	Egg cup, footed	135.00	165.00	80.00
Chl-80	Hot water jug	525.00	605.00	315.00
Chl-85	Jam pot with liner	175.00	210.00	160.00
Chl-90	Jug, 4"	425.00	510.00	250.00
Chl-91	Jug, 4 1/2"	475.00	570.00	275.00
Chl-92	Jug, 5"	525.00	605.00	300.00

Cat. No.	Shape	U.S. $	Can. $	U.K. £
Chl-97	Nut dish	50.00	60.00	55.00
Chl-201	Plate, 4" sq.	60.00	75.00	50.00
Chl-202	Plate, 5" sq.	70.00	85.00	55.00
Chl-203	Plate, 6" sq.	80.00	100.00	60.00
Chl-204	Plate, 7" sq.	100.00	120.00	75.00
Chl-205	Plate, 8" sq.	140.00	170.00	85.00
Chl-206	Plate, 9" sq.	165.00	200.00	100.00
Chl-207	Plate, 10" sq.	185.00	225.00	125.00
Chl-112	Relish dish, small	200.00	240.00	150.00
Chl-115	Salad bowl, chrome rim	395.00	475.00	195.00
Chl-117	Salt and pepper	145.00	175.00	80.00
Chl-118	Salt and pepper on tray	220.00	265.00	145.00
Chl-120	Sandwich tray, 10" x 6"	135.00	165.00	100.00
Chl-121	Sandwich tray, 12" x 7"	150.00	180.00	125.00
Chl-125	Sauce boat and liner	175.00	210.00	125.00
Chl-130	Teacup and saucer	135.00	165.00	80.00
Chl-135	Teapot, 2 cup	500.00	600.00	350.00
Chl-136	Teapot, 4 cup	700.00	805.00	525.00
Chl-137	Teapot, 6 cup	925.00	1,065.00	625.00
Chl-140	Teapot, stacking	1,300.00	1,430.00	700.00
Chl-145	Tennis set	125.00	150.00	85.00
Chl-150	Toast rack, 4 slice	375.00	450.00	225.00
Chl-151	Toast rack, 2 slice	300.00	360.00	165.00
Chl-155	Trivet	150.00	180.00	85.00
Chl-160	Vase, bud	195.00	235.00	100.00

CHINTZ

The pattern number is 2836 and was probably introduced in the mid-1930s. The pattern has elements of handpainting, including a butterfly. This pattern also comes in a brown colourway.

Cat. No.	Shape	U.S. $	Can. $	U.K. £
Chz-04	Bonbon dish	30.00	40.00	25.00
Chz-09	Bowl, 5"	30.00	40.00	25.00
Chz-14	Bowl, 8" soup	40.00	50.00	30.00
Chz-23	Breakfast set	495.00	595.00	325.00
Chz-28	Butter dish	100.00	120.00	65.00
Chz-30	Butter pat	25.00	30.00	20.00
Chz-35	Cake plate, open handles	100.00	120.00	65.00
Chz-37	Cake plate, 8" sq. pedestal	100.00	120.00	65.00
Chz-40	Cake stand, 2 tier	90.00	110.00	65.00
Chz-45	Canoe-shaped dish	135.00	165.00	85.00
Chz-50	Cheese keep	125.00	150.00	75.00
Chz-52	Coaster	25.00	30.00	20.00
Chz-55	Coffee pot	375.00	450.00	250.00
Chz-60	Compote, footed	80.00	100.00	50.00
Chz-65	Condiment set on tray	100.00	120.00	65.00
Chz-70	Cream and sugar	50.00	60.00	45.00
Chz-71	Cream and sugar on tray	100.00	120.00	65.00
Chz-75	Demi-tasse	40.00	50.00	30.00
Chz-77	Egg cup, footed	35.00	45.00	25.00
Chz-80	Hot water jug	160.00	195.00	125.00
Chz-85	Jam pot with liner	85.00	105.00	60.00
Chz-90	Jug, 4"	125.00	150.00	65.00
Chz-91	Jug, 4 1/2"	140.00	170.00	85.00
Chz-92	Jug, 5"	150.00	180.00	105.00

Cat. No.	Shape	U.S. $	Can. $	U.K. £
Chz-97	Nut dish	25.00	30.00	20.00
Chz-201	Plate, 4" sq.	30.00	40.00	20.00
Chz-202	Plate, 5" sq.	35.00	15.00	25.00
Chz-203	Plate, 6" sq.	40.00	45.00	30.00
Chz-204	Plate, 7" sq.	45.00	20.00	35.00
Chz-205	Plate, 8" sq.	65.00	55.00	45.00
Chz-206	Plate, 9" sq.	75.00	90.00	50.00
Chz-207	Plate, 10" sq .	85.00	105.00	55.00
Chz-112	Relish dish, small	85.00	105.00	60.00
Chz-115	Salad bowl, chrome rim	175.00	210.00	85.00
Chz-117	Salt and pepper	50.00	60.00	40.00
Chz-118	Salt and pepper on tray	100.00	120.00	80.00
Chz-120	Sandwich tray, 10" x 6"	60.00	75.00	45.00
Chz-121	Sandwich tray, 12" x 7"	75.00	90.00	50.00
Chz-125	Sauce boat and liner	65.00	55.00	45.00
Chz-130	Teacup and saucer	55.00	70.00	30.00
Chz-135	Teapot, 2 cup	175.00	210.00	125.00
Chz-136	Teapot, 4 cup	275.00	330.00	200.00
Chz-137	Teapot, 6 cup	325.00	390.00	225.00
Chz-140	Teapot, stacking	550.00	635.00	275.00
Chz-145	Tennis set	55.00	70.00	40.00
Chz-150	Toast rack, 4 slice	150.00	180.00	100.00
Chz-151	Toast rack, 2 slice	115.00	140.00	85.00
Chz-155	Trivet	55.00	70.00	40.00
Chz-160	Vase, bud	85.00	105.00	45.00

CLEVEDON

The pattern number is 1844 with burgundy trim. This pattern was introduced in 1934 and is an alternate colourway to **Cranstone** pattern 1154. This pattern is becoming more sought after but it is difficult to find.

Cat. No.	Shape	U.S. $	Can. $	U.K. £
Cl-04	Bonbon dish	75.00	90.00	60.00
Cl-09	Bowl, 5"	50.00	60.00	40.00
Cl-14	Bowl, 8" soup	85.00	105.00	70.00
Cl-23	Breakfast set	1,500.00	1,650.00	775.00
Cl-28	Butter dish	225.00	270.00	175.00
Cl-30	Butter pat	65.00	80.00	55.00
Cl-35	Cake plate, open handles	265.00	320.00	175.00
Cl-37	Cake plate, 8" sq. pedestal	225.00	270.00	175.00
Cl-40	Cake stand, 2 tier	200.00	240.00	150.00
Cl-45	Canoe-shaped dish	275.00	330.00	250.00
Cl-50	Cheese keep	275.00	330.00	225.00
Cl-52	Coaster	125.00	150.00	60.00
Cl-55	Coffee pot	1,275.00	1,405.00	675.00
Cl-60	Compote, footed	175.00	210.00	150.00
Cl-65	Condiment set on tray	300.00	360.00	225.00
Cl-70	Cream and sugar	170.00	205.00	95.00
Cl-71	Cream and sugar on tray	235.00	285.00	225.00
Cl-75	Demi-tasse	125.00	150.00	75.00
Cl-77	Egg cup, footed	125.00	150.00	70.00
Cl-80	Hot water jug	535.00	615.00	300.00
Cl-85	Jam pot with liner	200.00	240.00	150.00
Cl-90	Jug, 4"	425.00	510.00	225.00
Cl-91	Jug, 4 1/2"	475.00	570.00	250.00
Cl-92	Jug, 5"	525.00	605.00	275.00

Cat. No.	Shape	U.S. $	Can. $	U.K. £
Cl-97	Nut dish	65.00	80.00	55.00
Cl-201	Plate, 4" sq.	50.00	60.00	35.00
Cl-202	Plate, 5" sq.	65.00	80.00	45.00
Cl-203	Plate, 6" sq.	75.00	90.00	55.00
Cl-204	Plate, 7" sq.	100.00	110.00	65.00
Cl-205	Plate, 8" sq.	135.00	165.00	85.00
Cl-206	Plate, 9" sq.	150.00	180.00	100.00
Cl-207	Plate, 10" sq.	165.00	200.00	125.00
Cl-112	Relish dish, small	200.00	240.00	150.00
Cl-115	Salad bowl, chrome rim	395.00	475.00	200.00
Cl-117	Salt and pepper	125.00	150.00	75.00
Cl-118	Salt and pepper on tray	210.00	255.00	145.00
Cl-120	Sandwich tray, 10" x 6"	150.00	180.00	120.00
Cl-121	Sandwich tray, 12" x 7"	165.00	200.00	145.00
Cl-125	Sauce boat and liner	165.00	200.00	150.00
Cl-130	Teacup and saucer	135.00	165.00	75.00
Cl-135	Teapot, 2 cup	650.00	750.00	350.00
Cl-136	Teapot, 4 cup	900.00	1,035.00	500.00
Cl-137	Teapot, 6 cup	1,100.00	1,210.00	575.00
Cl-140	Teapot, stacking	1,600.00	1,760.00	650.00
Cl-145	Tennis set	135.00	165.00	85.00
Cl-150	Toast rack, 4 slice	400.00	480.00	215.00
Cl-151	Toast rack, 2 slice	325.00	390.00	175.00
Cl-155	Trivet	150.00	180.00	90.00
Cl-160	Vase, bud	195.00	235.00	95.00

CLYDE

The pattern number is 5315 for the green-leaf version and 5637 for the brown-leaf version. **Clyde** was probably introduced late in 1939. The three versions of **Clyde** feature green, brown and blue leaves, but the brown and blue versions have not been found with a pattern name backstamp.

Cat. No.	Shape	U.S. $	Can. $	U.K. £
Cly-04	Bonbon dish	25.00	30.00	25.00
Cly-09	Bowl, 5"	25.00	30.00	25.00
Cly-14	Bowl, 8" soup	35.00	45.00	30.00
Cly-23	Breakfast set	350.00	420.00	275.00
Cly-28	Butter dish	90.00	110.00	65.00
Cly-30	Butter pat	25.00	30.00	20.00
Cly-35	Cake plate, open handles	90.00	110.00	75.00
Cly-37	Cake plate, 8" sq. pedestal	90.00	110.00	65.00
Cly-40	Cake stand, 2 tier	90.00	110.00	65.00
Cly-45	Canoe-shaped dish	120.00	145.00	85.00
Cly-50	Cheese keep	115.00	140.00	100.00
Cly-52	Coaster	25.00	30.00	20.00
Cly-55	Coffee pot	350.00	420.00	200.00
Cly-60	Compote, footed	65.00	80.00	50.00
Cly-65	Condiment set on tray	90.00	110.00	65.00
Cly-70	Cream and sugar	55.00	70.00	45.00
Cly-71	Cream and sugar on tray	90.00	110.00	65.00
Cly-75	Demi-tasse	35.00	45.00	30.00
Cly-77	Egg cup, footed	35.00	45.00	25.00
Cly-80	Hot water jug	165.00	200.00	125.00
Cly-85	Jam pot with liner	75.00	90.00	60.00
Cly-90	Jug, 4"	135.00	165.00	65.00
Cly-91	Jug, 4 1/2"	150.00	180.00	75.00
Cly-92	Jug, 5"	165.00	200.00	95.00

Cat. No.	Shape	U.S. $	Can. $	U.K. £
Cly-97	Nut dish	25.00	30.00	20.00
Cly-201	Plate, 4" sq.	30.00	40.00	25.00
Cly-202	Plate, 5" sq.	35.00	45.00	25.00
Cly-203	Plate, 6" sq.	40.00	50.00	30.00
Cly-204	Plate, 7" sq.	45.00	55.00	35.00
Cly-205	Plate, 8" sq.	55.00	70.00	45.00
Cly-206	Plate, 9" sq.	65.00	80.00	50.00
Cly-207	Plate, 10" sq.	75.00	90.00	55.00
Cly-112	Relish dish, small	75.00	90.00	60.00
Cly-115	Salad bowl, chrome rim	145.00	175.00	75.00
Cly-117	Salt and pepper	45.00	55.00	40.00
Cly-118	Salt and pepper on tray	100.00	120.00	80.00
Cly-120	Sandwich tray, 10" x 6"	45.00	55.00	45.00
Cly-121	Sandwich tray, 12" x 7"	65.00	80.00	50.00
Cly-125	Sauce boat and liner	65.00	80.00	45.00
Cly-130	Teacup and saucer	35.00	45.00	30.00
Cly-135	Teapot, 2 cup	150.00	180.00	100.00
Cly-136	Teapot, 4 cup	225.00	270.00	150.00
Cly-137	Teapot, 6 cup	275.00	330.00	200.00
Cly-140	Teapot, stacking	300.00	360.00	275.00
Cly-145	Tennis set	45.00	55.00	40.00
Cly-150	Toast rack, 4 slice	150.00	180.00	90.00
Cly-151	Toast rack, 2 slice	90.00	110.00	65.00
Cly-155	Trivet	45.00	55.00	40.00
Cly-160	Vase, bud	65.00	80.00	45.00

COTSWOLD

The pattern number is 408 and the pattern was registered in Canada in 1952. This pattern was also used occasionally on bone china in the 1950s. Cotswold has become increasingly popular in England but it is difficult to find.

Cat. No.	Shape	U.S. $	Can. $	U.K. £
Co-04	Bonbon dish	50.00	60.00	50.00
Co-09	Bowl, 5"	50.00	60.00	45.00
Co-14	Bowl, 8" soup	75.00	90.00	60.00
Co-23	Breakfast set	1,000.00	1,150.00	650.00
Co-28	Butter dish	165.00	200.00	15.00
Co-30	Butter pat	45.00	55.00	40.00
Co-35	Cake plate, open handles	175.00	210.00	150.00
Co-37	Cake plate, 8" sq. pedestal	175.00	210.00	150.00
Co-40	Cake stand, 2 tier	150.00	180.00	150.00
Co-45	Canoe-shaped dish	200.00	240.00	195.00
Co-50	Cheese keep	200.00	240.00	175.00
Co-52	Coaster	85.00	105.00	35.00
Co-55	Coffee pot	750.00	865.00	500.00
Co-60	Compote, footed	135.00	165.00	105.00
Co-65	Condiment set on tray	200.00	240.00	165.00
Co-70	Cream and sugar	145.00	175.00	75.00
Co-71	Cream and sugar on tray	195.00	235.00	150.00
Co-75	Demi-tasse	95.00	115.00	60.00
Co-77	Egg cup, footed	105.00	130.00	55.00
Co-80	Hot water jug	400.00	480.00	225.00
Co-85	Jam pot with liner	150.00	180.00	120.00
Co-90	Jug, 4"	325.00	390.00	150.00
Co-91	Jug, 4 1/2"	375.00	450.00	175.00
Co-92	Jug, 5"	400.00	480.00	200.00

Cat. No.	Shape	U.S. $	Can. $	U.K. £
Co-97	Nut dish	45.00	55.00	40.00
Co-201	Plate, 4" sq.	50.00	60.00	40.00
Co-202	Plate, 5" sq.	55.00	70.00	50.00
Co-203	Plate, 6" sq.	60.00	75.00	55.00
Co-204	Plate, 7" sq.	75.00	90.00	65.00
Co-205	Plate, 8" sq.	100.00	120.00	75.00
Co-206	Plate, 9" sq.	120.00	145.00	85.00
Co-207	Plate, 10" sq.	135.00	65.00	95.00
Co-112	Relish dish, small	150.00	180.00	125.00
Co-115	Salad bowl, chrome rim	325.00	390.00	175.00
Co-117	Salt and pepper	100.00	120.00	60.00
Co-118	Salt and pepper on tray	175.00	210.00	120.00
Co-120	Sandwich tray, 10" x 6"	100.00	120.00	75.00
Co-121	Sandwich tray, 12" x 7"	125.00	150.00	95.00
Co-125	Sauce boat and liner	150.00	180.00	120.00
Co-130	Teacup and saucer	115.00	140.00	60.00
Co-135	Teapot, 2 cup	325.00	390.00	250.00
Co-136	Teapot, 4 cup	500.00	600.00	375.00
Co-137	Teapot, 6 cup	600.00	690.00	475.00
Co-140	Teapot, stacking	950.00	1,095.00	575.00
Co-145	Tennis set	110.00	135.00	75.00
Co-150	Toast rack, 4 slice	295.00	355.00	150.00
Co-151	Toast rack, 2 slice	225.00	270.00	110.00
Co-155	Trivet	115.00	140.00	75.00
Co-160	Vase, bud	165.00	200.00	75.00

CRANSTONE

The pattern number is 1154 with gold trim and an example was purchased by the Queen at the 1935 British Industries Fair. The pattern number for burgundy trim is 1877 and for green trim 2256. The alternate colourway is **Clevedon** 1844. This pattern has become very popular this year but it is difficult to find.

Cat. No.	Shape	U.S. $	Can. $	U.K. £
Cr-04	Bonbon dish	90.00	110.00	65.00
Cr-09	Bowl, 5"	65.00	80.00	50.00
Cr-14	Bowl, 8" soup	110.00	140.00	75.00
Cr-23	Breakfast set	1,450.00	1,595.00	800.00
Cr-28	Butter dish	250.00	300.00	175.00
Cr-30	Butter pat	75.00	90.00	50.00
Cr-35	Cake plate, open handles	295.00	355.00	175.00
Cr-37	Cake plate, 8" sq. pedestal	275.00	330.00	200.00
Cr-40	Cake stand, 2 tier	250.00	300.00	200.00
Cr-45	Canoe-shaped dish	325.00	390.00	250.00
Cr-50	Cheese keep	310.00	375.00	225.00
Cr-52	Coaster	125.00	150.00	55.00
Cr-55	Coffee pot	1,350.00	1,485.00	700.00
Cr-60	Compote, footed	230.00	280.00	150.00
Cr-65	Condiment set on tray	325.00	390.00	215.00
Cr-70	Cream and sugar	185.00	225.00	100.00
Cr-71	Cream and sugar on tray	300.00	360.00	185.00
Cr-75	Demi-tasse	135.00	165.00	75.00
Cr-77	Egg cup, footed	130.00	160.00	70.00
Cr-80	Hot water jug	575.00	665.00	325.00
Cr-85	Jam pot with liner	250.00	300.00	150.00
Cr-90	Jug, 4"	450.00	540.00	275.00
Cr-91	Jug, 4 1/2"	500.00	600.00	300.00
Cr-92	Jug, 5"	550.00	660.00	325.00

Cat. No.	Shape	U.S. $	Can. $	U.K. £
Cr-97	Nut dish	75.00	90.00	50.00
Cr-201	Plate, 4" sq.	70.00	85.00	45.00
Cr-202	Plate, 5" sq.	80.00	100.00	50.00
Cr-203	Plate, 6" sq.	90.00	110.00	55.00
Cr-204	Plate, 7" sq.	120.00	145.00	65.00
Cr-205	Plate, 8" sq.	150.00	180.00	80.00
Cr-206	Plate, 9" sq.	175.00	210.00	95.00
Cr-207	Plate, 10" sq.	190.00	230.00	115.00
Cr-112	Relish dish, small	220.00	265.00	175.00
Cr-115	Salad bowl, chrome rim	395.00	475.00	195.00
Cr-117	Salt and pepper	135.00	165.00	75.00
Cr-118	Salt and pepper on tray	225.00	270.00	175.00
Cr-120	Sandwich tray, 10" x 6"	165.00	200.00	125.00
Cr-121	Sandwich tray, 12" x 7"	195.00	235.00	150.00
Cr-125	Sauce boat and liner	195.00	235.00	150.00
Cr-130	Teacup and saucer	145.00	175.00	75.00
Cr-135	Teapot, 2 cup	650.00	750.00	375.00
Cr-136	Teapot, 4 cup	900.00	1,035.00	525.00
Cr-137	Teapot, 6 cup	1,100.00	1,210.00	625.00
Cr-140	Teapot, stacking	1,600.00	1,760.00	700.00
Cr-145	Tennis set	150.00	180.00	120.00
Cr-150	Toast rack, 4 slice	400.00	480.00	225.00
Cr-151	Toast rack, 2 slice	325.00	390.00	175.00
Cr-155	Trivet	150.00	180.00	120.00
Cr-160	Vase, bud	195.00	235.00	105.00

CROCUS

The pattern number of the white background **Crocus** is 111. The pattern number for the black background is 112 and a piece was found in 1997 with the pattern name **Triumph**. The pattern is mentioned in a 1939 article but it is the one of the few Royal Winton chintz patterns that have never been found with a pattern name backstamp. See **Triumph** page 114.

Cat. No.	Shape	U.S. $	Can. $	U.K. £
Cro-04	Bonbon dish	75.00	90.00	50.00
Cro-09	Bowl, 5"	50.00	60.00	35.00
Cro-14	Bowl, 8" soup	80.00	100.00	50.00
Cro-23	Breakfast set	1,000.00	1,150.00	600.00
Cro-28	Butter dish	200.00	240.00	150.00
Cro-30	Butter pat	60.00	75.00	45.00
Cro-35	Cake plate, open handles	200.00	240.00	150.00
Cro-37	Cake plate, 8" sq. pedestal	225.00	270.00	150.00
Cro-40	Cake stand, 2 tier	150.00	180.00	150.00
Cro-45	Canoe-shaped dish	225.00	270.00	150.00
Cro-50	Cheese keep	250.00	200.00	175.00
Cro-52	Coaster	85.00	105.00	40.00
Cro-55	Coffee pot	750.00	865.00	600.00
Cro-60	Compote, footed	175.00	210.00	125.00
Cro-65	Condiment set on tray	225.00	270.00	175.00
Cro-70	Cream and sugar	150.00	180.00	85.00
Cro-71	Cream and sugar on tray	225.00	270.00	175.00
Cro-75	Demi-tasse	100.00	120.00	65.00
Cro-77	Egg cup, footed	105.00	130.00	50.00
Cro-80	Hot water jug	400.00	480.00	250.00
Cro-85	Jam pot with liner	165.00	200.00	135.00
Cro-90	Jug, 4"	325.00	390.00	225.00
Cro-91	Jug, 4 1/2"	375.00	450.00	250.00
Cro-92	Jug, 5"	400.00	480.00	275.00

Cat. No.	Shape	U.S. $	Can. $	U.K. £
Cro-97	Nut dish	50.00	60.00	40.00
Cro-201	Plate, 4" sq.	50.00	60.00	40.00
Cro-202	Plate, 5" sq.	65.00	80.00	45.00
Cro-203	Plate, 6" sq.	75.00	90.00	50.00
Cro-204	Plate, 7" sq.	100.00	120.00	65.00
Cro-205	Plate, 8" sq.	135.00	155.00	75.00
Cro-206	Plate, 9" sq.	150.00	180.00	85.00
Cro-207	Plate, 10" sq .	165.00	200.00	105.00
Cro-112	Relish dish, small	200.00	240.00	125.00
Cro-115	Salad bowl, chrome rim	350.00	420.00	160.00
Cro-117	Salt and pepper	110.00	135.00	65.00
Cro-118	Salt and pepper on tray	185.00	225.00	125.00
Cro-120	Sandwich tray, 10" x 6"	135.00	165.00	95.00
Cro-121	Sandwich tray, 12" x 7"	165.00	200.00	115.00
Cro-125	Sauce boat and liner	165.00	200.00	115.00
Cro-130	Teacup and saucer	110.00	135.00	65.00
Cro-135	Teapot, 2 cup	450.00	540.00	300.00
Cro-136	Teapot, 4 cup	650.00	750.00	450.00
Cro-137	Teapot, 6 cup	750.00	865.00	525.00
Cro-140	Teapot, stacking	1,000.00	1,150.00	550.00
Cro-145	Tennis set	125.00	150.00	75.00
Cro-150	Toast rack, 4 slice	295.00	355.00	175.00
Cro-151	Toast rack, 2 slice	225.00	270.00	125.00
Cro-155	Trivet	125.00	150.00	75.00
Cro-160	Vase, bud	165.00	200.00	75.00

CROMER

The pattern number is 2078 and belongs to the all-over non-chintz pattern group.

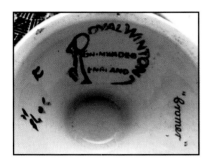 

Cat. No.	Shape	U.S. $	Can. $	U.K. £
Crom-04	Bonbon dish	30.00	40.00	25.00
Crom-09	Bowl, 5"	30.00	40.00	25.00
Crom-14	Bowl, 8" soup	40.00	50.00	35.00
Crom-23	Breakfast set	495.00	595.00	325.00
Crom-28	Butter dish	100.00	120.00	65.00
Crom-30	Butter pat	25.00	30.00	20.00
Crom-35	Cake plate, open handles	100.00	120.00	75.00
Crom-37	Cake plate, 8" sq. pedestal	100.00	120.00	75.00
Crom-40	Cake stand, 2 tier	100.00	120.00	65.00
Crom-45	Canoe-shaped dish	135.00	165.00	85.00
Crom-50	Cheese keep	125.00	150.00	85.00
Crom-52	Coaster	30.00	40.00	20.00
Crom-55	Coffee pot	375.00	450.00	275.00
Crom-60	Compote, footed	80.00	100.00	60.00
Crom-65	Condiment set on tray	110.00	135.00	75.00
Crom-70	Cream and sugar	55.00	70.00	55.00
Crom-71	Cream and sugar on tray	100.00	120.00	75.00
Crom-75	Demi-tasse	40.00	50.00	30.00
Crom-77	Egg cup, footed	55.00	70.00	35.00
Crom-80	Hot water jug	175.00	210.00	125.00
Crom-85	Jam pot with liner	95.00	115.00	70.00
Crom-90	Jug, 4"	125.00	150.00	75.00
Crom-91	Jug, 4 1/2"	150.00	180.00	95.00
Crom-92	Jug, 5"	165.00	200.00	105.00

Cat. No.	Shape	U.S. $	Can. $	U.K. £
Crom-97	Nut dish	25.00	30.00	20.00
Crom-201	Plate, 4" sq.	30.00	40.00	20.00
Crom-202	Plate, 5" sq.	35.00	45.00	25.00
Crom-203	Plate, 6" sq.	40.00	50.00	30.00
Crom-204	Plate, 7" sq.	45.00	55.00	35.00
Crom-205	Plate, 8" sq.	65.00	80.00	45.00
Crom-206	Plate, 9" sq.	75.00	90.00	50.00
Crom-207	Plate, 10" sq .	85.00	105.00	55.00
Crom-112	Relish dish, small	90.00	110.00	60.00
Crom-115	Salad bowl, chrome rim	175.00	210.00	95.00
Crom-117	Salt and pepper	55.00	70.00	40.00
Crom-118	Salt and pepper on tray	105.00	130.00	75.00
Crom-120	Sandwich tray, 10" x 6"	65.00	80.00	45.00
Crom-121	Sandwich tray, 12" x 7"	75.00	90.00	50.00
Crom-125	Sauce boat and liner	75.00	90.00	50.00
Crom-130	Teacup and saucer	55.00	70.00	30.00
Crom-135	Teapot, 2 cup	175.00	210.00	125.00
Crom-136	Teapot, 4 cup	275.00	330.00	200.00
Crom-137	Teapot, 6 cup	325.00	390.00	275.00
Crom-140	Teapot, stacking	550.00	635.00	325.00
Crom-145	Tennis set	65.00	80.00	45.00
Crom-150	Toast rack, 4 slice	150.00	180.00	115.00
Crom-151	Toast rack, 2 slice	115.00	140.00	85.00
Crom-155	Trivet	65.00	80.00	45.00
Crom-160	Vase, bud	85.00	105.00	55.00

DELPHINIUM CHINTZ

The pattern number is 9889. This pattern was introduced in 1931 in an advertisement in the *Pottery Gazette*. It first appeared a year earlier as a single spray on an ivory ground.

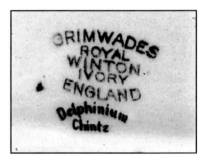

Cat. No.	Shape	U.S. $	Can. $	U.K. £
De-04	Bonbon dish	45.00	55.00	35.00
De-09	Bowl, 5"	40.00	50.00	30.00
De-14	Bowl, 8" soup	75.00	90.00	50.00
De-23	Breakfast set	800.00	920.00	450.00
De-28	Butter dish	135.00	165.00	85.00
De-30	Butter pat	40.00	50.00	30.00
De-35	Cake plate, open handles	155.00	190.00	85.00
De-37	Cake plate, 8" sq. pedestal	150.00	180.00	100.00
De-40	Cake stand, 2 tier	150.00	180.00	100.00
De-45	Canoe-shaped dish	200.00	240.00	125.00
De-50	Cheese keep	175.00	210.00	125.00
De-52	Coaster	85.00	105.00	35.00
De-55	Coffee pot	575.00	665.00	375.00
De-60	Compote, footed	100.00	120.00	65.00
De-65	Condiment set on tray	150.00	180.00	100.00
De-70	Cream and sugar	85.00	105.00	60.00
De-71	Cream and sugar on tray	150.00	180.00	100.00
De-75	Demi-tasse	60.00	75.00	45.00
De-77	Egg cup, footed	90.00	110.00	45.00
De-80	Hot water jug	275.00	330.00	150.00
De-85	Jam pot with liner	125.00	150.00	75.00
De-90	Jug, 4"	275.00	330.00	115.00
De-91	Jug, 4 1/2"	300.00	360.00	135.00
De-92	Jug, 5"	325.00	390.00	150.00

Cat. No.	Shape	U.S. $	Can. $	U.K. £
De-97	Nut dish	40.00	50.00	30.00
De-201	Plate, 4" sq.	35.00	45.00	20.00
De-202	Plate, 5" sq.	40.00	50.00	25.00
De-203	Plate, 6" sq.	45.00	55.00	30.00
De-204	Plate, 7" sq.	50.00	60.00	35.00
De-205	Plate, 8" sq.	60.00	75.00	40.00
De-206	Plate, 9" sq.	75.00	90.00	50.00
De-207	Plate, 10" sq.	95.00	115.00	60.00
De-112	Relish dish, small	125.00	150.00	75.00
De-115	Salad bowl, chrome rim	275.00	330.00	95.00
De-117	Salt and pepper	75.00	90.00	45.00
De-118	Salt and pepper on tray	140.00	170.00	85.00
De-120	Sandwich tray, 10" x 6"	85.00	105.00	60.00
De-121	Sandwich tray, 12" x 7"	100.00	120.00	65.00
De-125	Sauce boat and liner	125.00	150.00	75.00
De-130	Teacup and saucer	85.00	105.00	45.00
De-135	Teapot, 2 cup	275.00	330.00	175.00
De-136	Teapot, 4 cup	375.00	450.00	250.00
De-137	Teapot, 6 cup	475.00	570.00	325.00
De-140	Teapot, stacking	950.00	1,095.00	425.00
De-145	Tennis set	95.00	115.00	50.00
De-150	Toast rack, 4 slice	175.00	210.00	125.00
De-151	Toast rack, 2 slice	125.00	150.00	75.00
De-155	Trivet	75.00	90.00	50.00
De-160	Vase, bud	135.00	165.00	60.00

DORSET

The pattern number is 274, and this pattern was featured in an advertisement in Toronto, Canada, in 1949. The pattern number of the brown version is 294.

Cat. No.	Shape	U.S. $	Can. $	U.K. £
Do-04	Bonbon dish	25.00	30.00	25.00
Do-09	Bowl, 5"	25.00	30.00	25.00
Do-14	Bowl, 8" soup	35.00	45.00	30.00
Do-23	Breakfast set	350.00	420.00	300.00
Do-28	Butter dish	90.00	110.00	65.00
Do-30	Butter pat	25.00	30.00	20.00
Do-35	Cake plate, open handles	95.00	115.00	75.00
Do-37	Cake plate, 8" sq. pedestal	95.00	115.00	65.00
Do-40	Cake stand, 2 tier	95.00	115.00	65.00
Do-45	Canoe-shaped dish	135.00	165.00	100.00
Do-50	Cheese keep	115.00	140.00	90.00
Do-52	Coaster	30.00	40.00	20.00
Do-55	Coffee pot	375.00	450.00	250.00
Do-60	Compote, footed	65.00	80.00	50.00
Do-65	Condiment set on tray	90.00	110.00	65.00
Do-70	Cream and sugar	55.00	70.00	45.00
Do-71	Cream and sugar on tray	90.00	110.00	65.00
Do-75	Demi-tasse	40.00	50.00	30.00
Do-77	Egg cup, footed	45.00	55.00	30.00
Do-80	Hot water jug	165.00	200.00	125.00
Do-85	Jam pot with liner	75.00	90.00	60.00
Do-90	Jug, 4"	135.00	165.00	75.00
Do-91	Jug, 4 1/2	150.00	180.00	90.00
Do-92	Jug, 5"	165.00	200.00	100.00

Cat. No.	Shape	U.S. $	Can. $	U.K. £
Do-97	Nut dish	25.00	30.00	20.00
Do-201	Plate, 4" sq.	30.00	40.00	20.00
Do-202	Plate, 5" sq.	35.00	45.00	25.00
Do-203	Plate, 6" sq.	40.00	50.00	30.00
Do-204	Plate, 7" sq.	45.00	55.00	35.00
Do-205	Plate, 8" sq.	55.00	70.00	40.00
Do-206	Plate, 9" sq.	65.00	80.00	45.00
Do-207	Plate, 10" sq.	75.00	90.00	50.00
Do-112	Relish dish, small	75.00	90.00	55.00
Do-115	Salad bowl, chrome rim	145.00	175.00	85.00
Do-117	Salt and pepper	45.00	55.00	35.00
Do-118	Salt and pepper on tray	95.00	115.00	65.00
Do-120	Sandwich tray, 10" x 6"	50.00	60.00	40.00
Do-121	Sandwich tray, 12" x 7"	65.00	80.00	50.00
Do-125	Sauce boat and liner	65.00	80.00	45.00
Do-130	Teacup and saucer	40.00	50.00	30.00
Do-135	Teapot, 2 cup	150.00	180.00	100.00
Do-136	Teapot, 4 cup	225.00	270.00	150.00
Do-137	Teapot, 6 cup	275.00	330.00	225.00
Do-140	Teapot, stacking	300.00	360.00	300.00
Do-145	Tennis set	45.00	55.00	35.00
Do-150	Toast rack, 4 slice	145.00	175.00	90.00
Do-151	Toast rack, 2 slice	95.00	115.00	60.00
Do-155	Trivet	45.00	55.00	35.00
Do-160	Vase, bud	65.00	80.00	50.00

ELEANOR

The pattern number is 375, and was introduced early in the 1950s and remained in production well into the 1960s.

Cat. No.	Shape	U.S. $	Can. $	U.K. £
El-04	Bonbon dish	45.00	55.00	35.00
El-09	Bowl, 5"	40.00	50.00	30.00
El-14	Bowl, 8" soup	75.00	90.00	50.00
El-23	Breakfast set	800.00	920.00	400.00
El-28	Butter dish	135.00	165.00	85.00
El-30	Butter pat	40.00	50.00	30.00
El-35	Cake plate, open handles	155.00	190.00	95.00
El-37	Cake plate, 8" sq. pedestal	150.00	180.00	100.00
El-40	Cake stand, 2 tier	150.00	180.00	75.00
El-45	Canoe-shaped dish	200.00	240.00	125.00
El-50	Cheese keep	175.00	210.00	125.00
El-52	Coaster	85.00	105.00	45.00
El-55	Coffee pot	575.00	665.00	375.00
El-60	Compote, footed	100.00	120.00	65.00
El-65	Condiment set on tray	150.00	180.00	100.00
El-70	Cream and sugar	85.00	105.00	60.00
El-71	Cream and sugar on tray	150.00	180.00	100.00
El-75	Demi-tasse	60.00	75.00	45.00
El-77	Egg cup, footed	90.00	110.00	55.00
El-80	Hot water jug	275.00	330.00	150.00
El-85	Jam pot with liner	125.00	150.00	75.00
El-90	Jug, 4"	275.00	330.00	150.00
El-91	Jug, 4 1/2"	300.00	360.00	160.00
El-92	Jug, 5"	325.00	390.00	175.00

Cat. No.	Shape	U.S. $	Can. $	U.K. £
El-97	Nut dish	40.00	50.00	30.00
El-201	Plate, 4" sq.	35.00	45.00	20.00
El-202	Plate, 5" sq.	40.00	50.00	25.00
El-203	Plate, 6" sq.	45.00	55.00	30.00
El-204	Plate, 7" sq.	50.00	60.00	35.00
El-205	Plate, 8" sq.	75.00	90.00	40.00
El-206	Plate, 9" sq.	85.00	105.00	50.00
El-207	Plate, 10" sq.	100.00	120.00	60.00
El-112	Relish dish, small	125.00	150.00	75.00
El-115	Salad bowl, chrome rim	275.00	330.00	150.00
El-117	Salt and pepper	65.00	80.00	45.00
El-118	Salt and pepper on tray	140.00	170.00	85.00
El-120	Sandwich tray, 10" x 6"	85.00	105.00	60.00
El-121	Sandwich tray, 12" x 7"	100.00	120.00	65.00
El-125	Sauce boat and liner	125.00	150.00	75.00
El-130	Teacup and saucer	85.00	105.00	45.00
El-135	Teapot, 2 cup	275.00	330.00	150.00
El-136	Teapot, 4 cup	375.00	450.00	225.00
El-137	Teapot, 6 cup	475.00	570.00	275.00
El-140	Teapot, stacking	950.00	1,095.00	475.00
El-145	Tennis set	95.00	115.00	50.00
El-150	Toast rack, 4 slice	175.00	210.00	125.00
El-151	Toast rack, 2 slice	125.00	150.00	85.00
El-155	Trivet	75.00	90.00	50.00
El-160	Vase, bud	135.00	165.00	80.00

ENGLISH ROSE

The pattern number is 381 and this pattern has become increasingly popular with North American collectors. The pattern was introduced into Canada in 1951 and described in an advertisement as a warm and colourful pattern depicting the beauty of the English Rose in full bloom. The pattern was exclusive to Dingle, Davidson, Ltd. Toronto. Cups and saucers and 7 plates were available with a black or dark green border. **English Rose** has appeared occasionally on 1960s bone china cups and saucers made by Crown Staffordshire China.

Cat. No.	Shape	U.S. $	Can. $	U.K. £
ER-04	Bonbon dish	85.00	105.00	60.00
ER-09	Bowl, 5"	55.00	70.00	50.00
ER-14	Bowl, 8" soup	110.00	120.00	75.00
ER-23	Breakfast set	1,450.00	1,595.00	850.00
ER-28	Butter dish	250.00	300.00	175.00
ER-30	Butter pat	75.00	90.00	55.00
ER-35	Cake plate, open handles	295.00	355.00	195.00
ER-37	Cake plate, 8" sq. pedestal	275.00	330.00	200.00
ER-40	Cake stand, 2 tier	250.00	300.00	150.00
ER-45	Canoe-shaped dish	325.00	390.00	225.00
ER-50	Cheese keep	330.00	400.00	225.00
ER-52	Coaster	125.00	150.00	65.00
ER-55	Coffee pot	1,350.00	1,650.00	700.00
ER-60	Compote, footed	225.00	270.00	150.00
ER-65	Condiment set on tray	325.00	390.00	215.00
ER-70	Cream and sugar	195.00	235.00	150.00
ER-71	Cream and sugar on tray	325.00	390.00	220.00
ER-75	Demi-tasse	135.00	165.00	85.00
ER-77	Egg cup, footed	130.00	160.00	85.00
ER-80	Hot water jug	575.00	665.00	350.00
ER-85	Jam pot with liner	220.00	265.00	175.00
ER-90	Jug, 4"	450.00	540.00	250.00
ER-91	Jug, 4 1/2"	500.00	600.00	275.00
ER-92	Jug, 5"	550.00	635.00	300.00

Cat. No.	Shape	U.S. $	Can. $	U.K. £
ER-97	Nut dish	75.00	90.00	50.00
ER-201	Plate, 4" sq.	65.00	80.00	45.00
ER-202	Plate, 5" sq.	70.00	85.00	55.00
ER-203	Plate, 6" sq.	75.00	90.00	60.00
ER-204	Plate, 7" sq.	110.00	135.00	75.00
ER-205	Plate, 8" sq.	150.00	180.00	85.00
ER-206	Plate, 9" sq.	165.00	200.00	120.00
ER-207	Plate, 10" sq.	195.00	235.00	145.00
ER-112	Relish dish, small	220.00	265.00	150.00
ER-115	Salad bowl, chrome rim	395.00	475.00	225.00
ER-117	Salt and pepper	125.00	150.00	85.00
ER-118	Salt and pepper on tray	220.00	265.00	175.00
ER-120	Sandwich tray, 10" x 6"	165.00	200.00	125.00
ER-121	Sandwich tray, 12" x 7"	195.00	235.00	145.00
ER-125	Sauce boat and liner	195.00	235.00	125.00
ER-130	Teacup and saucer	135.00	165.00	80.00
ER-135	Teapot, 2 cup	650.00	750.00	375.00
ER-136	Teapot, 4 cup	900.00	1,035.00	525.00
ER-137	Teapot, 6 cup	1,100.00	1,210.00	625.00
ER-140	Teapot, stacking	1,600.00	1,760.00	750.00
ER-145	Tennis set	165.00	200.00	120.00
ER-150	Toast rack, 4 slice	400.00	480.00	215.00
ER-151	Toast rack, 2 slice	325.00	390.00	175.00
ER-155	Trivet	150.00	180.00	100.00
ER-160	Vase, bud	195.00	235.00	115.00

ESTELLE

The pattern number is 423, and the pattern was introduced early in the 1950s. This pattern is not easy to find but growing in popularity in the United States.

Cat. No.	Shape	U.S. $	Can. $	U.K. £
Esl-04	Bonbon dish	60.00	75.00	45.00
Esl-09	Bowl, 5"	50.00	60.00	40.00
Esl-14	Bowl, 8" soup	75.00	90.00	60.00
Esl-23	Breakfast set	1,250.00	1,375.00	550.00
Esl-28	Butter dish	175.00	210.00	120.00
Esl-30	Butter pat	50.00	60.00	40.00
Esl-35	Cake plate, open handles	235.00	285.00	125.00
Esl-37	Cake plate, 8" sq. pedestal	200.00	240.00	125.00
Esl-40	Cake stand, 2 tier	175.00	210.00	125.00
Esl-45	Canoe-shaped dish	225.00	270.00	150.00
Esl-50	Cheese keep	240.00	290.00	175.00
Esl-52	Coaster	110.00	135.00	40.00
Esl-55	Coffee pot	1,050.00	1,150.00	525.00
Esl-60	Compote, footed	150.00	180.00	95.00
Esl-65	Condiment set on tray	275.00	330.00	175.00
Esl-70	Cream and sugar	175.00	210.00	75.00
Esl-71	Cream and sugar on tray	250.00	300.00	175.00
Esl-75	Demi-tasse	115.00	140.00	60.00
Esl-77	Egg cup, footed	125.00	150.00	55.00
Esl-80	Hot water jug	450.00	540.00	225.00
Esl-85	Jam pot with liner	150.00	180.00	120.00
Esl-90	Jug, 4"	400.00	480.00	175.00
Esl-91	Jug, 4 1/2"	450.00	540.00	200.00
Esl-92	Jug, 5"	500.00	600.00	225.00

Cat. No.	Shape	U.S. $	Can. $	U.K. £
Esl-97	Nut dish	50.00	60.00	35.00
Esl-201	Plate, 4" sq.	55.00	70.00	40.00
Esl-202	Plate, 5" sq.	65.00	80.00	45.00
Esl-203	Plate, 6" sq.	75.00	90.00	50.00
Esl-204	Plate, 7" sq.	95.00	115.00	55.00
Esl-205	Plate, 8" sq.	130.00	160.00	65.00
Esl-206	Plate, 9" sq.	150.00	180.00	80.00
Esl-207	Plate, 10" sq.	165.00	200.00	95.00
Esl-112	Relish dish, small	150.00	180.00	125.00
Esl-115	Salad bowl, chrome rim	375.00	450.00	175.00
Esl-117	Salt and pepper	125.00	150.00	60.00
Esl-118	Salt and pepper on tray	200.00	240.00	120.00
Esl-120	Sandwich tray, 10" x 6"	115.00	140.00	75.00
Esl-121	Sandwich tray, 12" x 7"	135.00	165.00	95.00
Esl-125	Sauce boat and liner	165.00	200.00	120.00
Esl-130	Teacup and saucer	125.00	150.00	60.00
Esl-135	Teapot, 2 cup	475.00	570.00	250.00
Esl-136	Teapot, 4 cup	675.00	780.00	375.00
Esl-137	Teapot, 6 cup	900.00	1,035.00	450.00
Esl-140	Teapot, stacking	1,200.00	1,320.00	550.00
Esl-145	Tennis set	135.00	165.00	75.00
Esl-150	Toast rack, 4 slice	365.00	440.00	155.00
Esl-151	Toast rack, 2 slice	285.00	345.00	115.00
Esl-155	Trivet	140.00	170.00	75.00
Esl-160	Vase, bud	185.00	225.00	85.00

ESTHER

The pattern number is 473, and the pattern was registered in Canada in 1952. This pattern is still very popular in the United States and England.

Cat. No.	Shape	U.S. $	Can. $	U.K. £
Est-04	Bonbon dish	65.00	80.00	55.00
Est-09	Bowl, 5"	50.00	60.00	40.00
Est-14	Bowl, 8" soup	75.00	90.00	60.00
Est-23	Breakfast set	1,250.00	1,375.00	800.00
Est-28	Butter dish	175.00	210.00	150.00
Est-30	Butter pat	50.00	60.00	50.00
Est-35	Cake plate, open handles	235.00	285.00	160.00
Est-37	Cake plate, 8" sq. pedestal	200.00	240.00	150.00
Est-40	Cake stand, 2 tier	200.00	240.00	145.00
Est-45	Canoe-shaped dish	225.00	270.00	150.00
Est-50	Cheese keep	240.00	290.00	175.00
Est-52	Coaster	110.00	135.00	70.00
Est-55	Coffee pot	1,050.00	1,155.00	675.00
Est-60	Compote, footed	175.00	210.00	125.00
Est-65	Condiment set on tray	275.00	330.00	175.00
Est-70	Cream and sugar	175.00	210.00	115.00
Est-71	Cream and sugar on tray	250.00	300.00	175.00
Est-75	Demi-tasse	115.00	140.00	75.00
Est-77	Egg cup, footed	125.00	150.00	75.00
Est-80	Hot water jug	450.00	540.00	295.00
Est-85	Jam pot with liner	175.00	210.00	125.00
Est-90	Jug, 4"	400.00	480.00	275.00
Est-91	Jug, 4 1/2"	450.00	540.00	300.00
Est-92	Jug, 5"	500.00	600.00	325.00

Cat. No.	Shape	U.S. $	Can. $	U.K. £
Est-97	Nut dish	50.00	60.00	40.00
Est-201	Plate, 4" sq.	55.00	70.00	40.00
Est-202	Plate, 5" sq.	65.00	80.00	45.00
Est-203	Plate, 6" sq.	75.00	90.00	50.00
Est-204	Plate, 7" sq.	95.00	115.00	60.00
Est-205	Plate, 8" sq.	130.00	160.00	75.00
Est-206	Plate, 9" sq.	150.00	180.00	95.00
Est-207	Plate, 10" sq.	165.00	200.00	110.00
Est-112	Relish dish, small	175.00	210.00	125.00
Est-115	Salad bowl, chrome rim	375.00	450.00	225.00
Est-117	Salt and pepper	125.00	150.00	70.00
Est-118	Salt and pepper on tray	200.00	240.00	120.00
Est-120	Sandwich tray, 10" x 6"	175.00	210.00	120.00
Est-121	Sandwich tray, 12" x 7"	195.00	235.00	140.00
Est-125	Sauce boat and liner	175.00	210.00	120.00
Est-130	Teacup and saucer	135.00	165.00	85.00
Est-135	Teapot, 2 cup	475.00	570.00	375.00
Est-136	Teapot, 4 cup	675.00	780.00	475.00
Est-137	Teapot, 6 cup	900.00	1,035.00	600.00
Est-140	Teapot, stacking	1200.00	1,320.00	650.00
Est-145	Tennis set	145.00	175.00	95.00
Est-150	Toast rack, 4 slice	375.00	450.00	250.00
Est-151	Toast rack, 2 slice	295.00	355.00	200.00
Est-155	Trivet	150.00	180.00	125.00
Est-160	Vase, bud	195.00	235.00	105.00

EVESHAM

The pattern number is 404, and it was registered in Canada in 1951. The United States patent was issued March 25, 1952 at the same time as **Cheadle** — the designer of both patterns is listed as James Plant. The New Zealand patent was issued two weeks earlier on March 12, 1952. Interestingly, this pattern which is not really chintz has become one of the most sought after patterns around the world. In England prices have increased dramatically since the re-issue of **Julia** and **Welbeck**.

Cat. No.	Shape	U.S. $	Can. $	U.K. £
Ev-04	Bonbon dish	95.00	115.00	70.00
Ev-09	Bowl, 5"	60.00	75.00	60.00
Ev-14	Bowl, 8" soup	125.00	150.00	95.00
Ev-23	Breakfast set	1,550.00	1,750.00	1200.00
Ev-28	Butter dish	275.00	330.00	205.00
Ev-30	Butter pat	90.00	110.00	75.00
Ev-35	Cake plate, open handles	325.00	390.00	215.00
Ev-37	Cake plate, 8" sq. pedestal	300.00	360.00	235.00
Ev-40	Cake stand, 2 tier	275.00	330.00	225.00
Ev-45	Canoe-shaped dish	350.00	420.00	300.00
Ev-50	Cheese keep	375.00	450.00	350.00
Ev-52	Coaster	145.00	175.00	75.00
Ev-55	Coffee pot	1,400.00	1,540.00	900.00
Ev-60	Compote, footed	250.00	300.00	205.00
Ev-65	Condiment set on tray	375.00	450.00	275.00
Ev-70	Cream and sugar	225.00	270.00	150.00
Ev-71	Cream and sugar on tray	325.00	390.00	275.00
Ev-75	Demi-tasse	135.00	165.00	90.00
Ev-77	Egg cup, footed	150.00	180.00	100.00
Ev-80	Hot water jug	600.00	690.00	400.00
Ev-85	Jam pot with liner	275.00	330.00	215.00
Ev-90	Jug, 4"	500.00	600.00	375.00
Ev-91	Jug, 4 1/2"	550.00	635.00	400.00
Ev-92	Jug, 5"	600.00	690.00	425.00

Cat. No.	Shape	U.S. $	Can. $	U.K. £
Ev-97	Nut dish	75.00	90.00	65.00
Ev-201	Plate, 4" sq.	80.00	100.00	75.00
Ev-202	Plate, 5" sq.	85.00	105.00	80.00
Ev-203	Plate, 6" sq.	120.00	145.00	90.00
Ev-204	Plate, 7" sq.	165.00	200.00	100.00
Ev-205	Plate, 8" sq.	200.00	240.00	130.00
Ev-206	Plate, 9" sq.	220.00	265.00	150.00
Ev-207	Plate, 10" sq .	250.00	300.00	165.00
Ev-112	Relish dish, small	275.00	330.00	205.00
Ev-115	Salad bowl, chrome rim	425.00	510.00	250.00
Ev-117	Salt and pepper	165.00	200.00	95.00
Ev-118	Salt and pepper on tray	250.00	300.00	195.00
Ev-120	Sandwich tray, 10" x 6"	190.00	230.00	140.00
Ev-121	Sandwich tray, 12" x 7"	220.00	265.00	175.00
Ev-125	Sauce boat and liner	250.00	300.00	205.00
Ev-130	Teacup and saucer	145.00	175.00	100.00
Ev-135	Teapot, 2 cup	700.00	805.00	500.00
Ev-136	Teapot, 4 cup	950.00	1,095.00	650.00
Ev-137	Teapot, 6 cup	1,200.00	1,320.00	850.00
Ev-140	Teapot, stacking	1,750.00	1,925.00	900.00
Ev-145	Tennis set	175.00	210.00	135.00
Ev-150	Toast rack, 4 slice	400.00	480.00	275.00
Ev-151	Toast rack, 2 slice	350.00	420.00	225.00
Ev-155	Trivet	180.00	220.00	135.00
Ev-160	Vase, bud	210.00	255.00	135.00

"EXOTIC BIRD"

The pattern number for this pattern is 10011.Th s pattern must have been produced in 1931 at the same time as **Springtime** (pattern number 10017). This pattern has appeared on pieces produced by other factories; this may explain why it does not have a pattern name incorporated into the backstamp like the exclusive patterns **Delphinium Chintz** and **Springtime**.

Cat. No.	Shape	U.S. $	Can. $	U.K. £	Cat. No.	Shape	U.S. $	Can. $	U.K. £
EB-04	Bonbon dish	45.00	55.00	35.00	EB-97	Nut dish	45.00	55.00	30.00
EB-09	Bowl, 5"	40.00	50.00	30.00	EB-201	Plate, 4" sq.	35.00	45.00	25.00
EB-14	Bowl, 8" soup	70.00	85.00	50.00	EB-202	Plate, 5" sq.	40.00	50.00	30.00
EB-23	Breakfast set	950.00	1,095.00	450.00	EB-203	Plate, 6" sq.	45.00	55.00	35.00
EB-28	Butter dish	135.00	165.00	100.00	EB-204	Plate, 7" sq.	50.00	60.00	35.00
EB-30	Butter pat	45.00	55.00	30.00	EB-205	Plate, 8" sq.	85.00	105.00	65.00
EB-35	Cake plate, open handles	175.00	210.00	85.00	EB-206	Plate, 9" sq.	100.00	120.00	65.00
EB-36	Cake plate, tab handles	125.00	150.00	75.00	EB-207	Plate, 10" sq.	125.00	150.00	75.00
EB-37	Cake plate, 8" sq. pedestal	140.00	170.00	100.00	EB-112	Relish dish, small	125.00	150.00	75.00
EB-40	Cake stand, 2 tier	140.00	170.00	100.00	EB-115	Salad bowl, chrome rim	195.00	235.00	95.00
EB-45	Canoe-shaped dish	175.00	210.00	135.00	EB-117	Salt and pepper	75.00	90.00	45.00
EB-50	Cheese keep	195.00	235.00	125.00	EB-118	Salt and pepper on tray	150.00	180.00	100.00
EB-52	Coaster	85.00	105.00	25.00	EB-120	Sandwich tray, 10 x 6	95.00	115.00	60.00
EB-55	Coffee pot	550.00	635.00	350.00	EB-121	Sandwich tray, 12 x 7	110.00	135.00	65.00
EB-60	Compote, footed	100.00	120.00	65.00	EB-125	Sauce boat and liner	125.00	150.00	75.00
EB-65	Condiment set on tray	150.00	180.00	100.00	EB-130	Teacup and saucer	85.00	105.00	45.00
EB-70	Cream and sugar	85.00	105.00	60.00	EB-135	Teapot, 2 cup	300.00	360.00	175.00
EB-71	Cream and sugar on tray	150.00	180.00	100.00	EB-136	Teapot, 4 cup	400.00	480.00	250.00
EB-75	Demi-tasse	60.00	75.00	45.00	EB-137	Teapot, 6 cup	500.00	300.00	325.00
EB-77	Egg cup, footed	85.00	105.00	55.00	EB-140	Teapot, stacking	750.00	865.00	425.00
EB-80	Hot water jug	295.00	355.00	150.00	EB-145	Tennis set	90.00	110.00	50.00
EB-85	Jam pot with liner	135.00	165.00	75.00	EB-150	Toast rack, 4 slice	175.00	210.00	125.00
EB-90	Jug, 4"	225.00	270.00	125.00	EB-151	Toast rack, 2 slice	145.00	175.00	75.00
EB-91	Jug, 4 1/2"	250.00	300.00	135.00	EB-155	Trivet	80.00	100.00	50.00
EB-92	Jug, 5"	275.00	330.00	150.00	EB-160	Vase, bud	115.00	140.00	60.00

FERNESE

The original **Fernese,** pattern number 8786, dates to 1925 and the background is pale blue and there is a border of black and gold. The backstamp for this earlier pattern includes the pattern name. This pattern was reworked and issued again in the late 1930s with a deeper blue ground and hand colouring. The pattern number for this later **Fernese** is 4771. This pattern is rare in North America and available on a limited number of shapes. The prices are for the later version.

Cat. No.	Shape	U.S. $	Can. $	U.K. £
Fer -35	Cake plate, open handles	95.00	115.00	55.00
Fer-115	Salad bowl, chrome rim	175.00	210.00	80.00
Fer-130	Teacup and saucer	50.00	60.00	30.00

Cat. No.	Shape	U.S. $	Can. $	U.K. £
Fer-203	Plate, 6" sq.	35.00	45.00	25.00
Fer-206	Plate, 9" sq.	65.00	80.00	40.00

FIREGLOW BLACK

There are two totally unrelated patterns with the backstamp **Fireglow**. The black background has the pattern number 533, which is the last known chintz pattern number. **Black Fireglow** does not appear to have been exclusive to Grimwades. Alfred Meakin used this pattern in the 1950s but called it **GLO-WHITE**. See **Fireglow White** (page 68) with the much earlier pattern number 2510. This black **Fireglow** pattern has become more popular in the last year or two.

Cat. No.	Shape	U.S. $	Can. $	U.K. £
FiB-04	Bonbon dish	45.00	55.00	35.00
FiB-09	Bowl, 5"	40.00	50.00	30.00
FiB-14	Bowl, 8" soup	75.00	90.00	50.00
FiB-23	Breakfast set	750.00	865.00	400.00
FiB-28	Butter dish	135.00	165.00	80.00
FiB-30	Butter pat	40.00	50.00	25.00
FiB-35	Cake plate, open handles	155.00	190.00	85.00
FiB-37	Cake plate, 8" sq. pedestal	150.00	180.00	95.00
FiB-40	Cake stand, 2 tier	135.00	165.00	75.00
FiB-45	Canoe-shaped dish	175.00	210.00	105.00
FiB-50	Cheese keep	175.00	210.00	95.00
FiB-52	Coaster	85.00	105.00	40.00
FiB-55	Coffee pot	575.00	665.00	300.00
FiB-60	Compote, footed	100.00	120.00	60.00
FiB-65	Condiment set on tray	150.00	180.00	100.00
FiB-70	Cream and sugar	125.00	150.00	90.00
FiB-71	Cream and sugar on tray	175.00	210.00	125.00
FiB-75	Demi-tasse	75.00	90.00	50.00
FiB-77	Egg cup, footed	95.00	115.00	50.00
FiB-80	Hot water jug	275.00	330.00	175.00
FiB-85	Jam pot with liner	125.00	150.00	75.00
FiB-90	Jug, 4"	275.00	330.00	150.00
FiB-91	Jug, 4 1/2"	300.00	360.00	175.00
FiB-92	Jug, 5"	325.00	390.00	200.00

Cat. No.	Shape	U.S. $	Can. $	U.K. £
FiB-97	Nut dish	40.00	50.00	25.00
FiB-201	Plate, 4" sq.	35.00	45.00	25.00
FiB-202	Plate, 5" sq.	40.00	50.00	25.00
FiB-203	Plate, 6" sq.	45.00	55.00	30.00
FiB-204	Plate, 7" sq.	50.00	60.00	35.00
FiB-205	Plate, 8" sq.	60.00	75.00	40.00
FiB-206	Plate, 9" sq.	75.00	90.00	50.00
FiB-207	Plate, 10" sq.	95.00	115.00	60.00
FiB-112	Relish dish, small	125.00	150.00	75.00
FiB-115	Salad bowl, chrome rim	250.00	300.00	150.00
FiB-117	Salt and pepper	65.00	80.00	45.00
FiB-118	Salt and pepper on tray	130.00	160.00	85.00
FiB-120	Sandwich tray, 10" x 6"	85.00	105.00	60.00
FiB-121	Sandwich tray, 12" x 7"	100.00	120.00	70.00
FiB-125	Sauce boat and liner	125.00	150.00	75.00
FiB-130	Teacup and saucer	85.00	105.00	45.00
FiB-135	Teapot, 2 cup	275.00	330.00	175.00
FiB-136	Teapot, 4 cup	375.00	450.00	250.00
FiB-137	Teapot, 6 cup	475.00	570.00	275.00
FiB-140	Teapot, stacking	900.00	1,035.00	375.00
FiB-145	Tennis set	95.00	115.00	50.00
FiB-150	Toast rack, 4 slice	195.00	235.00	135.00
FiB-151	Toast rack, 2 slice	145.00	175.00	100.00
FiB-155	Trivet	75.00	90.00	50.00
FiB-160	Vase, bud	135.00	165.00	65.00

FIREGLOW WHITE

The pattern number for the white background **Fireglow** is 2510 which means it was likely introduced in 1935. It is totally unrelated to the black **Fireglow** from the 1950s. See **Fireglow Black** page 67.

Cat. No.	Shape	U.S. $	Can. $	U.K. £
FiW-04	Bonbon dish	50.00	60.00	35.00
FiW-09	Bowl, 5"	45.00	55.00	35.00
FiW-14	Bowl, 8" soup	75.00	90.00	50.00
FiW-23	Breakfast set	850.00	980.00	475.00
FiW-28	Butter dish	150.00	180.00	100.00
FiW-30	Butter pat	45.00	55.00	35.00
FiW-35	Cake plate, open handles	175.00	210.00	100.00
FiW-37	Cake plate, 8" sq. pedestal	150.00	180.00	125.00
FiW-40	Cake stand, 2 tier	150.00	180.00	105.00
FiW-45	Canoe-shaped dish	225.00	270.00	150.00
FiW-50	Cheese keep	200.00	240.00	150.00
FiW-52	Coaster	90.00	110.00	30.00
FiW-55	Coffee pot	600.00	690.00	375.00
FiW-60	Compote, footed	135.00	165.00	85.00
FiW-65	Condiment set on tray	175.00	210.00	125.00
FiW-70	Cream and sugar	135.00	165.00	105.00
FiW-71	Cream and sugar on tray	195.00	235.00	135.00
FiW-75	Demi-tasse	80.00	100.00	50.00
FiW-77	Egg cup, footed	100.00	120.00	65.00
FiW-80	Hot water jug	300.00	360.00	175.00
FiW-85	Jam pot with liner	140.00	170.00	100.00
FiW-90	Jug, 4"	300.00	360.00	150.00
FiW-91	Jug, 4 1/2"	325.00	390.00	175.00
FiW-92	Jug, 5"	350.00	420.00	200.00

Cat. No.	Shape	U.S. $	Can. $	U.K. £
FiW-97	Nut dish	45.00	55.00	35.00
FiW-201	Plate, 4" sq.	50.00	60.00	30.00
FiW-202	Plate, 5" sq.	55.00	70.00	35.00
FiW-203	Plate, 6" sq.	60.00	75.00	40.00
FiW-204	Plate, 7" sq.	75.00	90.00	50.00
FiW-205	Plate, 8" sq.	95.00	115.00	65.00
FiW-206	Plate, 9" sq.	115.00	140.00	70.00
FiW-207	Plate, 10" sq .	125.00	150.00	75.00
FiW-112	Relish dish, small	150.00	180.00	100.00
FiW-115	Salad bowl, chrome rim	300.00	360.00	175.00
FiW-117	Salt and pepper	85.00	105.00	50.00
FiW-118	Salt and pepper on tray	150.00	180.00	95.00
FiW-120	Sandwich tray, 10" x 6"	100.00	120.00	65.00
FiW-121	Sandwich tray, 12" x 7"	125.00	150.00	75.00
FiW-125	Sauce boat and liner	135.00	165.00	85.00
FiW-130	Teacup and saucer	105.00	130.00	50.00
FiW-135	Teapot, 2 cup	325.00	390.00	250.00
FiW-136	Teapot, 4 cup	425.00	510.00	300.00
FiW-137	Teapot, 6 cup	525.00	605.00	375.00
FiW-140	Teapot, stacking	950.00	1,095.00	425.00
FiW-145	Tennis set	110.00	135.00	65.00
FiW-150	Toast rack, 4 slice	225.00	270.00	150.00
FiW-151	Toast rack, 2 slice	175.00	210.00	100.00
FiW-155	Trivet	100.00	120.00	65.00
FiW-160	Vase, bud	150.00	180.00	95.00

FLORAL FEAST

The pattern number is 1394. This was one of the three new patterns along with **Summertime** and **Somerset** advertised by Wright, Tyndale & van Roden, Inc. of Philadelphia in the *Crockery and Glass Journal* of May 1933. The patterns were backstamped COPYRIGHT Wright, Tyndal & van Roden in an attempt to discourage pattern theft. **Floral Feast** is described "with large sprays and delicate blossoms gracefully intermingled on a deep ivory ground." A 1936 Australian Export Catalogue shows **Floral Feast** with blue trim and the pattern number 2255.

Cat. No.	Shape	U.S. $	Can. $	U.K. £
FF-04	Bonbon dish	50.00	60.00	35.00
FF-09	Bowl, 5"	45.00	55.00	35.00
FF-14	Bowl, 8" soup	75.00	90.00	50.00
FF-23	Breakfast set	850.00	980.00	475.00
FF-28	Butter dish	150.00	180.00	100.00
FF-30	Butter pat	45.00	55.00	35.00
FF-35	Cake plate, open handles	175.00	210.00	100.00
FF-37	Cake Plate, 8" sq. pedestal	150.00	180.00	115.00
FF-40	Cake stand, 2 tier	150.00	180.00	105.00
FF-45	Canoe-shaped dish	225.00	270.00	150.00
FF-50	Cheese keep	200.00	240.00	125.00
FF-52	Coaster	90.00	110.00	50.00
FF-55	Coffee pot	600.00	690.00	375.00
FF-60	Compote, footed	125.00	150.00	75.00
FF-65	Condiment set on tray	175.00	210.00	125.00
FF-70	Cream and sugar	135.00	165.00	90.00
FF-71	Cream and sugar on tray	195.00	235.00	135.00
FF-75	Demi-tasse	85.00	105.00	50.00
FF-77	Egg cup, footed	105.00	125.00	65.00
FF-80	Hot water jug	300.00	360.00	175.00
FF-85	Jam pot with liner	150.00	180.00	100.00
FF-90	Jug, 4"	300.00	360.00	150.00
FF-91	Jug, 4 1/2"	325.00	390.00	175.00
FF-92	Jug, 5"	350.00	420.00	200.00

Cat. No.	Shape	U.S. $	Can. $	U.K. £
FF-97	Nut dish	45.00	55.00	35.00
FF-201	Plate, 4" sq.	50.00	60.00	30.00
FF-202	Plate, 5" sq.	55.00	70.00	35.00
FF-203	Plate, 6" sq.	60.00	75.00	40.00
FF-204	Plate, 7" sq.	75.00	90.00	45.00
FF-205	Plate, 8" sq.	100.00	120.00	60.00
FF-206	Plate, 9" sq.	115.00	140.00	65.00
FF-207	Plate, 10" sq .	125.00	150.00	75.00
FF-112	Relish dish, small	150.00	180.00	100.00
FF-115	Salad bowl, chrome rim	300.00	360.00	175.00
FF-117	Salt and pepper	85.00	105.00	50.00
FF-118	Salt and pepper on tray	150.00	180.00	95.00
FF-120	Sandwich tray, 10" x 6"	100.00	120.00	65.00
FF-121	Sandwich tray, 12" x 7"	125.00	150.00	75.00
FF-125	Sauce boat and liner	125.00	150.00	75.00
FF-130	Teacup and saucer	105.00	125.00	60.00
FF-135	Teapot, 2 cup	350.00	420.00	225.00
FF-136	Teapot, 4 cup	450.00	540.00	275.00
FF-137	Teapot, 6 cup	550.00	660.00	350.00
FF-140	Teapot, stacking	950.00	1,140.00	425.00
FF-145	Tennis set	110.00	135.00	65.00
FF-150	Toast rack, 4 slice	250.00	300.00	150.00
FF-151	Toast rack, 2 slice	195.00	235.00	100.00
FF-155	Trivet	100.00	120.00	60.00
FF-160	Vase, bud	150.00	180.00	95.00

FLORAL GARDEN

The pattern number for the green colourway is 4547, and for the blue 4546. This pattern has been found in Australia with the name **Floral Garden** in the backstamp and probably dates to 1938.

Backstamp not available
at
press time

Cat. No.	Shape	U.S. $	Can. $	U.K. £
FG-04	Bonbon dish	35.00	45.00	25.00
FG-09	Bowl, 5"	25.00	30.00	20.00
FG-14	Bowl, 8" soup	35.00	45.00	25.00
FG-23	Breakfast set	450.00	540.00	290.00
FG-28	Butter dish	90.00	110.00	65.00
FG-30	Butter pat	25.00	30.00	20.00
FG-35	Cake plate, open handles	95.00	115.00	50.00
FG-37	Cake Plate, 8" sq. pedestal	95.00	115.00	50.00
FG-40	Cake stand, 2 tier	90.00	110.00	50.00
FG-45	Canoe-shaped dish	165.00	200.00	115.00
FG-50	Cheese keep	120.00	145.00	85.00
FG-52	Coaster	45.00	55.00	25.00
FG-55	Coffee pot	375.00	450.00	250.00
FG-60	Compote, footed	65.00	80.00	45.00
FG-65	Condiment set on tray	95.00	115.00	65.00
FG-70	Cream and sugar	55.00	70.00	40.00
FG-71	Cream and sugar on tray	95.00	115.00	75.00
FG-75	Demi-tasse	40.00	50.00	30.00
FG-77	Egg cup, footed	65.00	80.00	35.00
FG-80	Hot water jug	165.00	200.00	125.00
FG-85	Jam pot with liner	75.00	90.00	50.00
FG-90	Jug, 4"	135.00	165.00	85.00
FG-91	Jug, 4 1/2"	150.00	180.00	95.00
FG-92	Jug, 5"	165.00	200.00	110.00

Cat. No.	Shape	U.S. $	Can. $	U.K. £
FG-97	Nut dish	25.00	30.00	20.00
FG-201	Plate, 4" sq.	30.00	40.00	20.00
FG-202	Plate, 5" sq.	35.00	45.00	25.00
FG-203	Plate, 6" sq.	40.00	50.00	30.00
FG-204	Plate, 7" sq.	45.00	55.00	35.00
FG-205	Plate, 8" sq.	55.00	70.00	40.00
FG-206	Plate, 9" sq.	65.00	80.00	45.00
FG-207	Plate, 10" sq.	75.00	90.00	50.00
FG-112	Relish dish, small	75.00	90.00	55.00
FG-115	Salad bowl, chrome rim	145.00	175.00	80.00
FG-117	Salt and pepper	45.00	55.00	35.00
FG-118	Salt and pepper on tray	95.00	115.00	65.00
FG-120	Sandwich tray, 10" x 6"	50.00	60.00	35.00
FG-121	Sandwich tray, 12" x 7"	65.00	80.00	50.00
FG-125	Sauce boat and liner	65.00	80.00	45.00
FG-130	Teacup and saucer	45.00	55.00	30.00
FG-135	Teapot, 2 cup	175.00	210.00	150.00
FG-136	Teapot, 4 cup	250.00	300.00	175.00
FG-137	Teapot, 6 cup	350.00	420.00	225.00
FG-140	Teapot, stacking	400.00	480.00	300.00
FG-145	Tennis set	55.00	70.00	35.00
FG-150	Toast rack, 4 slice	150.00	180.00	105.00
FG-151	Toast rack, 2 slice	125.00	150.00	75.00
FG-155	Trivet	50.00	60.00	35.00
FG-160	Vase, bud	75.00	90.00	50.00

FLORENCE

The pattern number is 472, which would indicate that it is one of the last chintz patterns to be produced in the 1950s. The pattern was registered in Canada in 1953. This pattern is quite rare and very sought after by collectors worldwide. The pattern occasionally turns up on Royal Winton bone china. **Florence** is one of the patterns being reproduced by Royal Winton; this has had an effect on the price of vintage **Florence,** particularly in England.

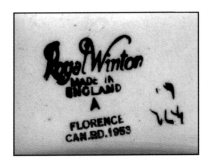

Cat. No.	Shape	U.S. $	Can. $	U.K. £
Fl-04	Bonbon dish	95.00	115.00	80.00
Fl-09	Bowl, 5"	75.00	90.00	60.00
Fl-14	Bowl, 8" soup	125.00	150.00	80.00
Fl-23	Breakfast set	1,550.00	1,750.00	1100.00
Fl-28	Butter dish	300.00	360.00	225.00
Fl-30	Butter pat	85.00	105.00	55.00
Fl-35	Cake plate, open handles	325.00	390.00	235.00
Fl-37	Cake Plate, 8" sq. pedestal	300.00	360.00	250.00
Fl-40	Cake stand, 2 tier	275.00	330.00	225.00
Fl-45	Canoe-shaped dish	350.00	420.00	300.00
Fl-50	Cheese keep	395.00	475.00	325.00
Fl-52	Coaster	145.00	175.00	65.00
Fl-55	Coffee pot	1,400.00	1,540.00	900.00
Fl-60	Compote, footed	245.00	295.00	195.00
Fl-65	Condiment set on tray	365.00	440.00	275.00
Fl-70	Cream and sugar	210.00	255.00	150.00
Fl-71	Cream and sugar on tray	325.00	390.00	250.00
Fl-75	Demi-tasse	150.00	180.00	90.00
Fl-77	Egg cup, footed	150.00	180.00	85.00
Fl-80	Hot water jug	600.00	690.00	425.00
Fl-85	Jam pot with liner	275.00	330.00	225.00
Fl-90	Jug, 4"	500.00	600.00	325.00
Fl-91	Jug, 4 1/2"	550.00	635.00	350.00
Fl-92	Jug, 5"	600.00	690.00	400.00

Cat. No.	Shape	U.S. $	Can. $	U.K. £
Fl-97	Nut dish	75.00	90.00	60.00
Fl-201	Plate, 4" sq.	85.00	105.00	60.00
Fl-202	Plate, 5" sq.	95.00	115.00	70.00
Fl-203	Plate, 6" sq.	135.00	165.00	80.00
Fl-204	Plate, 7" sq.	145.00	175.00	90.00
Fl-205	Plate, 8" sq.	195.00	235.00	130.00
Fl-206	Plate, 9" sq.	215.00	260.00	145.00
Fl-207	Plate, 10" sq .	230.00	280.00	165.00
Fl-112	Relish dish, small	275.00	330.00	225.00
Fl-115	Salad bowl, chrome rim	425.00	510.00	225.00
Fl-117	Salt and pepper	165.00	200.00	95.00
Fl-118	Salt and pepper on tray	250.00	300.00	175.00
Fl-120	Sandwich tray, 10" x 6"	195.00	235.00	150.00
Fl-121	Sandwich tray, 12" x 7"	220.00	265.00	175.00
Fl-125	Sauce boat and liner	245.00	295.00	145.00
Fl-130	Teacup and saucer	145.00	175.00	90.00
Fl-135	Teapot, 2 cup	700.00	805.00	450.00
Fl-136	Teapot, 4 cup	900.00	1,035.00	600.00
Fl-137	Teapot, 6 cup	1,200.00	1,320.00	750.00
Fl-140	Teapot, stacking	1,750.00	1,925.00	900.00
Fl-145	Tennis set	175.00	210.00	125.00
Fl-150	Toast rack, 4 slice	400.00	480.00	250.00
Fl-151	Toast rack, 2 slice	325.00	390.00	225.00
Fl-155	Trivet	175.00	210.00	125.00
Fl-160	Vase, bud	210.00	255.00	150.00

"GRAPES & ROSES"

This pattern has become very popular in North America. This pattern was used by Shelley, usually with a black and white chequered border, as well as by the American company Taylor, Smith & Taylor. Grimwades produced a limited range of pieces in the 1920s with this unnamed pattern.

Cat. No.	Shape	U.S. $	Can. $	U.K. £	Cat. No.	Shape	U.S. $	Can. $	U.K. £
GR-50	Cheese Keep	275.00	330.00	165.00	GR-164	Vase, 7"	295.00	355.00	200.00
GR-137	Teapot, 6 cup	850.00	980.00	400.00	GR-165	Vase, 9"	495.00	595.00	300.00
GR-155	Trivet	175.00	210.00	100.00	GR-166	Vase, 11"	695.00	800.00	400.00

HAZEL

The pattern number is 2208, and the pattern was mentioned in the *Pottery Gazette* several times in 1934. At the 1936 B.I.F. the *Pottery & Glass Record* commended "the lately introduced and strong-selling **Hazel Chintz**, more decisively decoratively treated (than the new **Sweet Pea**), specially good for the associative requirements of the furnishing trade." **Hazel** has a black background with the alternate colourways of a white background, **Spring** 2506, and the yellow **Welbeck** 2204. This pattern was much copied by the Japanese including a recent porcelain version by Fitz & Floyd called **Mille Fleurs**.

Cat. No.	Shape	U.S. $	Can. $	U.K. £
H-04	Bonbon dish	75.00	90.00	60.00
H-09	Bowl, 5"	50.00	60.00	45.00
H-14	Bowl, 8" soup	85.00	105.00	70.00
H-23	Breakfast set	1,350.00	1,485.00	800.00
H-28	Butter dish	225.00	270.00	195.00
H-30	Butter pat	65.00	80.00	55.00
H-35	Cake plate, open handles	265.00	320.00	195.00
H-37	Cake Plate, 8" sq. pedestal	225.00	270.00	185.00
H-40	Cake stand, 2 tier	200.00	240.00	150.00
H-45	Canoe-shaped dish	285.00	345.00	225.00
H-50	Cheese keep	275.00	330.00	250.00
H-52	Coaster	115.00	140.00	65.00
H-55	Coffee pot	1,150.00	1,265.00	725.00
H-60	Compote, footed	185.00	225.00	160.00
H-65	Condiment set on tray	300.00	360.00	225.00
H-70	Cream and sugar	165.00	200.00	125.00
H-71	Cream and sugar on tray	265.00	320.00	215.00
H-75	Demi-tasse	125.00	150.00	80.00
H-77	Egg cup, footed	125.00	150.00	75.00
H-80	Hot water jug	525.00	605.00	300.00
H-85	Jam pot with liner	225.00	270.00	175.00
H-90	Jug, 4"	425.00	510.00	250.00
H-91	Jug, 4 1/2"	475.00	570.00	275.00
H-92	Jug, 5"	525.00	605.00	300.00

Cat. No.	Shape	U.S. $	Can. $	U.K. £
H-97	Nut dish	65.00	80.00	50.00
H-201	Plate, 4" sq.	50.00	60.00	45.00
H-202	Plate, 5" sq.	65.00	80.00	50.00
H-203	Plate, 6" sq.	75.00	90.00	60.00
H-204	Plate, 7" sq.	100.00	120.00	70.00
H-205	Plate, 8" sq.	135.00	165.00	80.00
H-206	Plate, 9" sq.	150.00	180.00	95.00
H-207	Plate, 10" sq.	175.00	210.00	125.00
H-112	Relish dish, small	200.00	240.00	175.00
H-115	Salad bowl, chrome rim	350.00	420.00	195.00
H-117	Salt and pepper	120.00	145.00	80.00
H-118	Salt and pepper on tray	195.00	235.00	140.00
H-120	Sandwich tray, 10" x 6"	150.00	180.00	125.00
H-121	Sandwich tray, 12" x 7"	175.00	210.00	150.00
H-125	Sauce boat and liner	165.00	200.00	150.00
H-130	Teacup and saucer	125.00	150.00	75.00
H-135	Teapot, 2 cup	500.00	600.00	350.00
H-136	Teapot, 4 cup	750.00	865.00	550.00
H-137	Teapot, 6 cup	900.00	1,035.00	600.00
H-140	Teapot, stacking	1,400.00	1,540.00	700.00
H-145	Tennis set	125.00	150.00	85.00
H-150	Toast rack, 4 slice	375.00	450.00	225.00
H-151	Toast rack, 2 slice	300.00	360.00	175.00
H-155	Trivet	145.00	175.00	85.00
H-160	Vase, bud	175.00	210.00	125.00

JOYCE-LYNN

The pattern number is 275. This pattern was introduced into Canada in the fall of 1950. Enterprise Sales of Toronto, the exclusive Canadian distributor, urged retailers to carry the pattern because "The brilliance of colour, the red, blue and yellow blossoms with green leaves and highlights of gold coupled with the fine glazing of this beautiful open stock pattern will build sales volume for you." Early in 1999, Royal Winton produced several items — the stacking teapot, a non-Winton shape teapot and hot water on a tray and a breakfast set in **Joyce-Lynn** for the Magnolia Antique Mall in California.

Cat. No.	Shape	U.S. $	Can. $	U.K. £
JL-04	Bonbon dish	60.00	75.00	35.00
JL-09	Bowl, 5"	45.00	55.00	30.00
JL-14	Bowl, 8" soup	70.00	85.00	45.00
JL-23	Breakfast set	1,250.00	1,375.00	625.00
JL-28	Butter dish	175.00	210.00	100.00
JL-30	Butter pat	50.00	60.00	30.00
JL-35	Cake plate, open handles	235.00	285.00	125.00
JL-37	Cake Plate, 8" sq. pedestal	225.00	270.00	125.00
JL-40	Cake stand, 2 tier	165.00	200.00	100.00
JL-45	Canoe-shaped dish	225.00	270.00	150.00
JL-50	Cheese keep	240.00	290.00	125.00
JL-52	Coaster	110.00	135.00	65.00
JL-55	Coffee pot	1050.00	1,155.00	425.00
JL-60	Compote, footed	150.00	180.00	110.00
JL-65	Condiment set on tray	275.00	330.00	135.00
JL-70	Cream and sugar	175.00	210.00	95.00
JL-71	Cream and sugar on tray	250.00	300.00	145.00
JL-75	Demi-tasse	115.00	140.00	75.00
JL-77	Egg cup, footed	125.00	150.00	75.00
JL-80	Hot water jug	450.00	540.00	225.00
JL-85	Jam pot with liner	150.00	180.00	95.00
JL-90	Jug, 4"	375.00	450.00	175.00
JL-91	Jug, 4 1/2"	425.00	510.00	200.00
JL-92	Jug, 5"	475.00	570.00	225.00

Cat. No.	Shape	U.S. $	Can. $	U.K. £
JL-97	Nut dish	50.00	60.00	30.00
JL-201	Plate, 4" sq.	55.00	70.00	30.00
JL-202	Plate, 5" sq.	65.00	80.00	35.00
JL-203	Plate, 6" sq.	75.00	90.00	45.00
JL-204	Plate, 7" sq.	95.00	115.00	55.00
JL-205	Plate, 8" sq.	130.00	160.00	75.00
JL-206	Plate, 9" sq.	150.00	180.00	95.00
JL-207	Plate, 10" sq.	165.00	200.00	110.00
JL-112	Relish dish, small	150.00	180.00	100.00
JL-115	Salad bowl, chrome rim	375.00	450.00	175.00
JL-117	Salt and pepper	125.00	150.00	65.00
JL-118	Salt and pepper on tray	200.00	240.00	120.00
JL-120	Sandwich tray, 10" x 6"	115.00	140.00	75.00
JL-121	Sandwich tray, 12" x 7"	135.00	165.00	85.00
JL-125	Sauce boat and liner	165.00	200.00	110.00
JL-130	Teacup and saucer	125.00	150.00	75.00
JL-135	Teapot, 2 cup	450.00	540.00	275.00
JL-136	Teapot, 4 cup	650.00	750.00	325.00
JL-137	Teapot, 6 cup	850.00	980.00	400.00
JL-140	Teapot, stacking	1,200.00	1,320.00	525.00
JL-145	Tennis set	135.00	165.00	85.00
JL-150	Toast rack, 4 slice	350.00	420.00	180.00
JL-151	Toast rack, 2 slice	275.00	330.00	120.00
JL-155	Trivet	140.00	170.00	80.00
JL-160	Vase, bud	185.00	225.00	95.00

JULIA

The pattern number is 109 and probably appeared in 1939 and continued well into the 1950s. It is the favourite chintz pattern for collectors around the world and prices for unusual pieces with good colour are very high. Be aware that there are great variations in the depth of color in this pattern, with some examples appearing quite faded. A **Julia** breakfast set turned up in Canada recently with the original price tag still on the base — $7.95. Julia is one of the patterns Royal Winton is reproducing. This has had a slight impact on prices of vintage. Some new **Julia** has been produced for Clemetine Rusk, California with a special backstamp (see new chintz).

Cat. No.	Shape	U.S. $	Can. $	U.K. £
J-04	Bonbon dish	150.00	180.00	95.00
J-09	Bowl, 5"	110.00	135.00	65.00
J-14	Bowl, 8" soup	150.00	180.00	85.00
J-23	Breakfast set	2,500.00	2,750.00	1250.00
J-28	Butter dish	375.00	450.00	250.00
J-30	Butter pat	105.00	125.00	65.00
J-35	Cake plate, open handles	425.00	510.00	275.00
J-37	Cake Plate, 8" sq. pedestal	425.00	510.00	275.00
J-40	Cake stand, 2 tier	350.00	420.00	275.00
J-45	Canoe-shaped dish	450.00	540.00	350.00
J-50	Cheese keep	425.00	510.00	350.00
J-52	Coaster	155.00	190.00	85.00
J-55	Coffee pot	1,850.00	2,035.00	975.00
J-60	Compote, footed	300.00	360.00	200.00
J-65	Condiment set on tray	450.00	540.00	300.00
J-70	Cream and sugar	265.00	320.00	165.00
J-71	Cream and sugar on tray	395.00	475.00	300.00
J-75	Demi-tasse	175.00	210.00	95.00
J-77	Egg cup, footed	165.00	200.00	90.00
J-80	Hot water jug	700.00	805.00	450.00
J-85	Jam pot with liner	335.00	405.00	235.00
J-90	Jug, 4"	600.00	690.00	375.00
J-91	Jug, 4 1/2"	700.00	805.00	425.00
J-92	Jug, 5"	800.00	920.00	475.00

Cat. No.	Shape	U.S. $	Can. $	U.K. £
J-97	Nut dish	95.00	115.00	70.00
J-201	Plate, 4" sq.	90.00	110.00	65.00
J-202	Plate, 5" sq.	125.00	150.00	80.00
J-203	Plate, 6" sq.	140.00	170.00	85.00
J-204	Plate, 7" sq.	160.00	195.00	95.00
J-205	Plate, 8" sq.	200.00	240.00	125.00
J-206	Plate, 9" sq.	275.00	330.00	150.00
J-207	Plate, 10" sq.	335.00	405.00	160.00
J-112	Relish dish, small	310.00	375.00	225.00
J-115	Salad bowl, chrome rim	475.00	570.00	275.00
J-117	Salt and pepper	175.00	210.00	100.00
J-118	Salt and pepper on tray	275.00	330.00	195.00
J-120	Sandwich tray, 10" x 6"	250.00	300.00	165.00
J-121	Sandwich tray, 12" x 7"	295.00	355.00	185.00
J-125	Sauce boat and liner	300.00	360.00	185.00
J-130	Teacup and saucer	225.00	270.00	115.00
J-135	Teapot, 2 cup	800.00	920.00	450.00
J-136	Teapot, 4 cup	1,100.00	1,210.00	600.00
J-137	Teapot, 6 cup	1,400.00	1,540.00	700.00
J-140	Teapot, stacking	2,200.00	2,420.00	900.00
J-145	Tennis set	245.00	295.00	145.00
J-150	Toast rack, 4 slice	450.00	540.00	275.00
J-151	Toast rack, 2 slice	375.00	450.00	225.00
J-155	Trivet	225.00	270.00	175.00
J-160	Vase, bud	250.00	300.00	165.00

JUNE FESTIVAL

This pattern has a burgundy background and the pattern number is 137. **May Festival** is now known to be the name of the pattern when the background is either black (pattern number 135) or navy (pattern number 139). A Canadian advertisement in January, 1952 suggested that retailers carry "an entirely new pattern in Grimwades Royal Winton Ware to start 1952 — richly coloured in a deep maroon background with variegated coloured pansies."

Cat. No.	Shape	U.S. $	Can. $	U.K. £
JF-04	Bonbon dish	40.00	50.00	35.00
JF-09	Bowl, 5"	35.00	45.00	30.00
JF-14	Bowl, 8" soup	60.00	75.00	50.00
JF-23	Breakfast set	600.00	690.00	375.00
JF-28	Butter dish	120.00	145.00	85.00
JF-30	Butter pat	35.00	45.00	25.00
JF-35	Cake plate, open handles	125.00	150.00	85.00
JF-37	Cake Plate, 8" sq. pedestal	135.00	165.00	100.00
JF-40	Cake stand, 2 tier	100.00	120.00	65.00
JF-45	Canoe-shaped dish	125.00	150.00	95.00
JF-50	Cheese keep	155.00	190.00	125.00
JF-52	Coaster	35.00	45.00	20.00
JF-55	Coffee pot	400.00	480.00	295.00
JF-60	Compote, footed	90.00	110.00	65.00
JF-65	Condiment set on tray	135.00	165.00	100.00
JF-70	Cream and sugar	75.00	90.00	60.00
JF-71	Cream and sugar on tray	135.00	165.00	100.00
JF-75	Demi-tasse	75.00	90.00	45.00
JF-77	Egg cup, footed	75.00	90.00	45.00
JF-80	Hot water jug	200.00	240.00	170.00
JF-85	Jam pot with liner	115.00	140.00	80.00
JF-90	Jug, 4"	175.00	210.00	100.00
JF-91	Jug, 4 1/2"	200.00	240.00	115.00
JF-92	Jug, 5"	225.00	270.00	130.00

Cat. No.	Shape	U.S. $	Can. $	U.K. £
JF-97	Nut dish	35.00	45.00	25.00
JF-201	Plate, 4" sq.	30.00	40.00	20.00
JF-202	Plate, 5" sq.	35.00	45.00	25.00
JF-203	Plate, 6" sq.	40.00	50.00	30.00
JF-204	Plate, 7" sq.	45.00	55.00	35.00
JF-205	Plate, 8" sq.	65.00	80.00	40.00
JF-206	Plate, 9" sq.	85.00	105.00	50.00
JF-207	Plate, 10" sq .	105.00	125.00	60.00
JF-112	Relish dish, small	110.00	135.00	65.00
JF-115	Salad bowl, chrome rim	165.00	200.00	95.00
JF-117	Salt and pepper	60.00	75.00	45.00
JF-118	Salt and pepper on tray	100.00	120.00	75.00
JF-120	Sandwich tray, 10" x 6"	75.00	90.00	60.00
JF-121	Sandwich tray, 12" x 7"	90.00	110.00	65.00
JF-125	Sauce boat and liner	115.00	140.00	75.00
JF-130	Teacup and saucer	75.00	90.00	45.00
JF-135	Teapot, 2 cup	250.00	300.00	115.00
JF-136	Teapot, 4 cup	300.00	360.00	185.00
JF-137	Teapot, 6 cup	375.00	450.00	275.00
JF-140	Teapot, stacking	600.00	690.00	450.00
JF-145	Tennis set	65.00	80.00	50.00
JF-150	Toast rack, 4 slice	150.00	180.00	100.00
JF-151	Toast rack, 2 slice	125.00	150.00	65.00
JF-155	Trivet	65.00	80.00	50.00
JF-160	Vase, bud	95.00	115.00	55.00

JUNE ROSES

The pattern number is 1924 and was probably introduced in 1934. The pattern was also produced with silver trim (pattern number 1945) and with green trim (pattern number 2036). This pattern is often confused with **English Rose** and both patterns are highly collectible around the world and equally popular.

Cat. No.	Shape	U.S. $	Can. $	U.K. £
JR-04	Bonbon dish	85.00	105.00	60.00
JR-09	Bowl, 5"	55.00	70.00	50.00
JR-14	Bowl, 8" soup	110.00	135.00	75.00
JR-23	Breakfast set	1,450.00	1,595.00	850.00
JR-28	Butter dish	250.00	300.00	175.00
JR-30	Butter pat	75.00	90.00	55.00
JR-35	Cake plate, open handles	295.00	355.00	195.00
JR-37	Cake Plate, 8" sq. pedestal	275.00	330.00	200.00
JR-40	Cake stand, 2 tier	250.00	300.00	150.00
JR-45	Canoe-shaped dish	325.00	390.00	225.00
JR-50	Cheese keep	330.00	400.00	225.00
JR-52	Coaster	125.00	150.00	65.00
JR-55	Coffee pot	1,350.00	1,485.00	700.00
JR-60	Compote, footed	225.00	270.00	150.00
JR-65	Condiment set on tray	325.00	390.00	215.00
JR-70	Cream and sugar	195.00	235.00	150.00
JR-71	Cream and sugar on tray	325.00	390.00	220.00
JR-75	Demi-tasse	135.00	165.00	85.00
JR-77	Egg cup, footed	130.00	160.00	85.00
JR-80	Hot water jug	575.00	665.00	350.00
JR-85	Jam pot with liner	220.00	265.00	175.00
JR-90	Jug, 4"	450.00	540.00	250.00
JR-91	Jug, 4 1/2"	500.00	600.00	275.00
JR-92	Jug, 5"	550.00	635.00	300.00

Cat. No.	Shape	U.S. $	Can. $	U.K. £
JR-97	Nut dish	75.00	90.00	50.00
JR-201	Plate, 4" sq.	65.00	80.00	45.00
JR-202	Plate, 5" sq.	70.00	85.00	55.00
JR-203	Plate, 6" sq.	75.00	90.00	60.00
JR-204	Plate, 7" sq.	110.00	135.00	75.00
JR-205	Plate, 8" sq.	150.00	180.00	85.00
JR-206	Plate, 9" sq.	165.00	200.00	120.00
JR-207	Plate, 10" sq.	195.00	235.00	145.00
JR-112	Relish dish, small	220.00	265.00	150.00
JR-115	Salad bowl, chrome rim	395.00	475.00	225.00
JR-117	Salt and pepper	125.00	150.00	85.00
JR-118	Salt and pepper on tray	220.00	265.00	165.00
JR-120	Sandwich tray, 10" x 6"	165.00	200.00	125.00
JR-121	Sandwich tray, 12" x 7"	195.00	235.00	145.00
JR-125	Sauce boat and liner	195.00	235.00	125.00
JR-130	Teacup and saucer	135.00	165.00	80.00
JR-135	Teapot, 2 cup	650.00	750.00	375.00
JR-136	Teapot, 4 cup	900.00	1,035.00	525.00
JR-137	Teapot, 6 cup	1,100.00	1,210.00	625.00
JR-140	Teapot, stacking	1,600.00	1,760.00	750.00
JR-145	Tennis set	165.00	200.00	110.00
JR-150	Toast rack, 4 slice	400.00	480.00	215.00
JR-151	Toast rack, 2 slice	325.00	390.00	175.00
JR-155	Trivet	150.00	180.00	100.00
JR-160	Vase, bud	195.00	235.00	115.00

KEW

The pattern number is 240 and was widely produced in the 1950s. The pattern was exclusive to Dingle, Davidson, Toronto and was introduced as a new pattern in June 1949. The line is made up of giftware and teaware items, in prices ranging from $1.00 retail upwards. **Kew** has become more collectible in the past year.

Cat. No.	Shape	U.S. $	Can. $	U.K. £
Ke-04	Bonbon dish	60.00	75.00	40.00
Ke-09	Bowl, 5"	50.00	60.00	40.00
Ke-14	Bowl, 8" soup	75.00	90.00	55.00
Ke-23	Breakfast set	1,250.00	1,375.00	550.00
Ke-28	Butter dish	175.00	210.00	110.00
Ke-30	Butter pat	50.00	60.00	40.00
Ke-35	Cake plate, open handles	235.00	285.00	115.00
Ke-37	Cake Plate, 8" sq. pedestal	225.00	270.00	115.00
Ke-40	Cake stand, 2 tier	175.00	210.00	110.00
Ke-45	Canoe-shaped dish	225.00	270.00	165.00
Ke-50	Cheese keep	240.00	290.00	165.00
Ke-52	Coaster	110.00	135.00	65.00
Ke-55	Coffee pot	1,050.00	1,155.00	425.00
Ke-60	Compote, footed	150.00	180.00	95.00
Ke-65	Condiment set on tray	275.00	330.00	150.00
Ke-70	Cream and sugar	175.00	210.00	75.00
Ke-71	Cream and sugar on tray	250.00	300.00	140.00
Ke-75	Demi-tasse	115.00	140.00	60.00
Ke-77	Egg cup, footed	125.00	150.00	55.00
Ke-80	Hot water jug	450.00	540.00	225.00
Ke-85	Jam pot with liner	150.00	180.00	125.00
Ke-90	Jug, 4"	400.00	480.00	190.00
Ke-91	Jug, 4 1/2"	450.00	540.00	215.00
Ke-92	Jug, 5"	500.00	600.00	240.00

Cat. No.	Shape	U.S. $	Can. $	U.K. £
Ke-97	Nut dish	50.00	60.00	35.00
Ke-201	Plate, 4" sq.	55.00	70.00	25.00
Ke-202	Plate, 5" sq.	65.00	80.00	30.00
Ke-203	Plate, 6" sq.	75.00	90.00	35.00
Ke-204	Plate, 7" sq.	95.00	115.00	50.00
Ke-205	Plate, 8" sq.	130.00	160.00	60.00
Ke-206	Plate, 9" sq.	150.00	180.00	75.00
Ke-207	Plate, 10" sq.	165.00	200.00	95.00
Ke-112	Relish dish, small	150.00	180.00	110.00
Ke-115	Salad bowl, chrome rim	375.00	450.00	195.00
Ke-117	Salt and pepper	125.00	150.00	75.00
Ke-118	Salt and pepper on tray	200.00	240.00	130.00
Ke-120	Sandwich tray, 10" x 6"	115.00	140.00	70.00
Ke-121	Sandwich tray, 12" x 7"	135.00	165.00	80.00
Ke-125	Sauce boat and liner	165.00	200.00	95.00
Ke-130	Teacup and saucer	125.00	150.00	70.00
Ke-135	Teapot, 2 cup	475.00	570.00	300.00
Ke-136	Teapot, 4 cup	675.00	780.00	395.00
Ke-137	Teapot, 6 cup	900.00	1,035.00	525.00
Ke-140	Teapot, stacking	1,200.00	1,320.00	625.00
Ke-145	Tennis set	135.00	165.00	85.00
Ke-150	Toast rack, 4 slice	365.00	440.00	165.00
Ke-151	Toast rack, 2 slice	285.00	345.00	125.00
Ke-155	Trivet	140.00	170.00	85.00
Ke-160	Vase, bud	185.00	225.00	100.00

KINVER

The pattern number was 2254, and it was probably introduced in 1934. This is another pattern difficult to find but highly sought after.

Cat. No.	Shape	U.S. $	Can. $	U.K. £
Ki-04	Bonbon dish	85.00	105.00	60.00
Ki-09	Bowl, 5"	65.00	80.00	45.00
Ki-14	Bowl, 8" soup	95.00	115.00	70.00
Ki-23	Breakfast set	1,450.00	1,595.00	800.00
Ki-28	Butter dish	245.00	295.00	175.00
Ki-30	Butter pat	75.00	90.00	55.00
Ki-35	Cake plate, open handles	295.00	355.00	175.00
Ki-37	Cake plate, 8" sq. pedestal	285.00	345.00	175.00
Ki-40	Cake stand, 2 tier	225.00	270.00	175.00
Ki-45	Canoe-shaped dish	300.00	360.00	265.00
Ki-50	Cheese keep	300.00	360.00	225.00
Ki-52	Coaster	125.00	150.00	45.00
Ki-55	Coffee pot	1,350.00	1,485.00	700.00
Ki-60	Compote, footed	225.00	270.00	150.00
Ki-65	Condiment set on tray	325.00	390.00	215.00
Ki-70	Cream and sugar	185.00	225.00	125.00
Ki-71	Cream and sugar on tray	295.00	355.00	205.00
Ki-75	Demi-tasse	135.00	165.00	85.00
Ki-77	Egg cup, footed	130.00	160.00	60.00
Ki-80	Hot water jug	575.00	665.00	300.00
Ki-85	Jam pot with liner	225.00	270.00	175.00
Ki-90	Jug, 4"	450.00	540.00	275.00
Ki-91	Jug, 4 1/2"	500.00	600.00	300.00
Ki-92	Jug, 5"	550.00	635.00	325.00

Cat. No.	Shape	U.S. $	Can. $	U.K. £
Ki-97	Nut dish	75.00	90.00	50.00
Ki-201	Plate, 4" sq.	55.00	70.00	45.00
Ki-202	Plate, 5" sq.	65.00	80.00	55.00
Ki-203	Plate, 6" sq.	75.00	90.00	60.00
Ki-204	Plate, 7" sq.	110.00	135.00	75.00
Ki-205	Plate, 8" sq.	145.00	175.00	85.00
Ki-206	Plate, 9" sq.	160.00	195.00	120.00
Ki-207	Plate, 10" sq.	175.00	210.00	135.00
Ki-112	Relish dish, small	220.00	265.00	175.00
Ki-115	Salad bowl, chrome rim	395.00	475.00	195.00
Ki-117	Salt and pepper	125.00	150.00	80.00
Ki-118	Salt and pepper on tray	210.00	255.00	140.00
Ki-120	Sandwich tray, 10" x 6"	165.00	200.00	125.00
Ki-121	Sandwich tray, 12" x 7"	195.00	235.00	145.00
Ki-125	Sauce boat and liner	185.00	225.00	120.00
Ki-130	Teacup and saucer	135.00	165.00	75.00
Ki-135	Teapot, 2 cup	650.00	750.00	400.00
Ki-136	Teapot, 4 cup	900.00	1,035.00	500.00
Ki-137	Teapot, 6 cup	1,100.00	1,210.00	600.00
Ki-140	Teapot, stacking	1,600.00	1,760.00	650.00
Ki-145	Tennis set	135.00	165.00	95.00
Ki-150	Toast rack, 4 slice	400.00	480.00	205.00
Ki-151	Toast rack, 2 slice	325.00	390.00	150.00
Ki-155	Trivet	150.00	180.00	95.00
Ki-160	Vase, bud	195.00	235.00	110.00

MAJESTIC

The pattern number is 3311, this pattern with a black background was introduced in 1936 after **Royalty** 3079, the alternate colourway in yellow. This is one of the patterns Royal Winton plans to reproduce in 1999/2000.

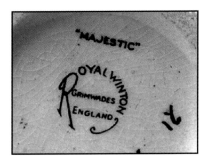

Cat. No.	Shape	U.S. $	Can. $	U.K. £
Maj-04	Bonbon dish	85.00	105.00	60.00
Maj-09	Bowl, 5"	55.00	70.00	45.00
Maj-14	Bowl, 8" soup	95.00	115.00	70.00
Maj-23	Breakfast set	1,450.00	1,595.00	1100.00
Maj-28	Butter dish	245.00	295.00	175.00
Maj-30	Butter pat	75.00	90.00	55.00
Maj-35	Cake plate, open handles	295.00	355.00	175.00
Maj-37	Cake plate, 8" sq. pedestal	270.00	325.00	175.00
Maj-40	Cake stand, 2 tier	210.00	255.00	175.00
Maj-45	Canoe-shaped dish	300.00	325.00	265.00
Maj-50	Cheese keep	300.00	360.00	225.00
Maj-52	Coaster	125.00	150.00	45.00
Maj-55	Coffee pot	1,350.00	1,485.00	700.00
Maj-60	Compote, footed	225.00	270.00	150.00
Maj-65	Condiment set on tray	325.00	390.00	215.00
Maj-70	Cream and sugar	185.00	225.00	125.00
Maj-71	Cream and sugar on tray	300.00	360.00	205.00
Maj-75	Demi-tasse	135.00	165.00	85.00
Maj-77	Egg cup, footed	130.00	160.00	60.00
Maj-80	Hot water jug	575.00	665.00	300.00
Maj-85	Jam pot with liner	225.00	270.00	175.00
Maj-90	Jug, 4"	450.00	540.00	275.00
Maj-91	Jug, 4 1/2"	500.00	600.00	300.00
Maj-92	Jug, 5"	550.00	635.00	325.00

Cat. No.	Shape	U.S. $	Can. $	U.K. £
Maj-97	Nut dish	75.00	90.00	50.00
Maj-201	Plate, 4" sq.	55.00	70.00	45.00
Maj-202	Plate, 5" sq.	65.00	80.00	55.00
Maj-203	Plate, 6" sq.	75.00	90.00	60.00
Maj-204	Plate, 7" sq.	110.00	135.00	75.00
Maj-205	Plate, 8" sq.	145.00	175.00	85.00
Maj-206	Plate, 9" sq.	160.00	195.00	120.00
Maj-207	Plate, 10" sq.	175.00	210.00	135.00
Maj-112	Relish dish, small	220.00	265.00	175.00
Maj-115	Salad bowl, chrome rim	395.00	475.00	225.00
Maj-117	Salt and pepper	125.00	150.00	80.00
Maj-118	Salt and pepper on tray	210.00	255.00	160.00
Maj-120	Sandwich tray, 10" x 6"	165.00	200.00	125.00
Maj-121	Sandwich tray, 12" x 7"	195.00	235.00	145.00
Maj-125	Sauce boat and liner	185.00	225.00	120.00
Maj-130	Teacup and saucer	135.00	165.00	75.00
Maj-135	Teapot, 2 cup	650.00	750.00	450.00
Maj-136	Teapot, 4 cup	900.00	1,035.00	600.00
Maj-137	Teapot, 6 cup	1,100.00	1,210.00	750.00
Maj-140	Teapot, stacking	1,600.00	1,760.00	825.00
Maj-145	Tennis set	135.00	165.00	120.00
Maj-150	Toast rack, 4 slice	400.00	480.00	250.00
Maj-151	Toast rack, 2 slice	325.00	390.00	150.00
Maj-155	Trivet	150.00	180.00	100.00
Maj-160	Vase, bud	195.00	235.00	125.00

MARGUERITE

The Pottery Gazette reported the pattern number as 9467 which is Marguerite with blue trim. Most pieces we see in North America have gold trim and pattern number 9432 is recorded on them. **Marguerite** is considered the first modern Winton chintz and was produced in 1928. The design was produced in great quantity for many years with gold, blue and burgundy trim. The blue trim sells for a premium over the burgundy and the gold. There are now some keen collectors for **Marguerite** in England, but it is still not popular in North America.

Cat. No.	Shape	U.S. $	Can. $	U.K. £
Mag-04	Bonbon dish	35.00	45.00	30.00
Mag-09	Bowl, 5"	30.00	40.00	25.00
Mag-14	Bowl, 8" soup	45.00	55.00	40.00
Mag-23	Breakfast set	750.00	865.00	450.00
Mag-28	Butter dish	115.00	140.00	75.00
Mag-30	Butter pat	35.00	45.00	25.00
Mag-35	Cake plate, open handles	135.00	165.00	100.00
Mag-37	Cake Plate, 8" sq. pedestal	135.00	165.00	100.00
Mag-40	Cake stand, 2 tier	125.00	150.00	100.00
Mag-45	Canoe-shaped dish	135.00	165.00	100.00
Mag-50	Cheese keep	175.00	210.00	150.00
Mag-52	Coaster	85.00	105.00	45.00
Mag-55	Coffee pot	400.00	480.00	375.00
Mag-60	Compote, footed	90.00	110.00	65.00
Mag-65	Condiment set on tray	135.00	165.00	85.00
Mag-70	Cream and sugar	85.00	105.00	50.00
Mag-71	Cream and sugar on tray	125.00	150.00	85.00
Mag-75	Demi-tasse	45.00	55.00	35.00
Mag-77	Egg cup, footed	85.00	105.00	45.00
Mag-80	Hot water jug	180.00	220.00	150.00
Mag-85	Jam pot with liner	90.00	110.00	65.00
Mag-90	Jug, 4"	175.00	210.00	150.00
Mag-91	Jug, 4 1/2"	200.00	240.00	160.00
Mag-92	Jug, 5"	225.00	270.00	175.00

Cat. No.	Shape	U.S. $	Can. $	U.K. £
Mag-97	Nut dish	35.00	45.00	25.00
Mag-201	Plate, 4" sq.	30.00	40.00	25.00
Mag-202	Plate, 5" sq.	35.00	45.00	30.00
Mag-203	Plate, 6" sq.	40.00	50.00	35.00
Mag-204	Plate, 7" sq.	45.00	55.00	40.00
Mag-205	Plate, 8" sq.	75.00	90.00	65.00
Mag-206	Plate, 9" sq.	85.00	105.00	70.00
Mag-207	Plate, 10" sq.	105.00	125.00	75.00
Mag-112	Relish dish, small	90.00	110.00	65.00
Mag-115	Salad bowl, chrome rim	125.00	150.00	75.00
Mag-117	Salt and pepper	65.00	80.00	40.00
Mag-118	Salt and pepper on tray	115.00	140.00	75.00
Mag-120	Sandwich tray, 10" x 6"	65.00	80.00	50.00
Mag-121	Sandwich tray, 12" x 7"	75.00	90.00	60.00
Mag-125	Sauce boat and liner	95.00	115.00	65.00
Mag-130	Teacup and saucer	70.00	85.00	45.00
Mag-135	Teapot, 2 cup	250.00	300.00	200.00
Mag-136	Teapot, 4 cup	300.00	360.00	250.00
Mag-137	Teapot, 6 cup	375.00	450.00	325.00
Mag-140	Teapot, stacking	575.00	665.00	350.00
Mag-145	Tennis set	80.00	100.00	50.00
Mag-150	Toast rack, 4 slice	150.00	180.00	115.00
Mag-151	Toast rack, 2 slice	125.00	150.00	85.00
Mag-155	Trivet	65.00	80.00	50.00
Mag-160	Vase, bud	100.00	120.00	60.00

MARION

The pattern number is 324. This post-war pattern was named after the daughter of a major Canadian importer, Rudolf van der Walde of Montreal, and the pattern was controlled to his company Waldonia Ltd. This pattern turns up occasionally on bone china. Royal Winton is also reproducing this pattern which has had a slight effect on the price of vintage **Marion.**

Cat. No.	Shape	U.S. $	Can. $	U.K. £
Mar-04	Bonbon dish	65.00	80 .00	60.00
Mar-09	Bowl, 5"	45.00	55.00	45.00
Mar-14	Bowl, 8" soup	80.00	100.00	75.00
Mar-23	Breakfast set	1,250.00	1,375.00	750.00
Mar-28	Butter dish	200.00	240.00	175.00
Mar-30	Butter pat	65.00	80.00	50.00
Mar-35	Cake plate, open handles	235.00	285.00	175.00
Mar-37	Cake Plate, 8" sq. pedestal	225.00	270.00	175.00
Mar-40	Cake stand, 2 tier	175.00	210.00	150.00
Mar-45	Canoe-shaped dish	225.00	270.00	200.00
Mar-50	Cheese keep	240.00	290.00	205.00
Mar-52	Coaster	110.00	135.00	60.00
Mar-55	Coffee pot	1,000.00	1,150.00	650.00
Mar-60	Compote, footed	175.00	210.00	135.00
Mar-65	Condiment set on tray	275.00	330.00	200.00
Mar-70	Cream and sugar	175.00	210.00	120.00
Mar-71	Cream and sugar on tray	250.00	300.00	195.00
Mar-75	Demi-tasse	125.00	150.00	85.00
Mar-77	Egg cup, footed	125.00	150.00	80.00
Mar-80	Hot water jug	450.00	540.00	300.00
Mar-85	Jam pot with liner	200.00	240.00	165.00
Mar-90	Jug, 4"	400.00	480.00	250.00
Mar-91	Jug, 4 1/2"	450.00	540.00	275.00
Mar-92	Jug, 5"	500.00	600.00	300.00

Cat. No.	Shape	U.S. $	Can. $	U.K. £
Mar-97	Nut dish	65.00	80.00	50.00
Mar-201	Plate, 4" sq.	55.00	70.00	45.00
Mar-202	Plate, 5" sq.	65.00	80.00	50.00
Mar-203	Plate, 6" sq.	75.00	90.00	55.00
Mar-204	Plate, 7" sq.	100.00	120.00	65.00
Mar-205	Plate, 8" sq.	135.00	165.00	85.00
Mar-206	Plate, 9" sq.	150.00	180.00	105.00
Mar-207	Plate, 10" sq.	165.00	200.00	125.00
Mar-112	Relish dish, small	180.00	220.00	175.00
Mar-115	Salad bowl, chrome rim	375.00	450.00	195.00
Mar-117	Salt and pepper	125.00	150.00	75.00
Mar-118	Salt and pepper on tray	200.00	240.00	145.00
Mar-120	Sandwich tray, 10" x 6"	125.00	150.00	120.00
Mar-121	Sandwich tray, 12" x 7"	145.00	175.00	145.00
Mar-125	Sauce boat and liner	165.00	135.00	135.00
Mar-130	Teacup and saucer	125.00	150.00	75.00
Mar-135	Teapot, 2 cup	475.00	570.00	325.00
Mar-136	Teapot, 4 cup	675.00	780.00	450.00
Mar-137	Teapot, 6 cup	900.00	1,035.00	550.00
Mar-140	Teapot, stacking	1,200.00	1,320.00	700.00
Mar-145	Tennis set	135.00	165.00	85.00
Mar-150	Toast rack, 4 slice	365.00	440.00	225.00
Mar-151	Toast rack, 2 slice	285.00	345.00	175.00
Mar-155	Trivet	150.00	180.00	85.00
Mar-160	Vase, bud	195.00	235.00	95.00

MAYFAIR

The pattern number is 392, and it was registered in Canada in 1951. This pattern is difficult to find in the United States but it remains very popular.

Cat. No.	Shape	U.S. $	Can. $	U.K. £
May-04	Bonbon dish	85.00	105.00	60.00
May-09	Bowl, 5"	55.00	70.00	45.00
May-14	Bowl, 8" soup	95.00	115.00	70.00
May-23	Breakfast set	1,450.00	1,595.00	625.00
May-28	Butter dish	245.00	295.00	175.00
May-30	Butter pat	75.00	90.00	55.00
May-35	Cake plate, open handles	295.00	355.00	175.00
May-37	Cake Plate, 8" sq. pedestal	245.00	295.00	175.00
May-40	Cake stand, 2 tier	210.00	255.00	175.00
May-45	Canoe-shaped dish	300.00	360.00	265.00
May-50	Cheese keep	300.00	360.00	225.00
May-52	Coaster	125.00	150.00	45.00
May-55	Coffee pot	1,350.00	1,485.00	700.00
May-60	Compote, footed	225.00	270.00	150.00
May-65	Condiment set on tray	325.00	390.00	215.00
May-70	Cream and sugar	185.00	225.00	125.00
May-71	Cream and sugar on tray	300.00	360.00	205.00
May-75	Demi-tasse	135.00	165.00	85.00
May-77	Egg cup, footed	130.00	160.00	60.00
May-80	Hot water jug	575.00	665.00	300.00
May-85	Jam pot with liner	225.00	270.00	175.00
May-90	Jug, 4"	450.00	540.00	250.00
May-91	Jug, 4 1/2"	500.00	600.00	375.00
May-92	Jug, 5"	550.00	635.00	300.00

Cat. No.	Shape	U.S. $	Can. $	U.K. £
May-97	Nut dish	75.00	90.00	40.00
May-201	Plate, 4" sq.	55.00	70.00	35.00
May-202	Plate, 5" sq.	65.00	80.00	45.00
May-203	Plate, 6" sq.	75.00	90.00	50.00
May-204	Plate, 7" sq.	110.00	135.00	60.00
May-205	Plate, 8" sq.	145.00	175.00	75.00
May-206	Plate, 9" sq.	160.00	195.00	95.00
May-207	Plate, 10" sq.	175.00	210.00	110.00
May-112	Relish dish, small	220.00	265.00	135.00
May-115	Salad bowl, chrome rim	395.00	475.00	215.00
May-117	Salt and pepper	125.00	150.00	65.00
May-118	Salt and pepper on tray	210.00	255.00	120.00
May-120	Sandwich tray, 10" x 6"	165.00	200.00	95.00
May-121	Sandwich tray, 12" x 7"	195.00	235.00	105.00
May-125	Sauce boat and liner	185.00	225.00	120.00
May-130	Teacup and saucer	135.00	165.00	85.00
May-135	Teapot, 2 cup	650.00	750.00	350.00
May-136	Teapot, 4 cup	900.00	1,035.00	495.00
May-137	Teapot, 6 cup	1,100.00	1,210.00	625.00
May-140	Teapot, stacking	1,600.00	1,760.00	750.00
May-145	Tennis set	135.00	165.00	95.00
May-150	Toast rack, 4 slice	400.00	480.00	225.00
May-151	Toast rack, 2 slice	325.00	390.00	175.00
May-155	Trivet	150.00	180.00	95.00
May-160	Vase, bud	195.00	235.00	100.00

MAY FESTIVAL

May Festival has been found with a pattern name in the backstamp with both the black and the navy background. The pattern number for the black background is 139, and 135 for the navy, and they are the alternate colourways to burgundy **June Festival.** Of the three, the black **May Festival** is the most popular and was introduced into Canada in 1952 after the other two colourways. **May Festival** is rarely found with a pattern name backstamp.

Cat. No.	Shape	U.S. $	Can. $	U.K. £
MF-04	Bonbon dish	45.00	55.00	35.00
MF-09	Bowl, 5"	40.00	50.00	30.00
MF-14	Bowl, 8" soup	70.00	85.00	50.00
MF-23	Breakfast set	950.00	1,095.00	375.00
MF-28	Butter dish	135.00	165.00	100.00
MF-30	Butter pat	45.00	55.00	30.00
MF-35	Cake plate, open handles	175.00	210.00	85.00
MF-37	Cake Plate, 8" sq. pedestal	165.00	200.00	100.00
MF-40	Cake stand, 2 tier	150.00	180.00	100.00
MF-45	Canoe-shaped dish	175.00	210.00	135.00
MF-50	Cheese keep	195.00	235.00	125.00
MF-52	Coaster	85.00	105.00	45.00
MF-55	Coffee pot	550.00	635.00	295.00
MF-60	Compote, footed	100.00	120.00	65.00
MF-65	Condiment set on tray	150.00	180.00	100.00
MF-70	Cream and sugar	85.00	105.00	60.00
MF-71	Cream and sugar on tray	150.00	180.00	100.00
MF-75	Demi-tasse	60.00	75.00	45.00
MF-77	Egg cup, footed	85.00	105.00	45.00
MF-80	Hot water jug	300.00	360.00	135.00
MF-85	Jam pot with liner	145.00	175.00	75.00
MF-90	Jug, 4"	250.00	300.00	135.00
MF-91	Jug, 4 1/2"	275.00	330.00	145.00
MF-92	Jug, 5"	300.00	360.00	165.00

Cat. No.	Shape	U.S. $	Can. $	U.K. £
MF-97	Nut dish	45.00	55.00	30.00
MF-201	Plate, 4" sq.	35.00	45.00	20.00
MF-202	Plate, 5" sq.	40.00	50.00	25.00
MF-203	Plate, 6" sq.	45.00	55.00	30.00
MF-204	Plate, 7" sq.	50.00	60.00	35.00
MF-205	Plate, 8" sq.	85.00	105.00	60.00
MF-206	Plate, 9" sq.	100.00	120.00	65.00
MF-207	Plate, 10" sq.	125.00	150.00	70.00
MF-112	Relish dish, small	125.00	150.00	75.00
MF-115	Salad bowl, chrome rim	195.00	235.00	100.00
MF-117	Salt and pepper	75.00	90.00	50.00
MF-118	Salt and pepper on tray	145.00	175.00	85.00
MF-120	Sandwich tray, 10" x 6"	95.00	115.00	60.00
MF-121	Sandwich tray, 12" x 7"	110.00	135.00	65.00
MF-125	Sauce boat and liner	125.00	150.00	75.00
MF-130	Teacup and saucer	85.00	105.00	50.00
MF-135	Teapot, 2 cup	300.00	360.00	150.00
MF-136	Teapot, 4 cup	400.00	480.00	225.00
MF-137	Teapot, 6 cup	500.00	600.00	300.00
MF-140	Teapot, stacking	850.00	980.00	475.00
MF-145	Tennis set	95.00	115.00	55.00
MF-150	Toast rack, 4 slice	175.00	210.00	125.00
MF-151	Toast rack, 2 slice	145.00	175.00	75.00
MF-155	Trivet	80.00	100.00	55.00
MF-160	Vase, bud	115.00	140.00	65.00

MERTON

The pattern is clearly one of the 1920s patterns and it is the Grimwades pattern which most closely resembles the A. G. Richardson chintzes of the same period. It is found in North America on a limited range of shapes. North American collectors of Crown Ducal like this pattern but it is difficult to find.

Cat. No.	Shape	U.S. $	Can. $	U.K. £
Mer-35	Cake plate, open handles	175.00	210.00	125.00
Mer-115	Salad bowl, chrome rim	195.00	235.00	100.00
Mer-130	Teacup and saucer	85.00	105.00	50.00

Cat. No.	Shape	U.S. $	Can. $	U.K. £
Mer-203	Plate, 6" sq.	60.00	75.00	40.00
Mer-206	Plate, 9" sq.	100.00	120.00	50.00

MORNING GLORY

The pattern has either a black or a burgundy background. The burgundy background is rarely seen in North America. Introduced into Canada in the spring of 1951 as an Enterprise Sales exclusive, it was described in one of their advertisements "Here is the perfect combination for the Canadian Trade. MORNING GLORY has a jet black background and is high-lighted by delicate pink, yellow and blue morning glories on a pale green vine. This beautiful under glaze pattern is a leader in the 1951 march of profits."

Cat. No.	Shape	U.S. $	Can. $	U.K. £
MG-04	Bonbon dish	45.00	55.00	35.00
MG-09	Bowl, 5"	40.00	50.00	30.00
MG-14	Bowl, 8" soup	70.00	85.00	50.00
MG-23	Breakfast set	950.00	1,095.00	375.00
MG-28	Butter dish	135.00	165.00	100.00
MG-30	Butter pat	45.00	55.00	30.00
MG-35	Cake plate, open handles	175.00	210.00	85.00
MG-37	Cake Plate, 8" sq. pedestal	165.00	200.00	100.00
MG-40	Cake stand, 2 tier	150.00	180.00	100.00
MG-45	Canoe-shaped dish	175.00	210.00	135.00
MG-50	Cheese keep	195.00	235.00	125.00
MG-52	Coaster	85.00	105.00	45.00
MG-55	Coffee pot	550.00	635.00	295.00
MG-60	Compote, footed	100.00	120.00	65.00
MG-65	Condiment set on tray	150.00	180.00	100.00
MG-70	Cream and sugar	85.00	105.00	60.00
MG-71	Cream and sugar on tray	150.00	180.00	100.00
MG-75	Demi-tasse	60.00	75.00	45.00
MG-77	Egg cup, footed	85.00	105.00	45.00
MG-80	Hot water jug	300.00	360.00	135.00
MG-85	Jam pot with liner	145.00	175.00	75.00
MG-90	Jug, 4"	250.00	300.00	135.00
MG-91	Jug, 4 1/2"	275.00	330.00	145.00
MG-92	Jug, 5"	300.00	360.00	165.00

Cat. No.	Shape	U.S. $	Can. $	U.K. £
MG-97	Nut dish	45.00	55.00	30.00
MG-201	Plate, 4" sq.	35.00	45.00	20.00
MG-202	Plate, 5" sq.	40.00	50.00	25.00
MG-203	Plate, 6" sq.	45.00	55.00	30.00
MG-204	Plate, 7" sq.	50.00	60.00	35.00
MG-205	Plate, 8" sq.	85.00	105.00	60.00
MG-206	Plate, 9" sq.	100.00	120.00	65.00
MG-207	Plate, 10" sq.	125.00	150.00	70.00
MG-112	Relish dish, small	125.00	150.00	75.00
MG-115	Salad bowl, chrome rim	195.00	235.00	100.00
MG-117	Salt and pepper	75.00	90.00	50.00
MG-118	Salt and pepper on tray	145.00	175.00	85.00
MG-120	Sandwich tray, 10" x 6"	95.00	115.00	60.00
MG-121	Sandwich tray, 12" x 7"	110.00	135.00	65.00
MG-125	Sauce boat and liner	125.00	150.00	75.00
MG-130	Teacup and saucer	85.00	105.00	50.00
MG-135	Teapot, 2 cup	300.00	360.00	150.00
MG-136	Teapot, 4 cup	400.00	480.00	225.00
MG-137	Teapot, 6 cup	500.00	600.00	300.00
MG-140	Teapot, stacking	850.00	980.00	475.00
MG-145	Tennis set	95.00	115.00	55.00
MG-150	Toast rack, 4 slice	175.00	210.00	105.00
MG-151	Toast rack, 2 slice	145.00	175.00	65.00
MG-155	Trivet	80.00	100.00	55.00
MG-160	Vase, bud	115.00	140.00	65.00

NANTWICH

The pattern number is 291. This pattern was exclusive to Cassidys and advertised in their 1953 catalogue. This pattern was exported in quantity to North America in the 1950s.

Cat. No.	Shape	U.S. $	Can. $	U.K. £
N-04	Bonbon dish	65.00	75.00	45.00
N-09	Bowl, 5"	50.00	60.00	40.00
N-14	Bowl, 8" soup	75.00	90.00	50.00
N-23	Breakfast set	1,200.00	1,320.00	650.00
N-28	Butter dish	175.00	210.00	150.00
N-30	Butter pat	50.00	60.00	40.00
N-35	Cake plate, open handles	200.00	240.00	150.00
N-37	Cake Plate, 8" sq. pedestal	200.00	240.00	150.00
N-40	Cake stand, 2 tier	185.00	225.00	135.00
N-45	Canoe-shaped dish	250.00	300.00	225.00
N-50	Cheese keep	225.00	270.00	175.00
N-52	Coaster	110.00	135.00	65.00
N-55	Coffee pot	975.00	1,125.00	575.00
N-60	Compote, footed	150.00	180.00	100.00
N-65	Condiment set on tray	225.00	270.00	150.00
N-70	Cream and sugar	125.00	150.00	85.00
N-71	Cream and sugar on tray	225.00	270.00	165.00
N-75	Demi-tasse	95.00	115.00	60.00
N-77	Egg cup, footed	110.00	135.00	65.00
N-80	Hot water jug	450.00	540.00	250.00
N-85	Jam pot with liner	175.00	210.00	125.00
N-90	Jug, 4"	400.00	480.00	175.00
N-91	Jug, 4 1/2"	450.00	540.00	200.00
N-92	Jug, 5"	500.00	600.00	225.00

Cat. No.	Shape	U.S. $	Can. $	U.K. £
N-97	Nut dish	50.00	60.00	40.00
N-201	Plate, 4" sq.	45.00	55.00	35.00
N-202	Plate, 5" sq.	50.00	60.00	40.00
N-203	Plate, 6" sq.	75.00	90.00	45.00
N-204	Plate, 7" sq.	85.00	105.00	60.00
N-205	Plate, 8" sq.	125.00	150.00	85.00
N-206	Plate, 9" sq.	150.00	180.00	100.00
N-207	Plate, 10" sq.	165.00	200.00	115.00
N-112	Relish dish, small	175.00	210.00	125.00
N-115	Salad bowl, chrome rim	300.00	360.00	165.00
N-117	Salt and pepper	95.00	115.00	60.00
N-118	Salt and pepper on tray	165.00	200.00	115.00
N-120	Sandwich tray, 10" x 6"	125.00	150.00	85.00
N-121	Sandwich tray, 12" x 7"	150.00	180.00	100.00
N-125	Sauce boat and liner	175.00	210.00	125.00
N-130	Teacup and saucer	110.00	135.00	60.00
N-135	Teapot, 2 cup	425.00	510.00	275.00
N-136	Teapot, 4 cup	650.00	750.00	400.00
N-137	Teapot, 6 cup	850.00	980.00	475.00
N-140	Teapot, stacking	1,200.00	1,320.00	550.00
N-145	Tennis set	125.00	150.00	75.00
N-150	Toast rack, 4 slice	300.00	360.00	200.00
N-151	Toast rack, 2 slice	225.00	270.00	160.00
N-155	Trivet	125.00	150.00	75.00
N-160	Vase, bud	150.00	180.00	85.00

OFFLEY

A breakfast set in this pattern was advertised in a Toronto newspaper in December 1938 for $9.50. Since **Sandon, Meaford** and **Offley** were introduced six months before and the description of **Offley** in the *Pottery Gazette* matches this pattern we are calling it **Offley** for the moment. This pattern also comes in a brown colourway. Neither pattern is particularly collectible.

Cat. No.	Shape	U.S. $	Can. $	U.K. £
Of-04	Bonbon dish	25.00	30.00	20.00
Of-09	Bowl, 5"	25.00	30.00	20.00
Of-14	Bowl, 8" soup	35.00	45.00	25.00
Of-23	Breakfast set	350.00	420.00	250.00
Of-28	Butter dish	90.00	110.00	60.00
Of-30	Butter pat	25.00	30.00	15.00
Of-35	Cake plate, open handles	90.00	110.00	65.00
Of-37	Cake Plate, 8" sq. pedestal	90.00	110.00	55.00
Of-40	Cake stand, 2 tier	90.00	110.00	45.00
Of-45	Canoe-shaped dish	120.00	145.00	75.00
Of-50	Cheese keep	115.00	140.00	90.00
Of-52	Coaster	35.00	45.00	20.00
Of-55	Coffee pot	350.00	420.00	200.00
Of-60	Compote, footed	65.00	80.00	50.00
Of-65	Condiment set on tray	90.00	110.00	65.00
Of-70	Cream and sugar	55.00	70.00	45.00
Of-71	Cream and sugar on tray	90.00	110.00	65.00
Of-75	Demi-tasse	35.00	45.00	25.00
Of-77	Egg cup, footed	45.00	55.00	25.00
Of-80	Hot water jug	165.00	200.00	125.00
Of-85	Jam pot with liner	75.00	90.00	50.00
Of-90	Jug, 4"	135.00	165.00	65.00
Of-91	Jug, 4 1/2"	150.00	180.00	75.00
Of-92	Jug, 5"	165.00	200.00	95.00

Cat. No.	Shape	U.S. $	Can. $	U.K. £
Of-97	Nut dish	25.00	30.00	15.00
Of-201	Plate, 4" sq.	30.00	40.00	15.00
Of-202	Plate, 5" sq.	35.00	45.00	20.00
Of-203	Plate, 6" sq.	40.00	50.00	25.00
Of-204	Plate, 7" sq.	45.00	55.00	30.00
Of-205	Plate, 8" sq.	55.00	70.00	40.00
Of-206	Plate, 9" sq.	65.00	80.00	45.00
Of-207	Plate, 10" sq.	75.00	90.00	50.00
Of-112	Relish dish, small	75.00	90.00	50.00
Of-115	Salad bowl, chrome rim	145.00	175.00	85.00
Of-117	Salt and pepper	45.00	55.00	30.00
Of-118	Salt and pepper on tray	95.00	115.00	60.00
Of-120	Sandwich tray, 10" x 6"	45.00	55.00	35.00
Of-121	Sandwich tray, 12" x 7"	65.00	80.00	40.00
Of-125	Sauce boat and liner	65.00	80.00	45.00
Of-130	Teacup and saucer	35.00	45.00	30.00
Of-135	Teapot, 2 cup	150.00	180.00	75.00
Of-136	Teapot, 4 cup	225.00	270.00	125.00
Of-137	Teapot, 6 cup	275.00	325.00	175.00
Of-140	Teapot, stacking	300.00	360.00	225.00
Of-145	Tennis set	45.00	55.00	35.00
Of-150	Toast rack, 4 slice	150.00	180.00	90.00
Of-151	Toast rack, 2 slice	90.00	110.00	65.00
Of-155	Trivet	45.00	55.00	30.00
Of-160	Vase, bud	65.00	80.00	45.00

OLD COTTAGE CHINTZ

The pattern number is 9632. The pattern was introduced very early in the 1930s and was produced in great quantities until the 1960s. It has been seen on an invoice as late as 1969. Be aware of the difference in the colour of the pre- and post-war transfer. **Old Cottage Chintz** turns up on bone china from time to time.

Cat. No.	Shape	U.S. $	Can. $	U.K. £
OC-04	Bonbon dish	50.00	60.00	35.00
OC-09	Bowl, 5"	45.00	55.00	35.00
OC-14	Bowl, 8" soup	75.00	90.00	50.00
OC-23	Breakfast set	950.00	1,095.00	400.00
OC-28	Butter dish	150.00	180.00	100.00
OC-30	Butter pat	45.00	55.00	35.00
OC-35	Cake plate, open handles	175.00	210.00	90.00
OC-37	Cake plate, 8" sq. pedestal	160.00	195.00	90.00
OC-40	Cake stand, 2 tier	150.00	180.00	80.00
OC-45	Canoe-shaped dish	195.00	235.00	150.00
OC-50	Cheese keep	200.00	240.00	125.00
OC-52	Coaster	95.00	115.00	50.00
OC-55	Coffee pot	700.00	805.00	375.00
OC-60	Compote, footed	125.00	150.00	75.00
OC-65	Condiment set on tray	175.00	210.00	125.00
OC-70	Cream and sugar	100.00	120.00	65.00
OC-71	Cream and sugar on tray	175.00	210.00	125.00
OC-75	Demi-tasse	75.00	90.00	50.00
OC-77	Egg cup, footed	95.00	115.00	55.00
OC-80	Hot water jug	275.00	325.00	175.00
OC-85	Jam pot with liner	150.00	180.00	100.00
OC-90	Jug, 4"	225.00	270.00	135.00
OC-91	Jug, 4 1/2"	275.00	330.00	145.00
OC-92	Jug, 5"	325.00	390.00	160.00

Cat. No.	Shape	U.S. $	Can. $	U.K. £
OC-97	Nut dish	45.00	55.00	30.00
OC-201	Plate, 4" sq.	50.00	60.00	30.00
OC-202	Plate, 5" sq.	50.00	60.00	35.00
OC-203	Plate, 6" sq.	60.00	75.00	40.00
OC-204	Plate, 7" sq.	75.00	90.00	45.00
OC-205	Plate, 8" sq.	100.00	120.00	60.00
OC-206	Plate, 9" sq.	125.00	150.00	70.00
OC-207	Plate, 10" sq.	135.00	165.00	75.00
OC-112	Relish dish, small	140.00	170.00	100.00
OC-115	Salad bowl, chrome rim	275.00	330.00	145.00
OC-117	Salt and pepper	75.00	90.00	50.00
OC-118	Salt and pepper on tray	150.00	180.00	85.00
OC-120	Sandwich tray, 10" x 6"	100.00	120.00	65.00
OC-121	Sandwich tray, 12" x 7"	125.00	150.00	75.00
OC-125	Sauce boat and liner	135.00	165.00	75.00
OC-130	Teacup and saucer	85.00	105.00	50.00
OC-135	Teapot, 2 cup	325.00	390.00	200.00
OC-136	Teapot, 4 cup	425.00	510.00	250.00
OC-137	Teapot, 6 cup	525.00	605.00	325.00
OC-140	Teapot, stacking	850.00	980.00	425.00
OC-145	Tennis set	100.00	120.00	65.00
OC-150	Toast rack, 4 slice	250.00	300.00	135.00
OC-151	Toast rack, 2 slice	195.00	235.00	75.00
OC-155	Trivet	100.00	120.00	50.00
OC-160	Vase, bud	135.00	165.00	65.00

ORIENT

The pattern number is 471, and the pattern was exclusive to Cassidys of Canada in 1954. Jack Robertson, who was the buyer for Cassidys, chose this pattern from a sample, but the finished product did not sell well. Although it is still not popular in North America, it is developing a following in England.

Cat. No.	Shape	U.S. $	Can. $	U.K. £	Cat. No.	Shape	U.S. $	Can. $	U.K. £
O-04	Bonbon dish	25.00	30.00	25.00	O-97	Nut dish	25.00	30.00	20.00
O-09	Bowl, 5"	25.00	35.00	25.00	O-201	Plate, 4" sq.	30.00	40.00	25.00
O-14	Bowl, 8" soup	35.00	45.00	30.00	O-202	Plate, 5" sq.	35.00	45.00	25.00
O-23	Breakfast set	450.00	540.00	350.00	O-203	Plate, 6" sq.	40.00	50.00	30.00
O-28	Butter dish	90.00	110.00	65.00	O-204	Plate, 7" sq.	45.00	55.00	35.00
O-30	Butter pat	25.00	30.00	20.00	O-205	Plate, 8" sq.	55.00	70.00	45.00
O-35	Cake plate, open handles	90.00	110.00	75.00	O-206	Plate, 9" sq.	65.00	80.00	50.00
O-37	Cake Plate, 8" sq. pedestal	90.00	110.00	65.00	O-207	Plate, 10" sq.	75.00	90.00	55.00
O-40	Cake stand, 2 tier	90.00	110.00	65.00	O-112	Relish dish, small	75.00	90.00	60.00
O-45	Canoe-shaped dish	120.00	145.00	85.00	O-115	Salad bowl, chrome rim	175.00	210.00	95.00
O-50	Cheese keep	125.00	150.00	100.00	O-117	Salt and pepper	65.00	80.00	40.00
O-52	Coaster	70.00	85.00	20.00	O-118	Salt and pepper on tray	115.00	140.00	80.00
O-55	Coffee pot	395.00	475.00	275.00	O-120	Sandwich tray, 10" x 6"	75.00	90.00	45.00
O-60	Compote, footed	65.00	80.00	50.00	O-121	Sandwich tray, 12" x 7"	85.00	105.00	50.00
O-65	Condiment set on tray	110.00	135.00	65.00	O-125	Sauce boat and liner	75.00	90.00	50.00
O-70	Cream and sugar	55.00	70.00	45.00	O-130	Teacup and saucer	65.00	80.00	35.00
O-71	Cream and sugar on tray	90.00	110.00	65.00	O-135	Teapot, 2 cup	175.00	210.00	150.00
O-75	Demi-tasse	60.00	75.00	35.00	O-136	Teapot, 4 cup	275.00	330.00	200.00
O-77	Egg cup, footed	75.00	90.00	25.00	O-137	Teapot, 6 cup	325.00	390.00	250.00
O-80	Hot water jug	165.00	200.00	125.00	O-140	Teapot, stacking	450.00	540.00	350.00
O-85	Jam pot with liner	95.00	115.00	60.00	O-145	Tennis set	75.00	90.00	40.00
O-90	Jug, 4"	145.00	175.00	75.00	O-150	Toast rack, 4 slice	165.00	200.00	125.00
O-91	Jug, 4 1/2"	160.00	195.00	95.00	O-151	Toast rack, 2 slice	115.00	140.00	65.00
O-92	Jug, 5"	175.00	210.00	125.00	O-155	Trivet	65.00	80.00	40.00
					O-160	Vase, bud	95.00	115.00	55.00

PAISLEY

This pattern was used by a number of companies including Wade throughout the 1920s and later James Kent produced blue paisley as pattern number 5663 in the late 1950s. The Grimwades version appeared in 1923 in both a rust and a green colorway (pattern number 8152). The blue colourway appeared some time later (pattern number 9154). This pattern has never been popular with chintz collectors but fits into the category of all over transfers including **Tartans** and **Quilt**.

Cat. No.	Shape	U.S. $	Can. $	U.K. £
Pa-04	Bonbon dish	25.00	30.00	25.00
Pa-09	Bowl, 5"	25.00	30.00	25.00
Pa-14	Bowl, 8" soup	35.00	45.00	30.00
Pa-23	Breakfast set	425.00	510.00	250.00
Pa-28	Butter dish	90.00	110.00	65.00
Pa-30	Butter pat	25.00	30.00	20.00
Pa-35	Cake plate, open handles	90.00	110.00	50.00
Pa-37	Cake Plate, 8" sq. pedestal	90.00	110.00	50.00
Pa-40	Cake stand, 2 tier	80.00	100.00	45.00
Pa-45	Canoe-shaped dish	120.00	145.00	65.00
Pa-50	Cheese keep	115.00	140.00	80.00
Pa-52	Coaster	65.00	80.00	25.00
Pa-55	Coffee pot	395.00	475.00	275.00
Pa-60	Compote, footed	65.00	80.00	50.00
Pa-65	Condiment set on tray	90.00	110.00	65.00
Pa-70	Cream and sugar	55.00	70.00	45.00
Pa-71	Cream and sugar on tray	90.00	110.00	65.00
Pa-75	Demi-tasse	35.00	45.00	30.00
Pa-77	Egg cup, footed	75.00	90.00	25.00
Pa-80	Hot water jug	135.00	165.00	75.00
Pa-85	Jam pot with liner	75.00	90.00	60.00
Pa-90	Jug, 4"	100.00	120.00	60.00
Pa-91	Jug, 4 1/2"	125.00	150.00	70.00
Pa-92	Jug, 5"	145.00	175.00	80.00

Cat. No.	Shape	U.S. $	Can. $	U.K. £
Pa-97	Nut dish	25.00	30.00	20.00
Pa-201	Plate, 4" sq.	30.00	40.00	25.00
Pa-202	Plate, 5" sq.	35.00	45.00	25.00
Pa-203	Plate, 6" sq.	40.00	50.00	30.00
Pa-204	Plate, 7" sq.	45.00	55.00	35.00
Pa-205	Plate, 8" sq.	55.00	70.00	45.00
Pa-206	Plate, 9" sq.	65.00	80.00	50.00
Pa-207	Plate, 10" sq.	75.00	90.00	55.00
Pa-112	Relish dish, small	75.00	90.00	60.00
Pa-115	Salad bowl, chrome rim	145.00	175.00	85.00
Pa-117	Salt and pepper	45.00	55.00	40.00
Pa-118	Salt and pepper on tray	95.00	115.00	75.00
Pa-120	Sandwich tray, 10" x 6"	45.00	55.00	45.00
Pa-121	Sandwich tray, 12" x 7"	65.00	80.00	50.00
Pa-125	Sauce boat and liner	65.00	80.00	45.00
Pa-130	Teacup and saucer	55.00	70.00	35.00
Pa-135	Teapot, 2 cup	175.00	210.00	125.00
Pa-136	Teapot, 4 cup	275.00	330.00	175.00
Pa-137	Teapot, 6 cup	325.00	390.00	225.00
Pa-140	Teapot, stacking	425.00	510.00	325.00
Pa-145	Tennis set	60.00	75.00	40.00
Pa-150	Toast rack, 4 slice	150.00	180.00	125.00
Pa-151	Toast rack, 2 slice	90.00	110.00	75.00
Pa-155	Trivet	45.00	55.00	40.00
Pa-160	Vase, bud	75.00	90.00	45.00

PEKIN

The pattern number for the 1950s version is 320, and it was produced with black, burgundy and dark green backgrounds. Waldonia Ltd. introduced this pattern into Canada in 1951 as Black Pekin; it was a huge success. The Ivory Pekin followed in 1953. Some of the earlier versions of this pattern are handpainted.

Cat. No.	Shape	U.S. $	Can. $	U.K. £
Pe-04	Bonbon dish	40.00	50.00	30.00
Pe-09	Bowl, 5"	35.00	45.00	25.00
Pe-14	Bowl, 8" soup	50.00	60.00	40.00
Pe-23	Breakfast set	550.00	635.00	375.00
Pe-28	Butter dish	100.00	120.00	75.00
Pe-30	Butter pat	25.00	30.00	25.00
Pe-35	Cake plate, open handles	125.00	150.00	95.00
Pe-37	Cake Plate, 8" sq. pedestal	125.00	150.00	95.00
Pe-40	Cake stand, 2 tier	95.00	115.00	90.00
Pe-45	Canoe-shaped dish	135.00	165.00	100.00
Pe-50	Cheese keep	125.00	150.00	100.00
Pe-52	Coaster	75.00	90.00	45.00
Pe-55	Coffee pot	375.00	450.00	325.00
Pe-60	Compote, footed	75.00	90.00	65.00
Pe-65	Condiment set on tray	125.00	150.00	85.00
Pe-70	Cream and sugar	65.00	80.00	50.00
Pe-71	Cream and sugar on tray	100.00	120.00	85.00
Pe-75	Demi-tasse	55.00	70.00	35.00
Pe-77	Egg cup, footed	75.00	90.00	35.00
Pe-80	Hot water jug	165.00	200.00	150.00
Pe-85	Jam pot with liner	85.00	105.00	65.00
Pe-90	Jug, 4"	135.00	165.00	100.00
Pe-91	Jug, 4 1/2"	150.00	180.00	125.00
Pe-92	Jug, 5"	165.00	200.00	150.00

Cat. No.	Shape	U.S. $	Can. $	U.K. £
Pe-97	Nut dish	25.00	30.00	25.00
Pe-201	Plate, 4" sq.	30.00	40.00	25.00
Pe-202	Plate, 5" sq.	35.00	45.00	30.00
Pe-203	Plate, 6" sq.	40.00	50.00	35.00
Pe-204	Plate, 7" sq.	45.00	55.00	40.00
Pe-205	Plate, 8" sq.	65.00	80.00	55.00
Pe-206	Plate, 9" sq.	75.00	90.00	65.00
Pe-207	Plate, 10" sq.	85.00	105.00	75.00
Pe-112	Relish dish, small	85.00	105.00	80.00
Pe-115	Salad bowl, chrome rim	165.00	200.00	95.00
Pe-117	Salt and pepper	65.00	80.00	40.00
Pe-118	Salt and pepper on tray	115.00	140.00	75.00
Pe-120	Sandwich tray, 10" x 6"	50.00	60.00	50.00
Pe-121	Sandwich tray, 12" x 7"	75.00	90.00	60.00
Pe-125	Sauce boat and liner	65.00	80.00	65.00
Pe-130	Teacup and saucer	65.00	80.00	35.00
Pe-135	Teapot, 2 cup	175.00	210.00	150.00
Pe-136	Teapot, 4 cup	275.00	330.00	200.00
Pe-137	Teapot, 6 cup	325.00	390.00	275.00
Pe-140	Teapot, stacking	450.00	540.00	350.00
Pe-145	Tennis set	75.00	90.00	50.00
Pe-150	Toast rack, 4 slice	150.00	180.00	115.00
Pe-151	Toast rack, 2 slice	100.00	120.00	85.00
Pe-155	Trivet	75.00	90.00	45.00
Pe-160	Vase, bud	95.00	115.00	50.00

PELHAM

The pattern number is 2201, and the pattern was purchased by Queen Mary at the 1935 British Industries Fair. It came with a teal trim. This pattern is also known as **Sampler**. Needlepoint patterns are not particularly collectible in general but some collectors love them.

Cat. No.	Shape	U.S. $	Can. $	U.K. £
Pel-04	Bonbon dish	45.00	55.00	35.00
Pel-09	Bowl, 5"	40.00	50.00	30.00
Pel-14	Bowl, 8" soup	50.00	60.00	40.00
Pel-23	Breakfast set	650.00	750.00	350.00
Pel-28	Butter dish	125.00	150.00	75.00
Pel-30	Butter pat	35.00	45.00	25.00
Pel-35	Cake plate, open handles	150.00	180.00	85.00
Pel-37	Cake Plate, 8" sq. pedestal	150.00	180.00	80.00
Pel-40	Cake stand, 2 tier	125.00	150.00	60.00
Pel-45	Canoe-shaped dish	145.00	175.00	75.00
Pel-50	Cheese keep	150.00	180.00	100.00
Pel-52	Coaster	75.00	90.00	35.00
Pel-55	Coffee pot	475.00	570.00	325.00
Pel-60	Compote, footed	100.00	120.00	65.00
Pel-65	Condiment set on tray	150.00	180.00	85.00
Pel-70	Cream and sugar	75.00	90.00	50.00
Pel-71	Cream and sugar on tray	135.00	165.00	85.00
Pel-75	Demi-tasse	60.00	75.00	40.00
Pel-77	Egg cup, footed	85.00	105.00	45.00
Pel-80	Hot water jug	225.00	270.00	150.00
Pel-85	Jam pot with liner	125.00	150.00	75.00
Pel-90	Jug, 4"	175.00	210.00	125.00
Pel-91	Jug, 4 1/2"	200.00	240.00	135.00
Pel-92	Jug, 5"	225.00	270.00	145.00

Cat. No.	Shape	U.S. $	Can. $	U.K. £
Pel-97	Nut dish	35.00	45.00	25.00
Pel-201	Plate, 4" sq.	35.00	45.00	20.00
Pel-202	Plate, 5" sq.	40.00	50.00	25.00
Pel-203	Plate, 6" sq.	45.00	55.00	30.00
Pel-204	Plate, 7" sq.	50.00	60.00	35.00
Pel-205	Plate, 8" sq.	75.00	90.00	40.00
Pel-206	Plate, 9" sq.	95.00	115.00	50.00
Pel-207	Plate, 10" sq.	125.00	150.00	55.00
Pel-112	Relish dish, small	125.00	150.00	75.00
Pel-115	Salad bowl, chrome rim	195.00	235.00	105.00
Pel-117	Salt and pepper	75.00	80.00	45.00
Pel-118	Salt and pepper on tray	135.00	165.00	85.00
Pel-120	Sandwich tray, 10" x 6"	75.00	90.00	50.00
Pel-121	Sandwich tray, 12" x 7"	100.00	120.00	65.00
Pel-125	Sauce boat and liner	125.00	150.00	75.00
Pel-130	Teacup and saucer	65.00	80.00	40.00
Pel-135	Teapot, 2 cup	300.00	360.00	150.00
Pel-136	Teapot, 4 cup	350.00	420.00	200.00
Pel-137	Teapot, 6 cup	400.00	480.00	250.00
Pel-140	Teapot, stacking	600.00	690.00	350.00
Pel-145	Tennis set	75.00	90.00	50.00
Pel-150	Toast rack, 4 slice	175.00	210.00	125.00
Pel-151	Toast rack, 2 slice	150.00	180.00	100.00
Pel-155	Trivet	75.00	90.00	50.00
Pel-160	Vase, bud	95.00	115.00	60.00

PEONY

This large flower chintz pattern is very much a 1950s chintz and was exported to North America in great quantities.

Cat. No.	Shape	U.S. $	Can. $	U.K. £
Peo-04	Bonbon dish	50.00	60.00	35.00
Peo-09	Bowl, 5"	45.00	55.00	30.00
Peo-14	Bowl, 8" soup	70.00	85.00	50.00
Peo-23	Breakfast set	950.00	1,095.00	375.00
Peo-28	Butter dish	135.00	165.00	100.00
Peo-30	Butter pat	45.00	55.00	30.00
Peo-35	Cake plate, open handles	175.00	210.00	105.00
Peo-37	Cake Plate, 8" sq. pedestal	165.00	200.00	105.00
Peo-40	Cake stand, 2 tier	140.00	170.00	95.00
Peo-45	Canoe-shaped dish	175.00	210.00	115.00
Peo-50	Cheese keep	195.00	235.00	125.00
Peo-52	Coaster	85.00	105.00	45.00
Peo-55	Coffee pot	550.00	635.00	295.00
Peo-60	Compote, footed	100.00	120.00	65.00
Peo-65	Condiment set on tray	150.00	180.00	100.00
Peo-70	Cream and sugar	85.00	105.00	60.00
Peo-71	Cream and sugar on tray	150.00	180.00	100.00
Peo-75	Demi-tasse	60.00	75.00	45.00
Peo-77	Egg cup, footed	85.00	105.00	50.00
Peo-80	Hot water jug	300.00	360.00	135.00
Peo-85	Jam pot with liner	150.00	180.00	85.00
Peo-90	Jug, 4"	250.00	300.00	135.00
Peo-91	Jug, 4 1/2"	275.00	330.00	145.00
Peo-92	Jug, 5"	300.00	360.00	165.00

Cat. No.	Shape	U.S. $	Can. $	U.K. £
Peo-97	Nut dish	45.00	55.00	30.00
Peo-201	Plate, 4" sq.	35.00	45.00	20.00
Peo-202	Plate, 5" sq.	40.00	50.00	25.00
Peo-203	Plate, 6" sq.	45.00	55.00	30.00
Peo-204	Plate, 7" sq.	50.00	60.00	35.00
Peo-205	Plate, 8" sq.	85.00	105.00	60.00
Peo-206	Plate, 9" sq.	100.00	120.00	65.00
Peo-207	Plate, 10" sq.	125.00	150.00	70.00
Peo-112	Relish dish, small	135.00	165.00	75.00
Peo-115	Salad bowl, chrome rim	195.00	235.00	100.00
Peo-117	Salt and pepper	85.00	105.00	50.00
Peo-118	Salt and pepper on tray	150.00	180.00	100.00
Peo-120	Sandwich tray, 10" x 6"	95.00	115.00	60.00
Peo-121	Sandwich tray, 12" x 7"	110.00	135.00	70.00
Peo-125	Sauce boat and liner	125.00	150.00	75.00
Peo-130	Teacup and saucer	85.00	105.00	40.00
Peo-135	Teapot, 2 cup	300.00	360.00	150.00
Peo-136	Teapot, 4 cup	400.00	480.00	225.00
Peo-137	Teapot, 6 cup	500.00	600.00	300.00
Peo-140	Teapot, stacking	850.00	980.00	425.00
Peo-145	Tennis set	95.00	115.00	45.00
Peo-150	Toast rack, 4 slice	175.00	210.00	105.00
Peo-151	Toast rack, 2 slice	145.00	175.00	65.00
Peo-155	Trivet	80.00	100.00	50.00
Peo-160	Vase, bud	115.00	140.00	60.00

PRIMROSE

Some collectors have called this pattern Cosmos but I think it is **Primrose** and dates to the late 1930s. There is a description of **Primrose** in the *Pottery & Glass Record* which fits this pattern: "Their **Primrose** was still showing and selling as easy as ever. A strong multi-colour scheme, warm and rich in consolidation of tones seen in a series of table and fancy sets, having a gold diaper print, on green, yellow, and pink bases, picked out in enamel flowers, gold finish." The yellow ground pattern number is 5995, pink is 5999 and green is 6001.

Cat. No.	Shape	U.S. $	Can. $	U.K. £
PRI-04	Bonbon dish	25.00	30.00	25.00
PRI-09	Bowl, 5"	25.00	30.00	25.00
PRI-14	Bowl, 8" soup	35.00	45.00	30.00
PRI-23	Breakfast set	350.00	420.00	325.00
PRI-28	Butter dish	90.00	110.00	65.00
PRI-30	Butter pat	25.00	30.00	20.00
PRI-35	Cake plate, open handles	100.00	120.00	75.00
PRI-37	Cake Plate, 8" sq. pedestal	100.00	120.00	75.00
PRI-40	Cake stand, 2 tier	90.00	110.00	65.00
PRI-45	Canoe-shaped dish	120.00	145.00	85.00
PRI-50	Cheese keep	115.00	140.00	100.00
PRI-52	Coaster	35.00	45.00	20.00
PRI-55	Coffee pot	375.00	450.00	250.00
PRI-60	Compote, footed	65.00	80.00	50.00
PRI-65	Condiment set on tray	125.00	150.00	75.00
PRI-70	Cream and sugar	55.00	70.00	45.00
PRI-71	Cream and sugar on tray	90.00	110.00	65.00
PRI-75	Demi-tasse	35.00	45.00	30.00
PRI-77	Egg cup, footed	45.00	55.00	25.00
PRI-80	Hot water jug	165.00	200.00	125.00
PRI-85	Jam pot with liner	75.00	90.00	60.00
PRI-90	Jug, 4"	135.00	165.00	65.00
PRI-91	Jug, 4 1/2"	150.00	180.00	75.00
PRI-92	Jug, 5"	165.00	200.00	95.00

Cat. No.	Shape	U.S. $	Can. $	U.K. £
PRI-97	Nut dish	25.00	30.00	20.00
PRI-201	Plate, 4" sq.	30.00	40.00	25.00
PRI-202	Plate, 5" sq.	35.00	45.00	25.00
PRI-203	Plate, 6" sq.	40.00	50.00	30.00
PRI-204	Plate, 7" sq.	45.00	55.00	35.00
PRI-205	Plate, 8" sq.	55.00	70.00	45.00
PRI-206	Plate, 9" sq.	65.00	80.00	50.00
PRI-207	Plate, 10" sq.	75.00	90.00	55.00
PRI-112	Relish dish, small	75.00	90.00	60.00
PRI-115	Salad bowl, chrome rim	145.00	175.00	85.00
PRI-117	Salt and pepper	55.00	70.00	40.00
PRI-118	Salt and pepper on tray	100.00	120.00	80.00
PRI-120	Sandwich tray, 10" x 6"	45.00	55.00	45.00
PRI-121	Sandwich tray, 12" x 7"	65.00	80.00	50.00
PRI-125	Sauce boat and liner	75.00	90.00	45.00
PRI-130	Teacup and saucer	35.00	45.00	30.00
PRI-135	Teapot, 2 cup	150.00	180.00	125.00
PRI-136	Teapot, 4 cup	225.00	270.00	175.00
PRI-137	Teapot, 6 cup	300.00	360.00	225.00
PRI-140	Teapot, stacking	400.00	480.00	275.00
PRI-145	Tennis set	45.00	55.00	40.00
PRI-150	Toast rack, 4 slice	150.00	180.00	125.00
PRI-151	Toast rack, 2 slice	90.00	110.00	65.00
PRI-155	Trivet	45.00	55.00	40.00
PRI-160	Vase, bud	65.00	80.00	45.00

QUEEN ANNE

The pattern number is 2995 and it was introduced at the 1936 British Industries Fair. The alternate colourway is **Victorian** 3164 with a black background. Neither has proved to be popular with chintz collectors but these needlepoint patterns do have some keen collectors.

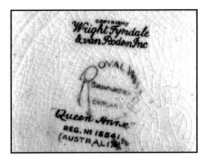

Cat. No.	Shape	U.S. $	Can. $	U.K. £
QA-04	Bonbon dish	45.00	55.00	35.00
QA-09	Bowl, 5"	40.00	50.00	30.00
QA-14	Bowl, 8" soup	50.00	60.00	40.00
QA-23	Breakfast set	650.00	750.00	350.00
QA-28	Butter dish	125.00	150.00	75.00
QA-30	Butter pat	35.00	45.00	25.00
QA-35	Cake plate, open handles	150.00	180.00	75.00
QA-37	Cake Plate, 8" sq. pedestal	150.00	180.00	75.00
QA-40	Cake stand, 2 tier	125.00	150.00	60.00
QA-45	Canoe-shaped dish	125.00	150.00	75.00
QA-50	Cheese keep	150.00	180.00	100.00
QA-52	Coaster	75.00	90.00	35.00
QA-55	Coffee pot	475.00	570.00	325.00
QA-60	Compote, footed	100.00	120.00	65.00
QA-65	Condiment set on tray	150.00	180.00	85.00
QA-70	Cream and sugar	75.00	90.00	50.00
QA-71	Cream and sugar on tray	135.00	165.00	85.00
QA-75	Demi-tasse	60.00	75.00	40.00
QA-77	Egg cup, footed	85.00	105.00	45.00
QA-80	Hot water jug	225.00	270.00	150.00
QA-85	Jam pot with liner	100.00	120.00	65.00
QA-90	Jug, 4"	175.00	210.00	125.00
QA-91	Jug, 4 1/2"	200.00	240.00	145.00
QA-92	Jug, 5"	225.00	270.00	165.00

Cat. No.	Shape	U.S. $	Can. $	U.K. £
QA-97	Nut dish	40.00	50.00	25.00
QA-201	Plate, 4" sq.	35.00	45.00	20.00
QA-202	Plate, 5" sq.	40.00	50.00	25.00
QA-203	Plate, 6" sq.	45.00	55.00	30.00
QA-204	Plate, 7" sq.	50.00	60.00	35.00
QA-205	Plate, 8" sq.	75.00	90.00	40.00
QA-206	Plate, 9" sq.	95.00	115.00	50.00
QA-207	Plate, 10" sq.	125.00	150.00	55.00
QA-112	Relish dish, small	125.00	150.00	75.00
QA-115	Salad bowl, chrome rim	175.00	210.00	95.00
QA-117	Salt and pepper	75.00	90.00	45.00
QA-118	Salt and pepper on tray	135.00	165.00	85.00
QA-120	Sandwich tray, 10" x 6"	75.00	90.00	50.00
QA-121	Sandwich tray, 12" x 7"	100.00	120.00	65.00
QA-125	Sauce boat and liner	125.00	150.00	75.00
QA-130	Teacup and saucer	65.00	80.00	40.00
QA-135	Teapot, 2 cup	300.00	360.00	150.00
QA-136	Teapot, 4 cup	350.00	420.00	200.00
QA-137	Teapot, 6 cup	400.00	480.00	250.00
QA-140	Teapot, stacking	600.00	690.00	300.00
QA-145	Tennis set	75.00	90.00	50.00
QA-150	Toast rack, 4 slice	175.00	210.00	125.00
QA-151	Toast rack, 2 slice	150.00	180.00	100.00
QA-155	Trivet	75.00	90.00	50.00
QA-160	Vase, bud	95.00	115.00	60.00

QUILT

The pattern number is 4515. This all-over pattern was clearly intended to be a companion pattern to **Tartans** 4514. Both were intended to appeal to the non-chintz customer and were produced late in the 1930s when chintz was no longer new and buyers were looking for something fresh.

Cat. No.	Shape	U.S. $	Can. $	U.K. £
Q-04	Bonbon dish	40.00	50.00	25.00
Q-09	Bowl, 5"	30.00	40.00	25.00
Q-14	Bowl, 8" soup	45.00	55.00	30.00
Q-23	Breakfast set	495.00	595.00	325.00
Q-28	Butter dish	100.00	120.00	65.00
Q-30	Butter pat	30.00	40.00	20.00
Q-35	Cake plate, open handles	125.00	150.00	75.00
Q-37	Cake Plate, 8" sq. pedestal	125.00	150.00	75.00
Q-40	Cake stand, 2 tier	100.00	120.00	65.00
Q-45	Canoe-shaped dish	135.00	165.00	85.00
Q-50	Cheese keep	125.00	150.00	75.00
Q-52	Coaster	45.00	55.00	25.00
Q-55	Coffee pot	375.00	450.00	250.00
Q-60	Compote, footed	80.00	100.00	50.00
Q-65	Condiment set on tray	135.00	165.00	65.00
Q-70	Cream and sugar	50.00	60.00	45.00
Q-71	Cream and sugar on tray	100.00	120.00	65.00
Q-75	Demi-tasse	45.00	55.00	30.00
Q-77	Egg cup, footed	50.00	60.00	35.00
Q-80	Hot water jug	160.00	195.00	125.00
Q-85	Jam pot with liner	95.00	115.00	60.00
Q-90	Jug, 4"	125.00	150.00	65.00
Q-91	Jug, 4 1/2"	140.00	170.00	85.00
Q-92	Jug, 5"	150.00	180.00	105.00

Cat. No.	Shape	U.S. $	Can. $	U.K. £
Q-97	Nut dish	25.00	30.00	20.00
Q-201	Plate, 4" sq.	30.00	40.00	20.00
Q-202	Plate, 5" sq.	35.00	45.00	25.00
Q-203	Plate, 6" sq.	40.00	50.00	30.00
Q-204	Plate, 7" sq.	45.00	55.00	35.00
Q-205	Plate, 8" sq.	65.00	80.00	45.00
Q-206	Plate, 9" sq.	75.00	90.00	50.00
Q-207	Plate, 10" sq .	85.00	105.00	55.00
Q-112	Relish dish, small	85.00	105.00	60.00
Q-115	Salad bowl, chrome rim	175.00	210.00	105.00
Q-117	Salt and pepper	50.00	60.00	40.00
Q-118	Salt and pepper on tray	100.00	120.00	80.00
Q-120	Sandwich tray, 10" x 6"	60.00	75.00	45.00
Q-121	Sandwich tray, 12" x 7"	75.00	90.00	50.00
Q-125	Sauce boat and liner	65.00	80.00	45.00
Q-130	Teacup and saucer	55.00	70.00	30.00
Q-135	Teapot, 2 cup	175.00	210.00	125.00
Q-136	Teapot, 4 cup	275.00	330.00	200.00
Q-137	Teapot, 6 cup	325.00	390.00	225.00
Q-140	Teapot, stacking	550.00	635.00	275.00
Q-145	Tennis set	65.00	80.00	40.00
Q-150	Toast rack, 4 slice	150.00	180.00	100.00
Q-151	Toast rack, 2 slice	115.00	140.00	85.00
Q-155	Trivet	55.00	70.00	40.00
Q-160	Vase, bud	85.00	105.00	50.00

RICHMOND

The pattern number is 4249, and the pattern was registered in Canada in 1938. This pattern is very difficult to find but very popular, and prices have risen accordingly. This is one of the patterns Royal Winton may reproduce in 1999/2000.

Cat. No.	Shape	U.S. $	Can. $	U.K. £
Ri-04	Bonbon dish	85.00	105.00	60.00
Ri-09	Bowl, 5"	55.00	70.00	50.00
Ri-14	Bowl, 8" soup	110.00	135.00	75.00
Ri-23	Breakfast set	1,450.00	1,595.00	850.00
Ri-28	Butter dish	250.00	300.00	175.00
Ri-30	Butter pat	75.00	90.00	55.00
Ri-35	Cake plate, open handles	295.00	355.00	195.00
Ri-37	Cake Plate, 8" sq. pedestal	275.00	330.00	200.00
Ri-40	Cake stand, 2 tier	250.00	300.00	150.00
Ri-45	Canoe-shaped dish	325.00	390.00	250.00
Ri-50	Cheese keep	330.00	400.00	250.00
Ri-52	Coaster	125.00	150.00	65.00
Ri-55	Coffee pot	1,350.00	1,485.00	650.00
Ri-60	Compote, footed	225.00	270.00	125.00
Ri-65	Condiment set on tray	325.00	390.00	215.00
Ri-70	Cream and sugar	195.00	235.00	120.00
Ri-71	Cream and sugar on tray	325.00	390.00	200.00
Ri-75	Demi-tasse	135.00	165.00	85.00
Ri-77	Egg cup, footed	130.00	160.00	75.00
Ri-80	Hot water jug	575.00	665.00	325.00
Ri-85	Jam pot with liner	220.00	265.00	145.00
Ri-90	Jug, 4"	450.00	540.00	200.00
Ri-91	Jug, 4 1/2"	500.00	600.00	250.00
Ri-92	Jug, 5"	550.00	635.00	275.00

Cat. No.	Shape	U.S. $	Can. $	U.K. £
Ri-97	Nut dish	75.00	90.00	50.00
Ri-201	Plate, 4" sq.	65.00	80.00	45.00
Ri-202	Plate, 5" sq.	70.00	85.00	55.00
Ri-203	Plate, 6" sq.	75.00	90.00	60.00
Ri-204	Plate, 7" sq.	110.00	135.00	75.00
Ri-205	Plate, 8" sq.	150.00	180.00	85.00
Ri-206	Plate, 9" sq.	165.00	200.00	110.00
Ri-207	Plate, 10" sq.	195.00	235.00	125.00
Ri-112	Relish dish, small	220.00	265.00	150.00
Ri-115	Salad bowl, chrome rim	395.00	475.00	225.00
Ri-117	Salt and pepper	125.00	150.00	85.00
Ri-118	Salt and pepper on tray	220.00	265.00	150.00
Ri-120	Sandwich tray, 10" x 6"	165.00	200.00	115.00
Ri-121	Sandwich tray, 12" x 7"	195.00	235.00	135.00
Ri-125	Sauce boat and liner	195.00	235.00	150.00
Ri-130	Teacup and saucer	135.00	165.00	80.00
Ri-135	Teapot, 2 cup	650.00	750.00	375.00
Ri-136	Teapot, 4 cup	900.00	1,035.00	525.00
Ri-137	Teapot, 6 cup	1,100.00	1,210.00	625.00
Ri-140	Teapot, stacking	1,600.00	1,760.00	750.00
Ri-145	Tennis set	165.00	200.00	120.00
Ri-150	Toast rack, 4 slice	400.00	480.00	215.00
Ri-151	Toast rack, 2 slice	325.00	390.00	175.00
Ri-155	Trivet	150.00	180.00	100.00
Ri-160	Vase, bud	195.00	235.00	115.00

ROSE BROCADE

Although this pattern has not been found with a backstamp, I found an advertisement in the Canadian *Gift Buyer* and the pattern was called **Rose Brocade** in the description. The pattern comes in a dark pink, a green, and a deep blue colourway. This pattern is usually found on the Rosebud shape and collectors sometimes call the pattern Rosebud. Although none of the colourways are particularly collectible, the pink is preferred.

Cat. No.	Shape	U.S. $	Can. $	U.K. £
RoB-04	Bonbon dish	30.00	40.00	25.00
RoB-09	Bowl, 5"	25.00	30.00	25.00
RoB-14	Bowl, 8" soup	40.00	50.00	35.00
RoB-23	Breakfast set	350.00	420.00	325.00
RoB-28	Butter dish	90.00	110.00	65.00
RoB-30	Butter pat	25.00	30.00	20.00
RoB-35	Cake plate, open handles	100.00	120.00	75.00
RoB-37	Cake plate, 8" sq. pedestal	100.00	120.00	65.00
RoB-40	Cake stand, 2 tier	90.00	110.00	55.00
RoB-45	Canoe-shaped dish	120.00	145.00	85.00
RoB-50	Cheese keep	115.00	140.00	100.00
RoB-52	Coaster	25.00	30.00	20.00
RoB-55	Coffee pot	375.00	450.00	250.00
RoB-60	Compote, footed	65.00	80.00	50.00
RoB-65	Condiment set on tray	125.00	150.00	75.00
RoB-70	Cream and sugar	55.00	70.00	45.00
RoB-71	Cream and sugar on tray	90.00	110.00	65.00
RoB-75	Demi-tasse	35.00	45.00	30.00
RoB-77	Egg cup, footed	40.00	50.00	30.00
RoB-80	Hot water jug	165.00	200.00	125.00
RoB-85	Jam pot with liner	75.00	90.00	60.00
RoB-90	Jug, 4"	135.00	165.00	65.00
RoB-91	Jug, 4 1/2"	150.00	180.00	75.00
RoB-92	Jug, 5"	165.00	200.00	95.00

Cat. No.	Shape	U.S. $	Can. $	U.K. £
RoB-97	Nut dish	25.00	30.00	20.00
RoB-201	Plate, 4" sq.	30.00	40.00	25.00
RoB-202	Plate, 5" sq.	35.00	45.00	25.00
RoB-203	Plate, 6" sq.	40.00	50.00	30.00
RoB-204	Plate, 7" sq.	45.00	55.00	35.00
RoB-205	Plate, 8" sq.	55.00	70.00	45.00
RoB-206	Plate, 9" sq.	65.00	80.00	50.00
RoB-207	Plate, 10" sq.	75.00	90.00	55.00
RoB-112	Relish dish, small	75.00	90.00	60.00
RoB-115	Salad bowl, chrome rim	145.00	175.00	75.00
RoB-117	Salt and pepper	55.00	70.00	40.00
RoB-118	Salt and pepper on tray	100.00	120.00	80.00
RoB-120	Sandwich tray, 10" x 6"	45.00	55.00	45.00
RoB-121	Sandwich tray, 12" x 7"	65.00	80.00	50.00
RoB-125	Sauce boat and liner	75.00	90.00	45.00
RoB-130	Teacup and saucer	40.00	50.00	30.00
RoB-135	Teapot, 2 cup	150.00	180.00	125.00
RoB-136	Teapot, 4 cup	225.00	270.00	150.00
RoB-137	Teapot, 6 cup	275.00	330.00	200.00
RoB-140	Teapot, stacking	350.00	420.00	250.00
RoB-145	Tennis set	55.00	70.00	40.00
RoB-150	Toast rack, 4 slice	150.00	180.00	125.00
RoB-151	Toast rack, 2 slice	90.00	110.00	65.00
RoB-155	Trivet	45.00	55.00	40.00
RoB-160	Vase, bud	65.00	80.00	45.00

ROSE DU BARRY

This pattern has a **Rose Du Barry** backstamp in North America, but in Australia the backstamp is **Chelsea Rose**. Ford & Sons used this litho as an unnamed Ford chintz while Shelley called the pattern **Briar Rose**. James Kent also used the same litho with the backstamp James Kent **Chelsea Rose** (James Kent pattern number 3014). Most of the Winton pieces found in North America have Henry Morgan & Co. Ltd. (a Canadian department store) as well as the pattern name in the backstamp. This may have been an exclusive name for Morgans. In 1938 Morgans advertised a **Rose Du Barry** breakfast set for sale at $2.50.

Cat. No.	Shape	U.S. $	Can. $	U.K. £
RD-04	Bonbon dish	45.00	55.00	35.00
RD-09	Bowl, 5"	40.00	50.00	30.00
RD-14	Bowl, 8" soup	75.00	90.00	50.00
RD-23	Breakfast set	750.00	865.00	400.00
RD-28	Butter dish	135.00	165.00	85.00
RD-30	Butter pat	40.00	50.00	30.00
RD-35	Cake plate, open handles	145.00	175.00	85.00
RD-37	Cake plate, 8" sq. pedestal	150.00	180.00	100.00
RD-40	Cake stand, 2 tier	135.00	165.00	90.00
RD-45	Canoe-shaped dish	200.00	240.00	125.00
RD-50	Cheese keep	175.00	210.00	125.00
RD-52	Coaster	75.00	90.00	35.00
RD-55	Coffee pot	525.00	605.00	375.00
RD-60	Compote, footed	100.00	120.00	65.00
RD-65	Condiment set on tray	150.00	180.00	100.00
RD-70	Cream and sugar	85.00	105.00	60.00
RD-71	Cream and sugar on tray	150.00	180.00	100.00
RD-75	Demi-tasse	60.00	75.00	45.00
RD-77	Egg cup, footed	95.00	115.00	55.00
RD-80	Hot water jug	225.00	270.00	150.00
RD-85	Jam pot with liner	125.00	150.00	75.00
RD-90	Jug, 4"	175.00	210.00	150.00
RD-91	Jug, 4 1/2"	200.00	240.00	160.00
RD-92	Jug, 5"	225.00	270.00	175.00

Cat. No.	Shape	U.S. $	Can. $	U.K. £
RD-97	Nut dish	40.00	50.00	30.00
RD-201	Plate, 4" sq.	35.00	45.00	25.00
RD-202	Plate, 5" sq.	40.00	50.00	30.00
RD-203	Plate, 6" sq.	45.00	55.00	35.00
RD-204	Plate, 7" sq.	50.00	60.00	35.00
RD-205	Plate, 8" sq.	85.00	105.00	60.00
RD-206	Plate, 9" sq.	100.00	120.00	65.00
RD-207	Plate, 10" sq.	125.00	150.00	75.00
RD-112	Relish dish, small	150.00	180.00	85.00
RD-115	Salad bowl, chrome rim	175.00	210.00	100.00
RD-117	Salt and pepper	65.00	80.00	45.00
RD-118	Salt and pepper on tray	115.00	140.00	90.00
RD-120	Sandwich tray, 10" x 6"	75.00	90.00	60.00
RD-121	Sandwich tray, 12" x 7"	95.00	115.00	65.00
RD-125	Sauce boat and liner	125.00	150.00	75.00
RD-130	Teacup and saucer	80.00	100.00	45.00
RD-135	Teapot, 2 cup	325.00	390.00	175.00
RD-136	Teapot, 4 cup	375.00	450.00	250.00
RD-137	Teapot, 6 cup	450.00	540.00	325.00
RD-140	Teapot, stacking	600.00	690.00	425.00
RD-145	Tennis set	90.00	110.00	50.00
RD-150	Toast rack, 4 slice	175.00	210.00	125.00
RD-151	Toast rack, 2 slice	135.00	165.00	85.00
RD-155	Trivet	90.00	110.00	50.00
RD-160	Vase, bud	110.00	135.00	60.00

ROYALTY

The pattern number is 3079. The pattern was introduced at the 1936 British Industries Fair. The *Pottery Gazette* mentioned **Royalty** again in describing the 1937 BIF: "Furnishers long catered for, and others, knowing Grimwades predilection for good chintz colourings, should be attracted to the new **Sweet Pea** and **Royalty** patterns." The alternate colourway is **Majestic** (3311) with a black background. **Royalty** continues to be very popular with chintz collectors around the world. This is one of the patterns Royal Winton is planning to reproduce in 1999/2000.

Cat. No.	Shape	U.S. $	Can. $	U.K. £
Roy-04	Bonbon dish	80.00	100.00	65.00
Roy-09	Bowl, 5"	50.00	60.00	55.00
Roy-14	Bowl, 8" soup	100.00	120.00	85.00
Roy-23	Breakfast set	1,300.00	1,430.00	975.00
Roy-28	Butter dish	225.00	270.00	205.00
Roy-30	Butter pat	75.00	90.00	65.00
Roy-35	Cake plate, open handles	250.00	300.00	175.00
Roy-37	Cake plate, 8" sq. pedestal	250.00	300.00	175.00
Roy-40	Cake stand, 2 tier	225.00	270.00	165.00
Roy-45	Canoe-shaped dish	300.00	360.00	200.00
Roy-50	Cheese keep	300.00	360.00	225.00
Roy-52	Coaster	125.00	150.00	55.00
Roy-55	Coffee pot	1,200.00	1,320.00	800.00
Roy-60	Compote, footed	200.00	240.00	150.00
Roy-65	Condiment set on tray	275.00	330.00	195.00
Roy-70	Cream and sugar	150.00	180.00	125.00
Roy-71	Cream and sugar on tray	275.00	330.00	195.00
Roy-75	Demi-tasse	125.00	150.00	80.00
Roy-77	Egg cup, footed	125.00	150.00	80.00
Roy-80	Hot water jug	550.00	635.00	350.00
Roy-85	Jam pot with liner	225.00	270.00	150.00
Roy-90	Jug, 4"	450.00	540.00	325.00
Roy-91	Jug, 4 1/2"	500.00	600.00	350.00
Roy-92	Jug, 5"	550.00	635.00	375.00

Cat. No.	Shape	U.S. $	Can. $	U.K. £
Roy-97	Nut dish	70.00	85.00	60.00
Roy-201	Plate, 4" sq.	65.00	80.00	55.00
Roy-202	Plate, 5" sq.	75.00	90.00	65.00
Roy-203	Plate, 6" sq.	100.00	120.00	75.00
Roy-204	Plate, 7" sq.	135.00	165.00	95.00
Roy-205	Plate, 8" sq.	165.00	200.00	115.00
Roy-206	Plate, 9" sq.	175.00	210.00	135.00
Roy-207	Plate, 10" sq.	200.00	240.00	145.00
Roy-112	Relish dish, small	225.00	270.00	160.00
Roy-115	Salad bowl, chrome rim	325.00	390.00	225.00
Roy-117	Salt and pepper	125.00	150.00	75.00
Roy-118	Salt and pepper on tray	200.00	240.00	150.00
Roy-120	Sandwich tray, 10" x 6"	150.00	180.00	125.00
Roy-121	Sandwich tray, 12" x 7"	175.00	210.00	145.00
Roy-125	Sauce boat and liner	195.00	235.00	165.00
Roy-130	Teacup and saucer	125.00	150.00	75.00
Roy-135	Teapot, 2 cup	550.00	635.00	375.00
Roy-136	Teapot, 4 cup	800.00	920.00	525.00
Roy-137	Teapot, 6 cup	950.00	1,095.00	600.00
Roy-140	Teapot, stacking	1,450.00	1,595.00	800.00
Roy-145	Tennis set	150.00	180.00	125.00
Roy-150	Toast rack, 4 slice	350.00	420.00	245.00
Roy-151	Toast rack, 2 slice	285.00	345.00	195.00
Roy-155	Trivet	150.00	180.00	95.00
Roy-160	Vase, bud	175.00	210.00	105.00

RUTLAND

The pattern number is 1470 with green trim, and the pattern was probably introduced in 1933. This pattern is very difficult to find both in England and in North America.

Cat. No.	Shape	U.S. $	Can. $	U.K. £
Ru-04	Bonbon dish	60.00	75.00	40.00
Ru-09	Bowl, 5"	50.00	60.00	35.00
Ru-14	Bowl, 8" soup	65.00	80.00	50.00
Ru-23	Breakfast set	1,050.00	1,155.00	525.00
Ru-28	Butter dish	150.00	180.00	120.00
Ru-30	Butter pat	40.00	50.00	35.00
Ru-35	Cake plate, open handles	195.00	235.00	145.00
Ru-37	Cake plate, 8" sq. pedestal	175.00	210.00	145.00
Ru-40	Cake stand, 2 tier	150.00	180.00	125.00
Ru-45	Canoe-shaped dish	200.00	240.00	175.00
Ru-50	Cheese keep	175.00	210.00	145.00
Ru-52	Coaster	90.00	110.00	40.00
Ru-55	Coffee pot	750.00	865.00	475.00
Ru-60	Compote, footed	120.00	145.00	85.00
Ru-65	Condiment set on tray	165.00	200.00	125.00
Ru-70	Cream and sugar	100.00	120.00	75.00
Ru-71	Cream and sugar on tray	175.00	210.00	145.00
Ru-75	Demi-tasse	85.00	105.00	50.00
Ru-77	Egg cup, footed	110.00	135.00	65.00
Ru-80	Hot water jug	350.00	420.00	200.00
Ru-85	Jam pot with liner	195.00	235.00	80.00
Ru-90	Jug, 4"	300.00	360.00	165.00
Ru-91	Jug, 4 1/2"	325.00	390.00	195.00
Ru-92	Jug, 5"	350.00	420.00	215.00

Cat. No.	Shape	U.S. $	Can. $	U.K. £
Ru-97	Nut dish	60.00	75.00	30.00
Ru-201	Plate, 4" sq.	55.00	70.00	40.00
Ru-202	Plate, 5" sq.	60.00	75.00	45.00
Ru-203	Plate, 6" sq.	70.00	85.00	50.00
Ru-204	Plate, 7" sq.	85.00	105.00	55.00
Ru-205	Plate, 8" sq.	95.00	115.00	60.00
Ru-206	Plate, 9" sq.	125.00	150.00	75.00
Ru-207	Plate, 10" sq.	145.00	175.00	85.00
Ru-112	Relish dish, small	155.00	190.00	120.00
Ru-115	Salad bowl, chrome rim	275.00	330.00	160.00
Ru-117	Salt and pepper	95.00	115.00	60.00
Ru-118	Salt and pepper on tray	150.00	180.00	110.00
Ru-120	Sandwich tray, 10" x 6"	100.00	120.00	70.00
Ru-121	Sandwich tray, 12" x 7"	125.00	150.00	85.00
Ru-125	Sauce boat and liner	195.00	235.00	85.00
Ru-130	Teacup and saucer	125.00	150.00	75.00
Ru-135	Teapot, 2 cup	325.00	390.00	250.00
Ru-136	Teapot, 4 cup	425.00	510.00	300.00
Ru-137	Teapot, 6 cup	525.00	605.00	375.00
Ru-140	Teapot, stacking	950.00	1,095.00	525.00
Ru-145	Tennis set	135.00	165.00	80.00
Ru-150	Toast rack, 4 slice	250.00	300.00	165.00
Ru-151	Toast rack, 2 slice	175.00	210.00	125.00
Ru-155	Trivet	100.00	120.00	70.00
Ru-160	Vase, bud	160.00	195.00	85.00

SHREWSBURY

The pattern number is 418. This post-war pattern was one of the Royal Winton patterns produced by Howard Potteries after the takeover in 1964. This pattern has become more popular in the past year. It is easier to find in North America than in England. This pattern turns up occasionally on bone china.

Cat. No.	Shape	U.S. $	Can. $	U.K. £
Sh-04	Bonbon dish	75.00	90.00	55.00
Sh-09	Bowl, 5"	60.00	75.00	40.00
Sh-14	Bowl, 8" soup	80.00	100.00	60.00
Sh-23	Breakfast set	1,350.00	1,485.00	550.00
Sh-28	Butter dish	195.00	235.00	150.00
Sh-30	Butter pat	50.00	60.00	45.00
Sh-35	Cake plate, open handles	235.00	285.00	175.00
Sh-37	Cake plate, 8" sq. pedestal	200.00	240.00	175.00
Sh-40	Cake stand, 2 tier	175.00	210.00	150.00
Sh-45	Canoe-shaped dish	225.00	270.00	195.00
Sh-50	Cheese keep	240.00	290.00	175.00
Sh-52	Coaster	110.00	135.00	55.00
Sh-55	Coffee pot	1,050.00	1,155.00	500.00
Sh-60	Compote, footed	150.00	180.00	125.00
Sh-65	Condiment set on tray	275.00	330.00	150.00
Sh-70	Cream and sugar	175.00	210.00	110.00
Sh-71	Cream and sugar on tray	250.00	300.00	150.00
Sh-75	Demi-tasse	115.00	140.00	60.00
Sh-77	Egg cup, footed	125.00	150.00	65.00
Sh-80	Hot water jug	450.00	540.00	250.00
Sh-85	Jam pot with liner	195.00	235.00	125.00
Sh-90	Jug, 4"	400.00	480.00	200.00
Sh-91	Jug, 4 1/2"	450.00	540.00	225.00
Sh-92	Jug, 5"	500.00	600.00	250.00

Cat. No.	Shape	U.S. $	Can. $	U.K. £
Sh-97	Nut dish	60.00	75.00	45.00
Sh-201	Plate, 4" sq.	55.00	70.00	40.00
Sh-202	Plate, 5" sq.	65.00	80.00	45.00
Sh-203	Plate, 6" sq.	75.00	90.00	50.00
Sh-204	Plate, 7" sq.	95.00	115.00	60.00
Sh-205	Plate, 8" sq.	130.00	160.00	75.00
Sh-206	Plate, 9" sq.	150.00	180.00	95.00
Sh-207	Plate, 10" sq.	165.00	200.00	110.00
Sh-112	Relish dish, small	150.00	180.00	125.00
Sh-115	Salad bowl, chrome rim	375.00	450.00	195.00
Sh-117	Salt and pepper	125.00	150.00	60.00
Sh-118	Salt and pepper on tray	200.00	240.00	120.00
Sh-120	Sandwich tray, 10" x 6"	115.00	140.00	75.00
Sh-121	Sandwich tray, 12" x 7"	135.00	165.00	85.00
Sh-125	Sauce boat and liner	165.00	200.00	120.00
Sh-130	Teacup and saucer	125.00	150.00	60.00
Sh-135	Teapot, 2 cup	475.00	570.00	275.00
Sh-136	Teapot, 4 cup	675.00	780.00	400.00
Sh-137	Teapot, 6 cup	900.00	1,035.00	475.00
Sh-140	Teapot, stacking	1,200.00	1,320.00	625.00
Sh-145	Tennis set	135.00	165.00	75.00
Sh-150	Toast rack, 4 slice	365.00	440.00	150.00
Sh-151	Toast rack, 2 slice	285.00	345.00	120.00
Sh-155	Trivet	140.00	170.00	75.00
Sh-160	Vase, bud	185.00	225.00	95.00

SOMERSET

Somerset was probably introduced late in 1932. This pattern came with both a gold trim (1420) and a blue trim (1611). This was one of the three new patterns along with **Summertime** and **Floral Feast** advertised by Wright, Tyndale & van Roden, Inc. of Philadelphia in the *Crockery and Glass Journal* of May 1933. The patterns were backstamped copyright Wright, Tyndal & van Roden in an attempt to discourage American companies from pattern theft. **Somerset** "boasts of varied colored delphiniums blue, rose and yellow in a well arranged pattern with the green leaves giving cool relief."

Cat. No.	Shape	U.S. $	Can. $	U.K. £		Cat. No.	Shape	U.S. $	Can. $	U.K. £
So-04	Bonbon dish	85.00	105.00	60.00		So-97	Nut dish	75.00	90.00	50.00
So-09	Bowl, 5"	55.00	70.00	50.00		So-201	Plate, 4" sq.	65.00	80.00	45.00
So-14	Bowl, 8" soup	110.00	135.00	75.00		So-202	Plate, 5" sq.	75.00	90.00	55.00
So-23	Breakfast set	1,450.00	1,595.00	900.00		So-203	Plate, 6" sq.	85.00	105.00	60.00
So-28	Butter dish	250.00	300.00	175.00		So-204	Plate, 7" sq.	110.00	135.00	75.00
So-30	Butter pat	75.00	90.00	55.00		So-205	Plate, 8" sq.	150.00	180.00	85.00
So-35	Cake plate, open handles	295.00	355.00	195.00		So-206	Plate, 9" sq.	165.00	200.00	120.00
So-37	Cake plate, 8" sq. pedestal	275.00	330.00	185.00		So-207	Plate, 10" sq.	195.00	235.00	145.00
So-40	Cake stand, 2 tier	250.00	300.00	150.00		So-112	Relish dish, small	220.00	265.00	150.00
So-45	Canoe-shaped dish	325.00	390.00	250.00		So-115	Salad bowl, chrome rim	395.00	475.00	235.00
So-50	Cheese keep	330.00	400.00	250.00		So-117	Salt and pepper	125.00	150.00	85.00
So-52	Coaster	125.00	150.00	65.00		So-118	Salt and pepper on tray	220.00	265.00	150.00
So-55	Coffee pot	1,350.00	1,485.00	700.00		So-120	Sandwich tray, 10" x 6"	165.00	200.00	125.00
So-60	Compote, footed	225.00	270.00	150.00		So-121	Sandwich tray, 12" x 7"	195.00	235.00	145.00
So-65	Condiment set on tray	325.00	390.00	215.00		So-125	Sauce boat and liner	195.00	235.00	125.00
So-70	Cream and sugar	195.00	235.00	130.00		So-130	Teacup and saucer	135.00	165.00	80.00
So-71	Cream and sugar on tray	325.00	390.00	195.00		So-135	Teapot, 2 cup	650.00	750.00	375.00
So-75	Demi-tasse	135.00	165.00	85.00		So-136	Teapot, 4 cup	900.00	1,035.00	525.00
So-77	Egg cup, footed	130.00	160.00	85.00		So-137	Teapot, 6 cup	1,100.00	1,210.00	625.00
So-80	Hot water jug	575.00	665.00	350.00		So-140	Teapot, stacking	1,600.00	1,760.00	750.00
So-85	Jam pot with liner	220.00	265.00	135.00		So-145	Tennis set	165.00	200.00	90.00
So-90	Jug, 4"	450.00	540.00	250.00		So-150	Toast rack, 4 slice	400.00	480.00	215.00
So-91	Jug, 4 1/2"	500.00	600.00	275.00		So-151	Toast rack, 2 slice	325.00	390.00	175.00
So-92	Jug, 5"	550.00	635.00	300.00		So-155	Trivet	150.00	180.00	95.00
						So-160	Vase, bud	195.00	235.00	115.00

SPRING

The pattern number is 2506, and it was introduced some months after the alternate colourways **Hazel** 2208 amd **Welbeck** 2204. Collectors like this pattern but it is difficult to find. Spring was also copied by the Japanese.

Cat. No.	Shape	U.S. $	Can. $	U.K. £	Cat. No.	Shape	U.S. $	Can. $	U.K. £
St-04	Bonbon dish	75.00	90.00	60.00	St-97	Nut dish	65.00	80.00	55.00
St-09	Bowl, 5"	50.00	60.00	45.00	St-201	Plate, 4" sq.	50.00	60.00	45.00
St-14	Bowl, 8" soup	85.00	105.00	70.00	St-202	Plate, 5" sq.	65.00	80.00	55.00
St-23	Breakfast set	1,350.00	1,485.00	800.00	St-203	Plate, 6" sq.	75.00	90.00	60.00
St-28	Butter dish	225.00	270.00	175.00	St-204	Plate, 7" sq.	100.00	120.00	75.00
St-30	Butter pat	65.00	80.00	55.00	St-205	Plate, 8" sq.	135.00	165.00	85.00
St-35	Cake plate, open handles	265.00	320.00	175.00	St-206	Plate, 9" sq.	150.00	180.00	115.00
St-37	Cake plate, 8" sq. pedestal	225.00	270.00	165.00	St-207	Plate, 10" sq.	175.00	210.00	135.00
St-40	Cake stand, 2 tier	200.00	240.00	150.00	St-112	Relish dish, small	200.00	240.00	175.00
St-45	Canoe-shaped dish	285.00	345.00	250.00	St-115	Salad bowl, chrome rim	350.00	420.00	225.00
St-50	Cheese keep	275.00	330.00	250.00	St-117	Salt and pepper	120.00	145.00	80.00
St-52	Coaster	115.00	140.00	65.00	St-118	Salt and pepper on tray	195.00	235.00	140.00
St-55	Coffee pot	1,150.00	1,265.00	700.00	St-120	Sandwich tray, 10" x 6"	150.00	180.00	125.00
St-60	Compote, footed	185.00	225.00	145.00	St-121	Sandwich tray, 12" x 7"	175.00	210.00	150.00
St-65	Condiment set on tray	300.00	360.00	215.00	St-125	Sauce boat and liner	165.00	200.00	125.00
St-70	Cream and sugar	165.00	200.00	120.00	St-130	Teacup and saucer	145.00	175.00	85.00
St-71	Cream and sugar on tray	265.00	320.00	225.00	St-135	Teapot, 2 cup	500.00	600.00	350.00
St-75	Demi-tasse	125.00	150.00	75.00	St-136	Teapot, 4 cup	750.00	865.00	500.00
St-77	Egg cup, footed	135.00	165.00	85.00	St-137	Teapot, 6 cup	900.00	1,035.00	600.00
St-80	Hot water jug	525.00	605.00	300.00	St-140	Teapot, stacking	1,400.00	1,540.00	700.00
St-85	Jam pot with liner	225.00	270.00	145.00	St-145	Tennis set	165.00	200.00	95.00
St-90	Jug, 4"	425.00	510.00	250.00	St-150	Toast rack, 4 slice	375.00	450.00	215.00
St-91	Jug, 4 1/2"	475.00	570.00	300.00	St-151	Toast rack, 2 slice	300.00	360.00	185.00
St-92	Jug, 5"	525.00	605.00	325.00	St-155	Trivet	145.00	175.00	85.00
					St-160	Vase, bud	195.00	235.00	110.00

SPRING GLORY

The pattern number is 402, and it is one of the series of 1950s large-flower open chintz patterns. The pattern usually comes with a black background and occasionally burgundy. The black background was advertised in Canada in March 1952 as available on all tableware except dinnerware pieces. These large patterns are not very popular in North America but they are rare in Australia and therefore of more interest to collectors there.

Cat. No.	Shape	U.S. $	Can. $	U.K. £
St-04	Bonbon dish	45.00	55.00	35.00
St-09	Bowl, 5"	50.00	60.00	40.00
St-14	Bowl, 8" soup	70.00	85.00	50.00
St-23	Breakfast set	950.00	1,095.00	375.00
St-28	Butter dish	135.00	165.00	80.00
St-30	Butter pat	45.00	55.00	30.00
St-35	Cake plate, open handles	175.00	210.00	85.00
St-37	Cake plate, 8" sq. pedestal	160.00	195.00	100.00
St-40	Cake stand, 2 tier	140.00	170.00	100.00
St-45	Canoe-shaped dish	175.00	210.00	125.00
St-50	Cheese keep	195.00	235.00	125.00
St-52	Coaster	85.00	105.00	45.00
St-55	Coffee pot	550.00	635.00	295.00
St-60	Compote, footed	100.00	120.00	65.00
St-65	Condiment set on tray	150.00	180.00	100.00
St-70	Cream and sugar	85.00	105.00	60.00
St-71	Cream and sugar on tray	150.00	180.00	100.00
St-75	Demi-tasse	60.00	75.00	45.00
St-77	Egg cup, footed	85.00	105.00	45.00
St-80	Hot water jug	300.00	360.00	135.00
St-85	Jam pot with liner	145.00	175.00	85.00
St-90	Jug, 4"	250.00	300.00	135.00
St-91	Jug, 4 1/2"	275.00	330.00	145.00
St-92	Jug, 5"	300.00	360.00	165.00

Cat. No.	Shape	U.S. $	Can. $	U.K. £
St-97	Nut dish	45.00	55.00	30.00
St-201	Plate, 4" sq.	35.00	45.00	20.00
St-202	Plate, 5" sq.	40.00	50.00	25.00
St-203	Plate, 6" sq.	45.00	55.00	30.00
St-204	Plate, 7" sq.	50.00	60.00	35.00
St-205	Plate, 8" sq.	85.00	105.00	60.00
St-206	Plate, 9" sq.	100.00	120.00	65.00
St-207	Plate, 10" sq.	125.00	150.00	70.00
St-112	Relish dish, small	125.00	150.00	75.00
St-115	Salad bowl, chrome rim	195.00	235.00	110.00
St-117	Salt and pepper	75.00	90.00	45.00
St-118	Salt and pepper on tray	150.00	180.00	90.00
St-120	Sandwich tray, 10" x 6"	95.00	115.00	60.00
St-121	Sandwich tray, 12" x 7"	110.00	135.00	70.00
St-125	Sauce boat and liner	125.00	150.00	75.00
St-130	Teacup and saucer	85.00	105.00	50.00
St-135	Teapot, 2 cup	300.00	360.00	150.00
St-136	Teapot, 4 cup	400.00	480.00	225.00
St-137	Teapot, 6 cup	500.00	600.00	300.00
St-140	Teapot, stacking	850.00	980.00	425.00
St-145	Tennis set	95.00	115.00	50.00
St-150	Toast rack, 4 slice	175.00	210.00	105.00
St-151	Toast rack, 2 slice	145.00	175.00	65.00
St-155	Trivet	80.00	100.00	50.00
St-160	Vase, bud	115.00	140.00	65.00

SPRINGTIME

The pattern, number 10017, was introduced in 1932 and was much in demand at the British Industries Fair that year. This pattern is difficult to find in North America.

Cat. No.	Shape	U.S. $	Can. $	U.K. £
St-04	Bonbon dish	65.00	80.00	45.00
St-09	Bowl, 5"	55.00	70.00	30.00
St-14	Bowl, 8" soup	85.00	105.00	40.00
St-23	Breakfast set	1,050.00	1,155.00	575.00
St-28	Butter dish	150.00	180.00	120.00
St-30	Butter pat	55.00	70.00	40.00
St-35	Cake plate, open handles	195.00	235.00	125.00
St-37	Cake plate, 8" sq. pedestal	185.00	225.00	125.00
St-40	Cake stand, 2 tier	150.00	180.00	125.00
St-45	Canoe-shaped dish	225.00	270.00	195.00
St-50	Cheese keep	250.00	300.00	200.00
St-52	Coaster	100.00	120.00	50.00
St-55	Coffee pot	750.00	865.00	475.00
St-60	Compote, footed	135.00	165.00	85.00
St-65	Condiment set on tray	175.00	210.00	145.00
St-70	Cream and sugar	150.00	180.00	75.00
St-71	Cream and sugar on tray	225.00	270.00	145.00
St-75	Demi-tasse	75.00	90.00	55.00
St-77	Egg cup, footed	100.00	120.00	60.00
St-80	Hot water jug	350.00	420.00	215.00
St-85	Jam pot with liner	150.00	180.00	85.00
St-90	Jug, 4"	300.00	360.00	175.00
St-91	Jug, 4 1/2"	325.00	390.00	200.00
St-92	Jug, 5"	350.00	420.00	225.00

Cat. No.	Shape	U.S. $	Can. $	U.K. £
St-97	Nut dish	45.00	55.00	35.00
St-201	Plate, 4" sq.	50.00	60.00	35.00
St-202	Plate, 5" sq.	55.00	70.00	40.00
St-203	Plate, 6" sq.	60.00	75.00	45.00
St-204	Plate, 7" sq.	75.00	90.00	55.00
St-205	Plate, 8" sq.	100.00	120.00	65.00
St-206	Plate, 9" sq.	125.00	150.00	85.00
St-207	Plate, 10" sq.	135.00	165.00	100.00
St-112	Relish dish, small	150.00	180.00	85.00
St-115	Salad bowl, chrome rim	275.00	330.00	175.00
St-117	Salt and pepper	75.00	90.00	55.00
St-118	Salt and pepper on tray	150.00	180.00	85.00
St-120	Sandwich tray, 10" x 6"	100.00	120.00	85.00
St-121	Sandwich tray, 12" x 7"	125.00	150.00	95.00
St-125	Sauce boat and liner	165.00	200.00	105.00
St-130	Teacup and saucer	95.00	115.00	55.00
St-135	Teapot, 2 cup	325.00	390.00	300.00
St-136	Teapot, 4 cup	425.00	510.00	350.00
St-137	Teapot, 6 cup	525.00	605.00	425.00
St-140	Teapot, stacking	950.00	1,095.00	475.00
St-145	Tennis set	115.00	140.00	70.00
St-150	Toast rack, 4 slice	250.00	300.00	175.00
St-151	Toast rack, 2 slice	175.00	210.00	145.00
St-155	Trivet	100.00	120.00	70.00
St-160	Vase, bud	165.00	200.00	95.00

STRATFORD

The pattern number is 493 and it was registered in Canada in 1953. One of the last of the Royal Winton chintz patterns to be produced, it is very difficult to find and much sought after. It is one of the patterns Royal Winton is considering reproducing in 1999/2000 which may affect values.

Cat. No.	Shape	U.S. $	Can. $	U.K. £
St-04	Bonbon dish	150.00	180.00	105.00
St-09	Bowl, 5"	110.00	135.00	75.00
St-14	Bowl, 8" soup	150.00	180.00	95.00
St-23	Breakfast set	2,500.00	2,750.00	1,300.00
St-28	Butter dish	375.00	450.00	250.00
St-30	Butter pat	105.00	125.00	65.00
St-35	Cake plate, open handles	450.00	540.00	275.00
St-37	Cake plate, 8" sq. pedestal	450.00	540.00	275.00
St-40	Cake stand, 2 tier	350.00	420.00	275.00
St-45	Canoe-shaped dish	450.00	540.00	365.00
St-50	Cheese keep	425.00	510.00	350.00
St-52	Coaster	155.00	190.00	85.00
St-55	Coffee pot	1,850.00	2,035.00	975.00
St-60	Compote, footed	300.00	360.00	225.00
St-65	Condiment set on tray	450.00	540.00	300.00
St-70	Cream and sugar	265.00	320.00	175.00
St-71	Cream and sugar on tray	400.00	480.00	310.00
St-75	Demi-tasse	175.00	210.00	95.00
St-77	Egg cup, footed	165.00	200.00	90.00
St-80	Hot water jug	700.00	805.00	450.00
St-85	Jam pot with liner	335.00	405.00	235.00
St-90	Jug, 4"	650.00	750.00	400.00
St-91	Jug, 4 1/2"	750.00	865.00	450.00
St-92	Jug, 5"	850.00	980.00	500.00

Cat. No.	Shape	U.S. $	Can. $	U.K. £
St-97	Nut dish	95.00	115.00	70.00
St-201	Plate, 4" sq.	90.00	110.00	65.00
St-202	Plate, 5" sq.	125.00	150.00	85.00
St-203	Plate, 6" sq.	140.00	170.00	95.00
St-204	Plate, 7" sq.	160.00	195.00	115.00
St-205	Plate, 8" sq.	200.00	240.00	135.00
St-206	Plate, 9" sq.	275.00	330.00	160.00
St-207	Plate, 10" sq.	335.00	405.00	175.00
St-112	Relish dish, small	310.00	375.00	225.00
St-115	Salad bowl, chrome rim	500.00	600.00	275.00
St-117	Salt and pepper	175.00	210.00	100.00
St-118	Salt and pepper on tray	295.00	355.00	195.00
St-120	Sandwich tray, 10" x 6"	250.00	300.00	165.00
St-121	Sandwich tray, 12" x 7"	295.00	355.00	185.00
St-125	Sauce boat and liner	300.00	360.00	185.00
St-130	Teacup and saucer	250.00	300.00	95.00
St-135	Teapot, 2 cup	800.00	920.00	50.00
St-136	Teapot, 4 cup	1,100.00	1,210.00	650.00
St-137	Teapot, 6 cup	1,400.00	1,540.00	850.00
St-140	Teapot, stacking	2,200.00	2,420.00	1,000.00
St-145	Tennis set	195.00	235.00	165.00
St-150	Toast rack, 4 slice	450.00	540.00	295.00
St-151	Toast rack, 2 slice	375.00	450.00	235.00
St-155	Trivet	225.00	270.00	150.00
St-160	Vase, bud	250.00	300.00	165.00

SUMMERTIME

The pattern number is 775 for the gold trim and 1612 for the green trim. This pattern was introduced in 1932. This was one of the three new patterns along with **Somerset** and **Floral Feast** advertised by Wright, Tyndale & van Roden, Inc. of Philadelphia in the *Crockery and Glass Journal* of May 1933. The alternate colourway is **Bedale** 1703. **Summertime** was perhaps the most popular and most widely produced Winton pattern until production ceased well into the 1960s. Complete dinner services were sold in this pattern and still turn up regularly in North America. Be aware of the difference in the colour of the pre- and post-war transfer. **Summertime** was occasionally produced in bone china. Both Royal Winton and House of Claridge have reproduced **Summertime** (see the section on new chintz).

Cat. No.	Shape	U.S. $	Can. $	U.K. £
Su-04	Bonbon dish	65.00	80.00	45.00
Su-09	Bowl, 5"	50.00	60.00	40.00
Su-14	Bowl, 8" soup	75.00	90.00	50.00
Su-23	Breakfast set	950.00	1,095.00	625.00
Su-28	Butter dish	190.00	230.00	135.00
Su-30	Butter pat	55.00	70.00	40.00
Su-35	Cake plate, open handles	225.00	270.00	135.00
Su-37	Cake plate, 8" sq. pedestal	225.00	270.00	135.00
Su-40	Cake stand, 2 tier	175.00	210.00	125.00
Su-45	Canoe-shaped dish	225.00	270.00	175.00
Su-50	Cheese keep	225.00	270.00	175.00
Su-52	Coaster	100.00	120.00	45.00
Su-55	Coffee pot	825.00	950.00	525.00
Su-60	Compote, footed	160.00	195.00	115.00
Su-65	Condiment set on tray	250.00	300.00	150.00
Su-70	Cream and sugar	150.00	180.00	75.00
Su-71	Cream and sugar on tray	250.00	300.00	160.00
Su-75	Demi-tasse	115.00	140.00	60.00
Su-77	Egg cup, footed	115.00	140.00	60.00
Su-80	Hot water jug	395.00	475.00	225.00
Su-85	Jam pot with liner	175.00	210.00	125.00
Su-90	Jug, 4"	300.00	360.00	185.00
Su-91	Jug, 4 1/2"	325.00	390.00	200.00
Su-92	Jug, 5"	350.00	420.00	225.00

Cat. No.	Shape	U.S. $	Can. $	U.K. £
Su-97	Nut dish	50.00	60.00	40.00
Su-201	Plate, 4" sq.	45.00	55.00	35.00
Su-202	Plate, 5" sq.	50.00	60.00	40.00
Su-203	Plate, 6" sq.	65.00	80.00	45.00
Su-204	Plate, 7" sq.	75.00	90.00	60.00
Su-205	Plate, 8" sq.	110.00	135.00	85.00
Su-206	Plate, 9" sq.	135.00	165.00	100.00
Su-207	Plate, 10" sq.	160.00	195.00	115.00
Su-112	Relish dish, small	175.00	210.00	125.00
Su-115	Salad bowl, chrome rim	325.00	390.00	165.00
Su-117	Salt and pepper	100.00	120.00	65.00
Su-118	Salt and pepper on tray	165.00	200.00	115.00
Su-120	Sandwich tray, 10" x 6"	125.00	150.00	75.00
Su-121	Sandwich tray, 12" x 7"	150.00	180.00	100.00
Su-125	Sauce boat and liner	175.00	210.00	125.00
Su-130	Teacup and saucer	100.00	120.00	60.00
Su-135	Teapot, 2 cup	475.00	570.00	325.00
Su-136	Teapot, 4 cup	575.00	665.00	375.00
Su-137	Teapot, 6 cup	675.00	780.00	450.00
Su-140	Teapot, stacking	950.00	1,095.00	550.00
Su-145	Tennis set	115.00	140.00	75.00
Su-150	Toast rack, 4 slice	325.00	390.00	200.00
Su-151	Toast rack, 2 slice	250.00	300.00	160.00
Su-155	Trivet	135.00	165.00	75.00
Su-160	Vase, bud	145.00	175.00	75.00

SUNSHINE

The pattern number is 4030, and the pattern was probably introduced in 1937. Be aware that this pattern sometimes has deep pink flowers and sometimes a burnt orange colour. Collectors no longer make much distinction between the two colourways. This is one of the patterns on the list for possible reproduction by Royal Winton in 1999/2000.

Cat. No.	Shape	U.S. $	Can. $	U.K. £
Sun-04	Bonbon dish	65.00	80.00	45.00
Sun-09	Bowl, 5"	50.00	60.00	30.00
Sun-14	Bowl, 8" soup	75.00	90.00	45.00
Sun-23	Breakfast set	1,050.00	1,155.00	550.00
Sun-28	Butter dish	190.00	230.00	125.00
Sun-30	Butter pat	55.00	70.00	35.00
Sun-35	Cake plate, open handles	250.00	300.00	135.00
Sun-37	Cake plate, 8" sq. pedestal	250.00	300.00	135.00
Sun-40	Cake stand, 2 tier	200.00	240.00	125.00
Sun-45	Canoe-shaped dish	250.00	300.00	175.00
Sun-50	Cheese keep	225.00	270.00	160.00
Sun-52	Coaster	110.00	135.00	45.00
Sun-55	Coffee pot	825.00	950.00	475.00
Sun-60	Compote, footed	160.00	195.00	105.00
Sun-65	Condiment set on tray	250.00	300.00	150.00
Sun-70	Cream and sugar	150.00	180.00	75.00
Sun-71	Cream and sugar on tray	250.00	300.00	140.00
Sun-75	Demi-tasse	115.00	140.00	60.00
Sun-77	Egg cup, footed	115.00	140.00	60.00
Sun-80	Hot water jug	395.00	475.00	215.00
Sun-85	Jam pot with liner	185.00	225.00	115.00
Sun-90	Jug, 4"	300.00	360.00	175.00
Sun-91	Jug, 4 1/2"	325.00	390.00	200.00
Sun-92	Jug, 5"	350.00	420.00	225.00

Cat. No.	Shape	U.S. $	Can. $	U.K. £
Sun-97	Nut dish	50.00	60.00	35.00
Sun-201	Plate, 4" sq.	45.00	55.00	25.00
Sun-202	Plate, 5" sq.	50.00	60.00	30.00
Sun-203	Plate, 6" sq.	65.00	80.00	35.00
Sun-204	Plate, 7" sq.	75.00	90.00	40.00
Sun-205	Plate, 8" sq.	110.00	135.00	50.00
Sun-206	Plate, 9" sq.	135.00	165.00	65.00
Sun-207	Plate, 10" sq.	160.00	195.00	75.00
Sun-112	Relish dish, small	175.00	210.00	115.00
Sun-115	Salad bowl, chrome rim	325.00	390.00	175.00
Sun-117	Salt and pepper	100.00	120.00	55.00
Sun-118	Salt and pepper on tray	175.00	210.00	100.00
Sun-120	Sandwich tray, 10" x 6"	125.00	150.00	75.00
Sun-121	Sandwich tray, 12" x 7"	150.00	180.00	95.00
Sun-125	Sauce boat and liner	185.00	225.00	135.00
Sun-130	Teacup and saucer	120.00	145.00	70.00
Sun-135	Teapot, 2 cup	475.00	570.00	300.00
Sun-136	Teapot, 4 cup	575.00	665.00	350.00
Sun-137	Teapot, 6 cup	675.00	780.00	400.00
Sun-140	Teapot, stacking	1,050.00	1,155.00	500.00
Sun-145	Tennis set	135.00	165.00	80.00
Sun-150	Toast rack, 4 slice	325.00	390.00	195.00
Sun-151	Toast rack, 2 slice	250.00	300.00	150.00
Sun-155	Trivet	145.00	175.00	85.00
Sun-160	Vase, bud	160.00	195.00	95.00

SWEET NANCY

The pattern number is 5828, and it was probably introduced in 1939.

Cat. No.	Shape	U.S. $	Can. $	U.K. £
SN-04	Bonbon dish	50.00	60.00	45.00
SN-09	Bowl, 5"	45.00	55.00	35.00
SN-14	Bowl, 8" soup	75.00	90.00	55.00
SN-23	Breakfast set	950.00	1,095.00	575.00
SN-28	Butter dish	150.00	180.00	100.00
SN-30	Butter pat	45.00	55.00	40.00
SN-35	Cake plate, open handles	185.00	225.00	115.00
SN-37	Cake plate, 8" sq. pedestal	185.00	225.00	115.00
SN-40	Cake stand, 2 tier	150.00	180.00	115.00
SN-45	Canoe-shaped dish	225.00	270.00	150.00
SN-50	Cheese keep	200.00	240.00	145.00
SN-52	Coaster	100.00	120.00	50.00
SN-55	Coffee pot	750.00	865.00	475.00
SN-60	Compote, footed	135.00	165.00	85.00
SN-65	Condiment set on tray	175.00	210.00	145.00
SN-70	Cream and sugar	110.00	135.00	85.00
SN-71	Cream and sugar on tray	175.00	210.00	125.00
SN-75	Demi-tasse	75.00	90.00	55.00
SN-77	Egg cup, footed	100.00	120.00	60.00
SN-80	Hot water jug	325.00	390.00	205.00
SN-85	Jam pot with liner	160.00	195.00	85.00
SN-90	Jug, 4"	250.00	300.00	145.00
SN-91	Jug, 4 1/2"	300.00	360.00	170.00
SN-92	Jug, 5"	350.00	420.00	195.00

Cat. No.	Shape	U.S. $	Can. $	U.K. £
SN-97	Nut dish	45.00	55.00	35.00
SN-201	Plate, 4" sq.	50.00	60.00	35.00
SN-202	Plate, 5" sq.	55.00	70.00	40.00
SN-203	Plate, 6" sq.	60.00	75.00	45.00
SN-204	Plate, 7" sq.	75.00	90.00	50.00
SN-205	Plate, 8" sq.	100.00	120.00	65.00
SN-206	Plate, 9" sq.	125.00	150.00	80.00
SN-207	Plate, 10" sq.	135.00	165.00	90.00
SN-112	Relish dish, small	150.00	180.00	85.00
SN-115	Salad bowl, chrome rim	275.00	330.00	175.00
SN-117	Salt and pepper	95.00	115.00	65.00
SN-118	Salt and pepper on tray	150.00	180.00	100.00
SN-120	Sandwich tray, 10" x 6"	100.00	120.00	80.00
SN-121	Sandwich tray, 12" x 7"	125.00	150.00	95.00
SN-125	Sauce boat and liner	145.00	175.00	95.00
SN-130	Teacup and saucer	95.00	115.00	55.00
SN-135	Teapot, 2 cup	325.00	390.00	225.00
SN-136	Teapot, 4 cup	425.00	510.00	300.00
SN-137	Teapot, 6 cup	525.00	605.00	375.00
SN-140	Teapot, stacking	950.00	1,095.00	500.00
SN-145	Tennis set	115.00	140.00	75.00
SN-150	Toast rack, 4 slice	250.00	300.00	145.00
SN-151	Toast rack, 2 slice	175.00	210.00	115.00
SN-155	Trivet	100.00	120.00	65.00
SN-160	Vase, bud	145.00	175.00	85.00

SWEET PEA

The pattern number is 3030, and the pattern was introduced in 1936 with great success. *The Pottery & Glass Record* mentioned that the Queen bought the **Sweet Pea** at the 1938 BIF and commended it "for its fresh bright unity of colour." It can be found with gold and deep blue trim. It is still a favorite with English collectors and may be the most popular with collectors in Australia. There are great variations in the depth of colour in examples of this pattern, with some pieces appearing very faded. **Sweet Pea** was occasionally produced in bone china.

Cat. No.	Shape	U.S. $	Can. $	U.K. £
SP-04	Bonbon dish	85.00	105.00	65.00
SP-09	Bowl, 5"	55.00	70.00	50.00
SP-14	Bowl, 8" soup	110.00	135.00	75.00
SP-23	Breakfast set	1,450.00	1,595.00	875.00
SP-28	Butter dish	250.00	300.00	195.00
SP-30	Butter pat	75.00	90.00	55.00
SP-35	Cake plate, open handles	295.00	355.00	195.00
SP-37	Cake plate, 8" sq. pedestal	275.00	330.00	200.00
SP-40	Cake stand, 2 tier	250.00	300.00	175.00
SP-45	Canoe-shaped dish	325.00	390.00	265.00
SP-50	Cheese keep	330.00	400.00	250.00
SP-52	Coaster	125.00	150.00	65.00
SP-55	Coffee pot	1,350.00	1,485.00	875.00
SP-60	Compote, footed	225.00	270.00	150.00
SP-65	Condiment set on tray	325.00	390.00	250.00
SP-70	Cream and sugar	195.00	235.00	145.00
SP-71	Cream and sugar on tray	325.00	390.00	215.00
SP-75	Demi-tasse	135.00	165.00	85.00
SP-77	Egg cup, footed	130.00	160.00	85.00
SP-80	Hot water jug	575.00	665.00	350.00
SP-85	Jam pot with liner	220.00	265.00	175.00
SP-90	Jug, 4"	450.00	540.00	295.00
SP-91	Jug, 4 1/2"	500.00	600.00	325.00
SP-92	Jug, 5"	550.00	635.00	350.00

Cat. No.	Shape	U.S. $	Can. $	U.K. £
SP-97	Nut dish	75.00	90.00	55.00
SP-201	Plate, 4" sq.	65.00	80.00	65.00
SP-202	Plate, 5" sq.	70.00	85.00	70.00
SP-203	Plate, 6" sq.	75.00	90.00	75.00
SP-204	Plate, 7" sq.	110.00	135.00	85.00
SP-205	Plate, 8" sq.	150.00	180.00	105.00
SP-206	Plate, 9" sq.	165.00	200.00	145.00
SP-207	Plate, 10" sq.	195.00	235.00	160.00
SP-112	Relish dish, small	220.00	265.00	175.00
SP-115	Salad bowl, chrome rim	395.00	475.00	200.00
SP-117	Salt and pepper	125.00	150.00	95.00
SP-118	Salt and pepper on tray	220.00	265.00	175.00
SP-120	Sandwich tray, 10" x 6"	165.00	200.00	145.00
SP-121	Sandwich tray, 12" x 7"	195.00	235.00	165.00
SP-125	Sauce boat and liner	225.00	270.00	155.00
SP-130	Teacup and saucer	135.00	165.00	90.00
SP-135	Teapot, 2 cup	650.00	750.00	375.00
SP-136	Teapot, 4 cup	900.00	1,035.00	525.00
SO-137	Teapot, 6 cup	1,100.00	1,210.00	625.00
SO-140	Teapot, stacking	1,600.00	1,760.00	850.00
SP-145	Tennis set	165.00	200.00	125.00
SP-150	Toast rack, 4 slice	400.00	480.00	275.00
SP-151	Toast rack, 2 slice	325.00	390.00	225.00
SP-155	Trivet	150.00	180.00	125.00
SP-160	Vase, bud	195.00	235.00	125.00

TARTANS

The pattern number is 4514. The pattern is clearly a companion to **Quilt** 4515, both patterns are intended for a non-chintz customer and were introduced late in the 1930s. Although not popular in North America, there are collectors of **Tartans** in the UK, mostly in Scotland as you might expect and this tends to make UK prices higher.

Cat. No.	Shape	U.S. $	Can. $	U.K. £
T-04	Bonbon dish	30.00	40.00	30.00
T-09	Bowl, 5"	30.00	40.00	30.00
T-14	Bowl, 8" soup	40.00	50.00	40.00
T-23	Breakfast set	450.00	540.00	375.00
T-28	Butter dish	95.00	115.00	75.00
T-30	Butter pat	25.00	30.00	20.00
T-35	Cake plate, open handles	100.00	120.00	95.00
T-37	Cake plate, 8" sq. pedestal	100.00	120.00	95.00
T-40	Cake stand, 2 tier	80.00	100.00	75.00
T-45	Canoe-shaped dish	125.00	150.00	95.00
T-50	Cheese keep	115.00	140.00	95.00
T-52	Coaster	35.00	45.00	20.00
T-55	Coffee pot	375.00	450.00	325.00
T-60	Compote, footed	75.00	90.00	60.00
T-65	Condiment set on tray	100.00	120.00	95.00
T-70	Cream and sugar	65.00	80.00	55.00
T-71	Cream and sugar on tray	100.00	120.00	95.00
T-75	Demi-tasse	40.00	50.00	30.00
T-77	Egg cup, footed	45.00	55.00	35.00
T-80	Hot water jug	160.00	195.00	150.00
T-85	Jam pot with liner	95.00	115.00	70.00
T-90	Jug, 4"	135.00	165.00	125.00
T-91	Jug, 4 1/2"	150.00	180.00	135.00
T-92	Jug, 5"	165.00	200.00	145.00

Cat. No.	Shape	U.S. $	Can. $	U.K. £
T-97	Nut dish	25.00	30.00	25.00
T-201	Plate, 4" sq.	30.00	40.00	20.00
T-202	Plate, 5" sq.	35.00	45.00	25.00
T 203	Plate, 6" sq.	40.00	50.00	30.00
T-204	Plate, 7" sq.	45.00	55.00	35.00
T-205	Plate, 8" sq.	65.00	80.00	45.00
T-206	Plate, 9" sq.	75.00	90.00	55.00
T-207	Plate, 10 sq .	85.00	105.00	60.00
T-112	Relish dish, small	85.00	105.00	70.00
T-115	Salad bowl, chrome rim	145.00	175.00	125.00
T-117	Salt and pepper	50.00	60.00	40.00
T-118	Salt and pepper on tray	95.00	115.00	80.00
T-120	Sandwich tray, 10" x 6"	50.00	60.00	50.00
T-121	Sandwich tray, 12" x 7"	70.00	85.00	65.00
T-125	Sauce boat and liner	75.00	90.00	65.00
T-130	Teacup and saucer	45.00	55.00	40.00
T-135	Teapot, 2 cup	150.00	180.00	175.00
T-136	Teapot, 4 cup	225.00	270.00	200.00
T-137	Teapot, 6 cup	275.00	330.00	225.00
T-140	Teapot, stacking	350.00	420.00	300.00
T-145	Tennis set	65.00	80.00	50.00
T-150	Toast rack, 4 slice	150.00	180.00	125.00
T-151	Toast rack, 2 slice	105.00	125.00	100.00
T-155	Trivet	45.00	55.00	40.00
T-160	Vase, bud	75.00	90.00	60.00

TRIUMPH

The pattern number is 112 and is the black background alternate to **White Crocus**, pattern number 111. This pattern was called **Black Crocus** until a piece was found in England in the summer of 1996 with the backstamp **Triumph.**

Cat. No.	Shape	U.S. $	Can. $	U.K. £
Tr-04	Bonbon dish	50.00	60.00	40.00
Tr-09	Bowl, 5"	40.00	50.00	35.00
Tr-14	Bowl, 8" soup	65.00	80.00	50.00
Tr-23	Breakfast set	1,000.00	1,150.00	500.00
Tr-28	Butter dish	140.00	170.00	125.00
Tr-30	Butter pat	40.00	50.00	35.00
Tr-35	Cake plate, open handles	175.00	210.00	125.00
Tr-37	Cake plate, 8" sq. pedestal	175.00	210.00	125.00
Tr-40	Cake stand, 2 tier	150.00	180.00	100.00
Tr-45	Canoe-shaped dish	200.00	240.00	135.00
Tr-50	Cheese keep	200.00	240.00	150.00
Tr-52	Coaster	85.00	105.00	40.00
Tr-55	Coffee pot	675.00	780.00	550.00
Tr-60	Compote, footed	125.00	150.00	85.00
Tr-65	Condiment set on tray	185.00	225.00	120.00
Tr-70	Cream and sugar	145.00	175.00	95.00
Tr-71	Cream and sugar on tray	195.00	235.00	145.00
Tr-75	Demi-tasse	90.00	110.00	50.00
Tr-77	Egg cup, footed	105.00	125.00	50.00
Tr-80	Hot water jug	400.00	480.00	225.00
Tr-85	Jam pot with liner	150.00	180.00	125.00
Tr-90	Jug, 4"	325.00	390.00	150.00
Tr-91	Jug, 4 1/2"	375.00	450.00	175.00
Tr-92	Jug, 5"	400.00	480.00	200.00

Cat. No.	Shape	U.S. $	Can. $	U.K. £
Tr-97	Nut dish	40.00	50.00	35.00
Tr-201	Plate, 4" sq.	45.00	55.00	35.00
Tr-202	Plate, 5" sq.	50.00	60.00	40.00
Tr-203	Plate, 6" sq.	55.00	70.00	45.00
Tr-204	Plate, 7" sq.	65.00	80.00	50.00
Tr-205	Plate, 8" sq.	85.00	105.00	60.00
Tr-206	Plate, 9" sq.	105.00	125.00	65.00
Tr-207	Plate, 10" sq.	135.00	165.00	85.00
Tr-112	Relish dish, small	145.00	175.00	125.00
Tr-115	Salad bowl, chrome rim	325.00	390.00	165.00
Tr-117	Salt and pepper	100.00	120.00	55.00
Tr-118	Salt and pepper on tray	175.00	210.00	95.00
Tr-120	Sandwich tray, 10" x 6"	100.00	120.00	85.00
Tr-121	Sandwich tray, 12" x 7"	125.00	150.00	95.00
Tr-125	Sauce boat and liner	165.00	200.00	100.00
Tr-130	Teacup and saucer	105.00	125.00	65.00
Tr-135	Teapot, 2 cup	350.00	420.00	200.00
Tr-136	Teapot, 4 cup	450.00	540.00	325.00
Tr-137	Teapot, 6 cup	550.00	635.00	375.00
Tr-140	Teapot, stacking	950.00	1,095.00	525.00
Tr-145	Tennis set	125.00	150.00	75.00
Tr-150	Toast rack, 4 slice	295.00	355.00	175.00
Tr-151	Toast rack, 2 slice	225.00	270.00	125.00
Tr-155	Trivet	135.00	165.00	80.00
Tr-160	Vase, bud	165.00	200.00	95.00

VICTORIAN

The pattern number is 3164 and it was introduced in 1936 shortly after the alternate colourway **Queen Anne** (2995). The pattern was very popular at the time and sold in quantity but it is not popular with collectors today.

Cat. No.	Shape	U.S. $	Can. $	U.K. £
V-04	Bonbon dish	40.00	50.00	35.00
V-09	Bowl, 5"	35.00	45.00	30.00
V-14	Bowl, 8" soup	45.00	55.00	40.00
V-23	Breakfast set	550.00	635.00	300.00
V-28	Butter dish	125.00	150.00	75.00
V-30	Butter pat	35.00	45.00	25.00
V-35	Cake plate, open handles	150.00	180.00	60.00
V-37	Cake plate, 8" sq. pedestal	150.00	180.00	60.00
V-40	Cake stand, 2 tier	125.00	150.00	50.00
V-45	Canoe-shaped dish	160.00	195.00	75.00
V-50	Cheese keep	160.00	195.00	100.00
V-52	Coaster	75.00	90.00	35.00
V-55	Coffee pot	475.00	570.00	325.00
V-60	Compote, footed	100.00	120.00	65.00
V-65	Condiment set on tray	150.00	180.00	85.00
V-70	Cream and sugar	75.00	90.00	50.00
V-71	Cream and sugar on tray	135.00	165.00	85.00
V-75	Demi-tasse	60.00	75.00	40.00
V-77	Egg cup, footed	75.00	90.00	35.00
V-80	Hot water jug	200.00	240.00	135.00
V-85	Jam pot with liner	100.00	120.00	65.00
V-90	Jug, 4"	150.00	180.00	95.00
V-91	Jug, 4 1/2"	170.00	205.00	115.00
V-92	Jug, 5"	195.00	235.00	125.00

Cat. No.	Shape	U.S. $	Can. $	U.K. £
V-97	Nut dish	35.00	45.00	20.00
V-201	Plate, 4" sq.	35.00	45.00	20.00
V-202	Plate, 5" sq.	40.00	50.00	25.00
V-203	Plate, 6" sq.	45.00	55.00	30.00
V-204	Plate, 7" sq.	50.00	60.00	35.00
V-205	Plate, 8" sq.	75.00	90.00	40.00
V-206	Plate, 9" sq.	95.00	115.00	50.00
V-207	Plate, 10" sq.	125.00	150.00	55.00
V-112	Relish dish, small	125.00	150.00	75.00
V-115	Salad bowl, chrome rim	175.00	210.00	85.00
V-117	Salt and pepper	65.00	80.00	45.00
V-118	Salt and pepper on tray	125.00	150.00	85.00
V-120	Sandwich tray, 10" x 6"	75.00	90.00	50.00
V-121	Sandwich tray, 12" x 7"	100.00	120.00	65.00
V-125	Sauce boat and liner	125.00	150.00	75.00
V-130	Teacup and saucer	65.00	80.00	40.00
V-135	Teapot, 2 cup	300.00	360.00	150.00
V-136	Teapot, 4 cup	350.00	420.00	200.00
V-137	Teapot, 6 cup	400.00	480.00	250.00
V-140	Teapot, stacking	600.00	690.00	300.00
V-145	Tennis set	75.00	90.00	50.00
V-150	Toast rack, 4 slice	175.00	210.00	125.00
V-151	Toast rack, 2 slice	150.00	180.00	100.00
V-155	Trivet	75.00	90.00	50.00
V-160	Vase, bud	95.00	115.00	50.00

VICTORIAN ROSE

The pattern number is 440, and was registered in Canada in 1953. It was one of the patterns produced by Howard Potteries after the takeover in 1964. This pattern is mentioned on a factory invoice dated as late as 1969. Although this is a widely spaced pattern, collectors love the big roses and it has become quite popular in the last year.

Cat. No.	Shape	U.S. $	Can. $	U.K. £
VR-04	Bonbon dish	65.00	80.00	45.00
VR-09	Bowl, 5"	50.00	60.00	40.00
VR-14	Bowl, 8" soup	75.00	90.00	50.00
VR-23	Breakfast set	1,050.00	1,155.00	625.00
VR-28	Butter dish	190.00	230.00	135.00
VR-30	Butter pat	55.00	70.00	30.00
VR-35	Cake plate, open handles	250.00	300.00	135.00
VR-37	Cake plate, 8" sq. pedestal	245.00	295.00	145.00
VR-40	Cake stand, 2 tier	200.00	240.00	125.00
VR-45	Canoe-shaped dish	250.00	300.00	175.00
VR-50	Cheese keep	225.00	270.00	175.00
VR-52	Coaster	110.00	135.00	45.00
VR-55	Coffee pot	825.00	950.00	525.00
VR-60	Compote, footed	160.00	195.00	115.00
VR-65	Condiment set on tray	250.00	300.00	150.00
VR-70	Cream and sugar	150.00	180.00	75.00
VR-71	Cream and sugar on tray	250.00	300.00	160.00
VR-75	Demi-tasse	115.00	140.00	70.00
VR-77	Egg cup, footed	115.00	140.00	60.00
VR-80	Hot water jug	395.00	475.00	225.00
VR-85	Jam pot with liner	175.00	210.00	125.00
VR-90	Jug, 4"	300.00	360.00	195.00
VR-91	Jug, 4 1/2"	325.00	390.00	215.00
VR-92	Jug, 5"	350.00	420.00	225.00

Cat. No.	Shape	U.S. $	Can. $	U.K. £
VR-97	Nut dish	50.00	60.00	40.00
VR-201	Plate, 4" sq.	45.00	55.00	35.00
VR-202	Plate, 5" sq.	50.00	60.00	40.00
VR-203	Plate, 6" sq.	65.00	80.00	45.00
VR-204	Plate, 7" sq.	75.00	90.00	60.00
VR-205	Plate, 8" sq.	110.00	135.00	85.00
VR-206	Plate, 9" sq.	135.00	165.00	100.00
VR-207	Plate, 10" sq.	160.00	195.00	115.00
VR-112	Relish dish, small	175.00	210.00	125.00
VR-115	Salad bowl, chrome rim	325.00	390.00	165.00
VR-117	Salt and pepper	100.00	120.00	65.00
VR-118	Salt and pepper on tray	165.00	200.00	115.00
VR-120	Sandwich tray, 10" x 6"	125.00	150.00	75.00
VR-121	Sandwich tray, 12" x 7"	150.00	180.00	100.00
VR-125	Sauce boat and liner	185.00	225.00	125.00
VR-130	Teacup and saucer	115.00	140.00	70.00
VR-135	Teapot, 2 cup	475.00	570.00	325.00
VR-136	Teapot, 4 cup	575.00	665.00	375.00
VR-137	Teapot, 6 cup	675.00	780.00	450.00
VR-140	Teapot, stacking	1,050.00	1,155.00	550.00
VR-145	Tennis set	135.00	165.00	85.00
VR-150	Toast rack, 4 slice	325.00	390.00	200.00
VR-151	Toast rack, 2 slice	250.00	300.00	160.00
VR-155	Trivet	135.00	165.00	85.00
VR-160	Vase, bud	150.00	180.00	95.00

WELBECK

The pattern number is 2204, and it was probably introduced in 1934 along with **Hazel** 2208. **Hazel** and **Spring** 2506 are the alternate colourways to **Welbeck**. This pattern was much copied by the Japanese. This pattern has been reproduced by Royal Winton and has been sold in large quantities in North America through *Victoria* magazine. The reproduction **Welbeck** lacks the warmth and depth of colour of the vintage and prices remain very high for the vintage pieces.

Cat. No.	Shape	U.S. $	Can. $	U.K. £
W-04	Bonbon dish	150.00	180.00	95.00
W-09	Bowl, 5"	110.00	135.00	65.00
W-14	Bowl, 8" soup	150.00	180.00	85.00
W-23	Breakfast set	2,500.00	2,750.00	1250.00
W-28	Butter dish	375.00	450.00	250.00
W-30	Butter pat	105.00	125.00	65.00
W-35	Cake plate, open handles	425.00	510.00	275.00
W-37	Cake plate, 8" sq. pedestal	425.00	510.00	275.00
W-40	Cake stand, 2 tier	325.00	390.00	275.00
W-45	Canoe-shaped dish	450.00	540.00	350.00
W-50	Cheese keep	425.00	510.00	350.00
W-52	Coaster	155.00	190.00	85.00
W-55	Coffee pot	1,850.00	2,035.00	975.00
W-60	Compote, footed	300.00	360.00	160.00
W-65	Condiment set on tray	450.00	540.00	300.00
W-70	Cream and sugar	265.00	320.00	165.00
W-71	Cream and sugar on tray	400.00	480.00	300.00
W-75	Demi-tasse	175.00	210.00	95.00
W-77	Egg cup, footed	165.00	200.00	90.00
W-80	Hot water jug	700.00	805.00	450.00
W-85	Jam pot with liner	335.00	405.00	235.00
W-90	Jug, 4"	650.00	750.00	375.00
W-91	Jug, 4 1/2"	750.00	865.00	425.00
W-92	Jug, 5"	850.00	980.00	475.00

Cat. No.	Shape	U.S. $	Can. $	U.K. £
W-97	Nut dish	95.00	115.00	70.00
W-201	Plate, 4" sq.	90.00	110.00	65.00
W-202	Plate, 5" sq.	125.00	150.00	80.00
W-203	Plate, 6" sq.	140.00	170.00	85.00
W-204	Plate, 7" sq.	160.00	195.00	95.00
W-205	Plate, 8" sq.	200.00	240.00	125.00
W-206	Plate, 9" sq.	275.00	330.00	150.00
W-207	Plate, 10" sq.	335.00	405.00	160.00
W-112	Relish dish, small	310.00	375.00	225.00
W-115	Salad bowl, chrome rim	500.00	600.00	275.00
W-117	Salt and pepper	175.00	210.00	100.00
W-118	Salt and pepper on tray	295.00	355.00	195.00
W-120	Sandwich tray, 10" x 6"	250.00	300.00	165.00
W-121	Sandwich tray, 12" x 7"	295.00	355.00	185.00
W-125	Sauce boat and liner	300.00	360.00	185.00
W-130	Teacup and saucer	225.00	270.00	105.00
W-135	Teapot, 2 cup	800.00	920.00	575.00
W-136	Teapot, 4 cup	1,100.00	1,210.00	800.00
W-137	Teapot, 6 cup	1,400.00	1,540.00	950.00
W-140	Teapot, stacking	2,200.00	2,420.00	1100.00
W-145	Tennis set	195.00	235.00	145.00
W-150	Toast rack, 4 slice	450.00	540.00	275.00
W-151	Toast rack, 2 slice	375.00	450.00	225.00
W-155	Trivet	225.00	270.00	175.00
W-160	Vase, bud	250.00	300.00	165.00

WILD FLOWERS

The pattern number is 3149, and it was probably introduced in 1936. This pattern is difficult to find in North America but it is becoming even more popular with American collectors.

Cat. No.	Shape	U.S. $	Can. $	U.K. £	Cat. No.	Shape	U.S. $	Can. $	U.K. £
WF-04	Bonbon dish	85.00	105.00	65.00	WF-97	Nut dish	75.00	90.00	45.00
WF-09	Bowl, 5"	55.00	70.00	50.00	WF-201	Plate, 4" sq.	65.00	80.00	50.00
WF-14	Bowl, 8" soup	110.00	135.00	75.00	WF-202	Plate, 5" sq.	70.00	85.00	60.00
WF-23	Breakfast set	1,250.00	1,375.00	725.00	WF-203	Plate, 6" sq.	75.00	90.00	65.00
WF-28	Butter dish	250.00	300.00	195.00	WF-204	Plate, 7" sq.	110.00	135.00	70.00
WF-30	Butter pat	75.00	90.00	55.00	WF-205	Plate, 8" sq.	150.00	180.00	80.00
WF-35	Cake plate, open handles	295.00	355.00	175.00	WF-206	Plate, 9" sq.	165.00	200.00	95.00
WF-37	Cake plate, 8" sq. pedestal	275.00	330.00	195.00	WF-207	Plate, 10" sq.	195.00	235.00	110.00
WF-40	Cake stand, 2 tier	225.00	270.00	165.00	WF-112	Relish dish, small	220.00	265.00	145.00
WF-45	Canoe-shaped dish	250.00	300.00	175.00	WF-115	Salad bowl, chrome rim	395.00	475.00	195.00
WF-50	Cheese keep	330.00	400.00	250.00	WF-117	Salt and pepper	125.00	150.00	95.00
WF-52	Coaster	125.00	150.00	65.00	WF-118	Salt and pepper on tray	220.00	265.00	150.00
WF-55	Coffee pot	1,050.00	1,155.00	550.00	WF-120	Sandwich tray, 10" x 6"	165.00	200.00	145.00
WF-60	Compote, footed	225.00	270.00	150.00	WF-121	Sandwich tray, 12" x 7"	195.00	235.00	165.00
WF-65	Condiment set on tray	325.00	390.00	250.00	WF-125	Sauce boat and liner	195.00	235.00	155.00
WF-70	Cream and sugar	175.00	210.00	115.00	WF-130	Teacup and saucer	135.00	165.00	90.00
WF-71	Cream and sugar on tray	275.00	330.00	165.00	WF-135	Teapot, 2 cup	650.00	750.00	375.00
WF-75	Demi-tasse	135.00	165.00	75.00	WF-136	Teapot, 4 cup	900.00	1,035.00	525.00
WF-77	Egg cup, footed	125.00	150.00	65.00	WF-137	Teapot, 6 cup	1,100.00	1,210.00	625.00
WF-80	Hot water jug	475.00	570.00	250.00	WF-140	Teapot, stacking	1,450.00	1,595.00	850.00
WF-85	Jam pot with liner	220.00	265.00	175.00	WF-145	Tennis set	165.00	200.00	125.00
WF-90	Jug, 4"	400.00	480.00	195.00	WF-150	Toast rack, 4 slice	400.00	480.00	250.00
WF-91	Jug, 4 1/2"	450.00	540.00	225.00	WF-151	Toast rack, 2 slice	325.00	390.00	195.00
WF-92	Jug, 5"	500.00	600.00	250.00	WF-155	Trivet	150.00	180.00	100.00
					WF-160	Vase, bud	195.00	235.00	105.00

WINIFRED

Unfortunately we have no information on this pattern at this time.

Cat. No.	Shape	U.S. $	Can. $	U.K. £
Wi-04	Bonbon dish	25.00	30.00	20.00
Wi-09	Bowl, 5"	20.00	25.00	20.00
Wi-14	Bowl, 8" soup	30.00	4.00	25.00
Wi-23	Breakfast set	375.00	450.00	295.00
Wi-28	Butter dish	80.00	100.00	60.00
Wi-30	Butter pat	20.00	25.00	20.00
Wi-35	Cake plate, open handles	80.00	100.00	60.00
Wi-37	Cake plate, 8" sq. pedestal	80.00	100.00	60.00
Wi-40	Cake stand, 2 tier	80.00	100.00	60.00
Wi-45	Canoe-shaped dish	105.00	125.00	75.00
Wi-50	Cheese keep	95.00	115.00	70.00
Wi-52	Coaster	20.00	25.00	20.00
Wi-55	Coffee pot	300.00	360.00	225.00
Wi-60	Compote, footed	60.00	75.00	45.00
Wi-65	Condiment set on tray	80.00	100.00	60.00
Wi-70	Cream and sugar	45.00	55.00	40.00
Wi-71	Cream and sugar on tray	80.00	100.00	60.00
Wi-75	Demi-tasse	30.00	40.00	25.00
Wi-77	Egg cup, footed	45.00	55.00	25.00
Wi-80	Hot water jug	125.00	150.00	105.00
Wi-85	Jam pot with liner	75.00	90.00	45.00
Wi-90	Jug, 4"	135.00	165.00	75.00
Wi-91	Jug, 4 1/2"	150.00	180.00	100.00
Wi-92	Jug, 5"	165.00	200.00	125.00

Cat. No.	Shape	U.S. $	Can. $	U.K. £
Wi-97	Nut dish	20.00	25.00	20.00
Wi-201	Plate, 4" sq.	20.00	25.00	20.00
Wi-202	Plate, 5" sq.	25.00	30.00	25.00
Wi-203	Plate, 6" sq.	30.00	40.00	30.00
Wi-204	Plate, 7" sq.	40.00	50.00	35.00
Wi-205	Plate, 8" sq.	55.00	70.00	40.00
Wi-206	Plate, 9" sq.	65.00	80.00	45.00
Wi-207	Plate, 10" sq.	75.00	90.00	50.00
Wi-112	Relish dish, small	65.00	80.00	50.00
Wi-115	Salad bowl, chrome rim	125.00	150.00	75.00
Wi-117	Salt and pepper	45.00	55.00	35.00
Wi-118	Salt and pepper on tray	90.00	110.00	60.00
Wi-120	Sandwich tray, 10" x 6"	50.00	60.00	40.00
Wi-121	Sandwich tray, 12" x 7"	60.00	75.00	45.00
Wi-125	Sauce boat and liner	55.00	70.00	40.00
Wi-130	Teacup and saucer	35.00	45.00	30.00
Wi-135	Teapot, 2 cup	150.00	180.00	105.00
Wi-136	Teapot, 4 cup	250.00	300.00	175.00
Wi-137	Teapot, 6 cup	300.00	360.00	200.00
Wi-140	Teapot, stacking	350.00	420.00	250.00
Wi-145	Tennis set	45.00	55.00	35.00
Wi-150	Toast rack, 4 slice	135.00	165.00	100.00
Wi-151	Toast rack, 2 slice	115.00	140.00	85.00
Wi-155	Trivet	45.00	55.00	35.00
Wi-160	Vase, bud	55.00	70.00	40.00

"Royal Winton"

Popular Old English Chintz Designs (a few of many).

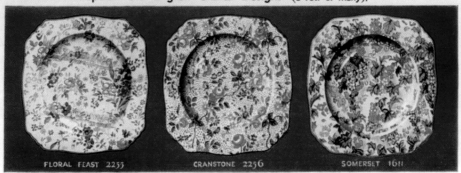

FLORAL FEAST 2255   CRANSTONE 2256   SOMERSET 1611

MARGUERITE 9467

KINVER 2254

JUNE ROSES 2056

Item No.		Price	
021.	"Canoe" Tray	24/-	Per doz.
022.	Butter, "Trefu"	4/-	,,
023.	Tray, "Fife"	L/s 24/-	S/s 21/- ,,
024.	Triple Dish, "Stafford"	21/-	,,
025.	Condiment Set, "Acme"		
	(2 piece on Tray)	14/-	,,
026.	Twin Dish "Stafford"	18/-	,,
027.	Tennis Set, 2 piece, "Ascot"	16/-	,,
028.	Toast, Butter and Marmalade		
	"Saville"	15/-	,,
029.	Triple Tray, "Viola"	33/-	,,
030.	Eggset—4 cup, "Saville"	24/-	,,
031.	Individual Breakfast Set,		
	6 piece, "Athena"	20/-	,,
032.	Cruet Set, "Egg and Clover Leaf"	21/-	,,
033.	Egg-Cruet Set, 5 piece, "Ascot"	18/-	,,
034.	Triple Tray, "Gem"	30/-	,,
035.	Egg-Cruet Set, 7 piece, "York"	27/-	,,
036.	Cruet Set, "Fife"	27/-	,,
037.	Bed Side Set, 6 piece, "Countess"	48/-	,,
038.	,, ,, ,, 7 piece, "Ascot"	66/-	,,
039.	,, ,, ,, 7 piece, "York"	66/-	,,
01.	4 Compartment Dish, "Ascot"	20/-	,,
02.	4 ,, ,, "Oval"	24/-	,,
03.	3 ,, ,, "Marina"	24/-	,,
	Also 5 Compartment	30/-	,,
04.	Mayonnaise Bowl & Stand "Saville"	14/-	,,
	and Ladle	4/-	,,
05.	5 Compartment Dish, "Duchess"	27/-	,,
06.	Mayonnaise Bowl & Stand, "Ascot"	14/-	,,
	and Ladle	4/-	,,
07.	Marmalade and Stand, "Ascot"	15/-	,,
08.	Cheese, "Ascot"	18/-	,,
09.	Covered Butter, "Ascot" L/s 18/-	S/s 15/-	,,
010.	Honey, fast stand, "Chelsea"	22/-	,,
011.	Nut Dish, "Ascot"	12/-	,,
	and Scoop	6/-	,,
012.	Mayonnaise Bowl and Stand,		
	"Norman"	14/-	,,
	and Ladle	4/-	,,
013.	Cheese, No. 3 "Dane"	24/-	,,
014.	Cake Set, 5 piece, "Saville"	3/6	Per set
015.	Sandwich Set, 7 piece,		
	10" x 5" "Ascot"	3/5	,,
016.	Cheese, "Marvel"	18/-	Per doz.
017.	Sandwich Set, 7 piece, "Ascot"		
	(12" Divided Tray & 6" Actual Plates)	4/9	Per set
018.	Fruit Set, 7 piece, "Stella"	5/-	,,
019.	,, ,, 7 piece, "Concave"	4/9	,,
020.	,, ,, 7 piece, "Ascot"	4/6	,,
040.	Sweet, "Holborn" 4" 10/- 5" 11/- 6"	13/-	Per doz.
041.	Sweet, "Bow" S/s 7/- M/s 7/6	L/s 8/6	,,
042.	Oatmeal	9/-	,,
043.	Mint Boat and Stand, "Era"	12/-	,,
044.	Low Comport, "Ascot"	22/-	,,
045.	Chocolate Comport, "Lily"	14/-	,,
	also larger size	18/-	,,
046.	Footed Nut, "Bow"	18/-	,,

Item No.		Price	
047.	Jug, "Cambridge" 30/42's	4/-	Per set
048.	,, "Globe"	4/-	,,
049.	Coffee Pot, "Perth"	39/-	Per doz.
050.	Chocolate Comport, "Greek"	14/-	,,
051.	,, ,, "Eton"	14/-	,,
052.	Jug, "Duval" 30/42's	4/-	Per set
053.	,, "Grafton"	4/6	,,
054.	Cake Plate, Handled, "Ascot"	18/-	Per doz.
055.	Coffee Pot, "Norman"	39/-	,,
056.	,, "Greek" 2 pints 45/- 1½ pints	39/-	,,
057.	Bowl, "Fife"	42/-	,,
058.	Plate, "Ascot" 3" 4" 5" 6" 7" 8" nominal		
	4/6 6/- 8/- 10/- 13/- 15/-		Per doz.
059.	Bowl, "King"	42/-	,,
060.	Teapot, 36's, "Hastings" (1 size)	32/-	,,
061.	Sugar, Tea set size, "Hastings"	} Per doz. pairs	
062.	Cream, ,,		18/-
063.	Tea and Saucer, "Hastings"	8/6	Per doz.
064.	Tea Plate, 4" nominal, "Ascot"	6/-	,,
	Tea Set, 21 piece, "Hastings"		
	with Round or Ascot Plates	10/6	Per set
065.	Sugar, Bridge, "Stuart"	} Per doz. pairs	
066.	Cream, ,, ,,		13/-
067.	Teapot, "Countess" 30's 36's 42's 48's 54's Per		
	34/- 32/- 30/- 21/- 17/- doz.		
068.	Sugar, Bridge, "Countess"	} Per doz. pairs	
069.	Cream, ,, ,,		12/-
070.	Sugar, Bridge, "Grecian"	}	
071.	Cream, ,, ,,		16/-
073.	Sugar, Bridge, "Norman"	}	
072.	Cream, ,, ,,		12/-
074.	Sugar, Bridge, "Ascot"	}	
075.	Cream, ,, ,,		12/-
076.	Teapot, "Ascot" 30's 36's 48's		
	34/- 32/- 21/-		Per doz.
078.	Sugar, Bridge, "Hector"	} Per doz. pairs	
077.	Cream, ,, ,,		12/-
079.	Teapot Stand, "Ascot"	8/-	Per doz.
080.	,, ,, Round	9/-	,,
081.	Eggcup, fast stand, Plain	12/-	,,
082.	Eggcup, footed, Plain	4/-	,,
083.	Eggcup, fast stand, "Ascot"	12/-	,,
084.	Tea and Saucer, "Ascot"	8/6	,,
	Tea Set, 21 piece, tall, "Ascot"	10/6	Per set
085.	Covered Jug, "Sexta" 1 pt. 24/-, ½ pt. 16/-		Per doz.
086.	Toast Rack, "Queen" 3 bar 10/-, 5 bar 12/-		,,
087.	Covered Jug, "Countess" 1 pt. 24/-, ½ pt. 16/-		,,
088.	Tea and Saucer, "King"	8/6	Per doz.
	Teaset, 21 piece, "King"	10/6	Per set
089.	Coffee and Saucer, "Can"	8/6	Per doz.
090.	Coffee and Saucer, "Ascot"	8/6	,,
	Coffee set, 16 piece, "Can" or "Ascot"	9/6	Per set
091.	Beaker, Handled, "Straight"	9/6	Per doz.
092.	,, Unhandled,	8/6	,,
093.	Bon-Bon, Handled, "Octagon" S/s L/s		
	12/- 18/-		,,
094.	,, Unhandled, 10/6 14/-		,,
095.	Covered Muffin, "Countess"	24/-	,,

All articles quoted above are illustrated on Supplement "C," and are the same prices in any one design or assorted.
These designs can be finished with Colour or Gilt Edge at the same prices.

GRIMWADES LTD.   ..   STOKE-ON-TRENT.

JAMES KENT, LTD.

James Kent, Ltd. was another of those Staffordshire factories that tried to serve as many mid- or low-priced markets as they could identify. As reported in the 1935 *Pottery Gazette*, Old Foley Pottery at Longton was one of the oldest factories in the potteries. John Wesley preached from the steps of the old house that was incorporated into the James Kent factory on his visit to the potteries in 1790. James Kent took over the factory in 1897 and for more than forty years continued to produce "earthenwares which catered for expressed needs." His three sons helped him to keep in touch with modern movements and the *Gazette* reported the Kent range to be thoroughly up to date.

After this extended report there is remarkably little reference to James Kent in any of the trade publications. The January 1934 *Pottery & Glass Record* reported that Messrs. James Kent Ltd. "have succeeded in producing something for all good tastes and that no pains have been spared in modeling shapes to meet the demands of utility and ornamentation." In 1939 there is a report of **Du Barry** being presented in the London showrooms. In 1941 Goodwin Johnson Inc. of New York City advertised for sale the following James Kent chintzes: **Harmony, Apple Blossom, Capri, Hydrangea, Du Barry, Pearl De Light, Mille Fleurs,** and **Rosalynde.** Later that year, they took out a full page advertisement showing a wide range of James Kent chintzes including mayonnaise bowls with ladles and nut dishes with scoops similar in shape to Grimwades. Ebeling & Reuss Co., with headquarters in Philadelphia, were the American distributors for Royal Winton and they also appear to have taken on James Kent in 1942. In April 1942 they advertised the six Kent chintz patterns in four place settings to the trade at $17.95. In 1949 they offered open stock in dinnerware and gift items in **Apple Blossom**; cups and saucers were $10.00 per dozen and luncheon plates $12.00 per dozen wholesale. By 1950 Ebeling & Reuss were urging retailers to stock up on assorted **Rosalynde**, offering coffee pots at $33.00 a dozen and small teapots at $24.00 a dozen. In January, 1951 *The Gift Buyer* reported that Miss Ruth Kent had toured Canada to study "the methods and requirements of pottery merchandising in Canada." Her 87-year-old father was still chairman and her brothers Phillip and Peter joint managing directors while Ruth served as Sales Director. The next report about the factory came in the 1958 *Gazette* and mentioned four new James Kent chintzes, including **Tapestry,** on display at the Blackpool Gift Fair.

We were fortunate to be able to spend a morning with one of Jimmy Kent's workers. Mrs. Doreen Donegan worked at James Kent in the 1930s, which she described as "hard work for small wages." She joined the factory in 1935 at the age of 16 and was paid 5 shillings and 9 pence a week. She remembers the women who worked on chintz were considered a little above the others. Two slightly stand-offish sisters called Ada and Maude Kent (no relation) did nearly all of the chintzware for many years. "Since you went onto piece work after a training period and chintz was much harder to do everyone wanted to be paid more for doing chintz. I was never able to do teapots .

. . they were beyond me." Doreen described cutting out all the little notches for the ruffled sweet dishes and how often the girls cut their fingers while they were working. She said that employees were allowed to buy thirds not seconds — the difference being that the thirds had obvious chips or cracks. When we asked about day after day of applying transfers, Doreen looked surprised and explained, "I couldn't grumble because I was working." After Jimmy Kent the factory was run by his son Peter and then by Peter's sister, Ruth Kent. By all accounts, Ruth Kent, who had never expected to be running the factory, did a splendid job and was well regarded throughout the potteries. Shortly after the first edition came out, we had a reply to our letter to Miss Ruth Kent: "Regarding the chintz patterns produced by our company, there was also another one called **Lichfield.** As far as I can remember **Du Barry** was the first produced around 1934/5 and the others followed; **Du Barry** and **Rosalynde** being the most popular. I do not remember the names of the designers. **Du Barry** remained in production up to 1980 but it was slow to produce and costly. I hope this information may be of some use to you."

In the 1980s James Kent went through turbulent times and various versions of the **Du Barry** chintz were produced either for the Next Interiors shops in England or for MIKASA. It has been very difficult to map out the timeline for this decade. I have reproduced two advertising leaflets in the new chintz section so you will have some idea which shapes were produced during this time. The trim for at least some of the pieces during this time was burgundy. I assume this was an economy measure, gold being much more expensive than enamel.

The pieces for Next Interiors were illustrated in a newspaper article in 1987. The Diamond shape teapot sold for £19.99, creamer £9.99, covered sugar £9.99, cup and saucer £7.99 and the teaplate £5.50. When I was at the factory, I found an ex works price list for July 1, 1988. I also found a shape page for the giftwares including the shaving mug we included in the first edition thinking it was much older. I have included the backstamp illustrated on the 1988 price list as well as one from the 1950s so that you can recognize the differences.

After being bought and sold several times through the 1980s, the firm went into receivership in 1989. It was bought by M.R. Hadida Ltd.— a bathroom furnishing company, and owner of Hadida Fine Bone China Ltd. Hadida immediately ceased production of chintz as too labour-intensive and not cost-effective. Fortunately, Clare Hadida is passionate about the past and insisted on keeping everything. It was extraordinary to see the original moulds for many of the chintz pieces still sitting on dusty shelves in the mould room when Mrs. Hadida took me on a tour of the factory in the summer of 1998. She allowed me to poke around in her office and I found all the Kent shape pages we have reproduced with her permission. Hadida produced a range of new chintz for The Old Chintz Company in 1998 and have recently begun to produce chintz in their own right.

JAMES KENT STANDARD BACKSTAMPS

c.1930s

c.1930s

c.1936 - 1939

c.1950 +

c.1950 +

c.1955 +

c.1988

1999

LIMITED and SPECIAL EDITION BACKSTAMPS

Made for Next Interiors c.1988

Made for Mikasa c.1988

Made for Old Chintz Company 1998

Old Chintz Company 1999

APPLE BLOSSOM

This pattern was introduced in the 1930s and exported in quantity to North America before and after the war. Complete dinner services still turn up occasionally in North America.

Cat. No.	Shape	U.S $	Can. $	U.K. £
AB-04	Bonbon dish	50.00	60.00	45.00
AB-10	Bowl, 6"	50.00	60.00	45.00
AB-15	Bowl, 9"	150.00	180.00	115.00
AB-23	Breakfast set	800.00	920.00	495.00
AB-28	Butter dish	150.00	180.00	120.00
AB-36	Cake plate, square, 11"	175.00	210.00	120.00
AB-55	Coffee pot, 4 cup	750.00	865.00	395.00
AB-60	Compote, footed	115.00	140.00	85.00
AB-65	Condiment set on tray	200.00	240.00	135.00
AB-70	Cream and sugar	150.00	180.00	115.00
AB-71	Cream and sugar on tray	225.00	270.00	150.00
AB-75	Demi-tasse	95.00	115.00	60.00
AB-85	Jam pot	150.00	180.00	115.00

Cat. No.	Shape	U.S. $	Can. $	U.K. £
AB-97	Nut dish	50.00	60.00	40.00
AB-103	Plate, 6 1/2"	75.00	90.00	55.00
AB-106	Plate, 9"	125.00	150.00	85.00
AB-112	Relish dish	125.00	150.00	95.00
AB-117	Salt and pepper	120.00	145.00	75.00
AB-118	Salt and pepper on tray	175.00	210.00	120.00
AB-120	Sandwich tray	100.00	120.00	85.00
AB-130	Teacup and saucer	110.00	135.00	65.00
AB-136	Teapot, 4 cup	595.00	685.00	375.00
AB-137	Teapot, 6 cup	695.00	800.00	450.00
AB-150	Toast rack, 4 slice	250.00	300.00	160.00
AB-160	Vase, bud	150.00	180.00	70.00

CRAZY PAVING

The pattern number is 2839. A reporter, looking at the James Kent stand at the 1934 British Industries Fair, saw "that an amusing new notion at this stand was a tea set in a pattern inspired by crazy paving! The irregular pattern was faithfully reproduced."

Cat. No.	Shape	U.S $	Can. $	U.K. £
CP-04	Bonbon dish	45.00	55.00	35.00
CP-10	Bowl, 6 1/2"	45.00	55.00	35.00
CP-15	Bowl, 9"	125.00	150.00	85.00
CP-23	Breakfast set	800.00	920.00	475.00
CP-28	Butter dish	125.00	150.00	95.00
CP-36	Cake plate, square, 11"	150.00	180.00	80.00
CP-55	Coffee pot, 4 cup	500.00	600.00	345.00
CP-60	Compote, footed	100.00	120.00	85.00
CP-65	Condiment set on tray	165.00	200.00	125.00
CP-70	Cream and sugar	100.00	120.00	80.00
CP-71	Cream and sugar on tray	150.00	180.00	120.00
CP-75	Demi-tasse	75.00	90.00	45.00
CP-85	Jam pot	120.00	145.00	85.00

Cat. No.	Shape	U.S. $	Can. $	U.K. £
CP-97	Nut dish	40.00	50.00	30.00
CP-103	Plate, 6 1/2"	65.00	80.00	35.00
CP-106	Plate, 9"	100.00	120.00	65.00
CP-112	Relish dish	100.00	120.00	75.00
CP-117	Salt and pepper	85.00	105.00	60.00
CP-118	Salt and pepper on tray	135.00	165.00	110.00
CP-120	Sandwich tray	85.00	105.00	70.00
CP-130	Teacup and saucer	85.00	105.00	60.00
CP-136	Teapot, 4 cup	450.00	540.00	320.00
CP-137	Teapot, 6 cup	550.00	635.00	360.00
CP-150	Toast rack, 4 slice	200.00	240.00	145.00
CP-160	Vase, bud	95.00	115.00	65.00

DU BARRY

This pattern was in the London showrooms in 1938 and exported in quantity to North America before and after the war. Complete dinner services still turn up occasionally in North America. According to Miss Ruth Kent, **Du Barry** was first produced around 1934/35 and remained in production up to 1980, but it was slow to produce and costly. Marked as Melody Chintz the **Du Barry** pattern also turns up on pieces backstamped "Royal Crown, Pasadena, Made in Great Britain." This may have been a special order produced by James Kent for a company in Pasadena, U.S.A. It was reproduced later in the 1980s with a MIKASA for James Kent backstamp. The **Du Barry** with the pink trim was also produced in the 1980s with a globe backstamp. **Du Barry** is one of the patterns being reproduced by Hadida (see the section on new chintz). In 1998, Hadida also created a new chintz — **Lydia,** a black background colourway of **Du Barry.**

Cat. No.	Shape	U.S $	Can. $	U.K. £
D-04	Bonbon dish	50.00	60.00	45.00
D-10	Bowl, 6"	50.00	60.00	45.00
D-15	Bowl, 9"	150.00	180.00	125.00
D-23	Breakfast set	800.00	920.00	550.00
D-28	Butter dish	150.00	180.00	140.00
D-36	Cake plate, square, 11"	175.00	210.00	115.00
D-55	Coffee pot, 4 cup	750.00	865.00	600.00
D-60	Compote, footed	115.00	140.00	95.00
D-65	Condiment set on tray	200.00	240.00	145.00
D-70	Cream and sugar	150.00	180.00	95.00
D-71	Cream and sugar on tray	225.00	270.00	150.00
D-75	Demi-tasse	95.00	115.00	65.00
D-85	Jam pot	150.00	180.00	115.00

Cat. No.	Shape	U.S $	Can. $	U.K. £
D-97	Nut dish	50.00	60.00	45.00
D-103	Plate, 6 1/2"	75.00	90.00	50.00
D-106	Plate, 9"	125.00	150.00	85.00
D-112	Relish dish	125.00	150.00	105.00
D-117	Salt and pepper	120.00	145.00	65.00
D-118	Salt and pepper on tray	175.00	210.00	115.00
D-120	Sandwich tray	100.00	120.00	85.00
D-130	Teacup and saucer	110.00	135.00	65.00
D-136	Teapot, 4 cup	595.00	685.00	395.00
D-137	Teapot, 6 cup	695.00	800.00	495.00
D-150	Toast rack, 4 slice	250.00	300.00	165.00
D-160	Vase, bud	150.00	180.00	85.00

FLORITA

The pattern number is 5008, and the pattern was probably introduced in early 1958. It has always been popular with North American collectors but is now sought after in New Zealand and Australia. Because the blue tends to fade, the more vivid the colour, the higher the price.

Cat. No.	Shape	U.S $	Can. $	U.K. £
F-04	Bonbon dish	65.00	80.00	50.00
F-10	Bowl, 6"	75.00	90.00	55.00
F-15	Bowl, 9"	175.00	210.00	135.00
F-23	Breakfast set	1,050.00	1,155.00	650.00
F-28	Butter dish	175.00	210.00	165.00
F-36	Cake plate, square, 11"	185.00	225.00	135.00
F-55	Coffee pot, 4 cup	750.00	865.00	595.00
F-60	Compote, footed	135.00	165.00	100.00
F-65	Condiment set on tray	225.00	270.00	165.00
F-70	Cream and sugar	175.00	210.00	110.00
F-71	Cream and sugar on tray	250.00	300.00	165.00
F-75	Demi-tasse	100.00	120.00	65.00
F-85	Jam pot	175.00	210.00	125.00

Cat. No.	Shape	U.S. $	Can. $	U.K. £
F-97	Nut dish	55.00	70.00	40.00
F-103	Plate, 6 1/2"	85.00	105.00	55.00
F-106	Plate, 9"	150.00	180.00	95.00
F-112	Relish dish	150.00	180.00	115.00
F-117	Salt and pepper	135.00	165.00	75.00
F-118	Salt and pepper on tray	200.00	240.00	125.00
F-120	Sandwich tray	135.00	165.00	110.00
F-130	Teacup and saucer	125.00	150.00	80.00
F-136	Teapot, 4 cup	725.00	835.00	475.00
F-137	Teapot, 6 cup	825.00	950.00	550.00
F-150	Toast rack, 4 slice	285.00	345.00	165.00
F-160	Vase, bud	165.00	200.00	95.00

HARMONY

This chintz pattern was an uncontrolled pattern and was used by a number of companies, including A.G. Richardson pattern number 3275, and Hollinshead & Kirkham. The Czechoslovakian version of this pattern is called **Chelsea**. The Dutch Societe Cramique also produced this chintz pattern. This pattern has never been popular with collectors no matter who made it.

Cat. No.	Shape	U.S $	Can. $	U.K. £
Ha-04	Bonbon dish	30.00	40.00	20.00
Ha-10	Bowl, 6"	45.00	55.00	30.00
Ha-15	Bowl, 9"	80.00	100.00	70.00
Ha-23	Breakfast set	400.00	480.00	350.00
Ha-28	Butter dish	75.00	90.00	70.00
Ha-36	Cake plate, square, 11"	90.00	110.00	70.00
Ha-55	Coffee pot, 4 cup	350.00	420.00	325.00
Ha-60	Compote, footed	60.00	75.00	55.00
Ha-65	Condiment set on tray	100.00	120.00	90.00
Ha-70	Cream and sugar	65.00	80.00	50.00
Ha-71	Cream and sugar on tray	105.00	125.00	85.00
Ha-75	Demi-tasse	40.00	50.00	35.00
Ha-85	Jam pot	75.00	90.00	65.00

Cat. No.	Shape	U.S. $	Can. $	U.K. £
Ha-97	Nut dish	35.00	45.00	30.00
Ha-103	Plate, 6 1/2"	35.00	45.00	25.00
Ha-106	Plate, 9"	55.00	70.00	40.00
Ha-112	Relish dish	65.00	80.00	55.00
Ha-117	Salt and pepper	55.00	70.00	40.00
Ha-118	Salt and pepper on tray	85.00	105.00	80.00
Ha-120	Sandwich tray	65.00	80.00	50.00
Ha-130	Teacup and saucer	45.00	55.00	35.00
Ha-136	Teapot, 4 cup	275.00	330.00	225.00
Ha-137	Teapot, 6 cup	325.00	390.00	275.00
Ha-150	Toast rack, 4 slice	135.00	165.00	95.00
Ha-160	Vase, bud	65.00	80.00	55.00

HYDRANGEA (WHITE)

This pattern is the most sought after James Kent pattern in North America. The pattern was also available with a black background, but this version is much preferred. Hydrangea cups and saucers were advertised for sale by Bullocks, Los Angeles in 1941 for 75¢ each. Hadida is reproducing **Hydrangea** which has had some impact on the price of vintage pieces.

Cat. No.	Shape	U.S $	Can. $	U.K. £
Hy-04	Bonbon dish	65.00	80.00	45.00
Hy-10	Bowl, 6"	75.00	90.00	45.00
Hy-15	Bowl, 9"	175.00	210.00	120.00
Hy-23	Breakfast set	1,050.00	1,155.00	650.00
Hy-28	Butter dish	175.00	210.00	135.00
Hy-36	Cake plate, square, 11"	185.00	225.00	115.00
Hy-55	Coffee pot, 4 cup	750.00	865.00	475.00
Hy-60	Compote, footed	135.00	165.00	90.00
Hy-65	Condiment set on tray	225.00	270.00	145.00
Hy-70	Cream and sugar	150.00	180.00	90.00
Hy-71	Cream and sugar on tray	250.00	300.00	135.00
Hy-75	Demi-tasse	100.00	120.00	65.00
Hy-85	Jam pot	175.00	210.00	95.00

Cat. No.	Shape	U.S. $	Can. $	U.K. £
Hy-97	Nut dish	50.00	60.00	40.00
Hy-103	Plate, 6 1/2"	85.00	105.00	50.00
Hy-106	Plate, 9"	150.00	180.00	80.00
Hy-112	Relish dish	150.00	180.00	90.00
Hy-117	Salt and pepper	125.00	150.00	65.00
Hy-118	Salt and pepper on tray	200.00	240.00	105.00
Hy-120	Sandwich tray	125.00	150.00	80.00
Hy-130	Teacup and saucer	125.00	150.00	55.00
Hy-136	Teapot, 4 cup	725.00	835.00	425.00
Hy-137	Teapot, 6 cup	825.00	950.00	475.00
Hy-150	Toast rack, 4 slice	285.00	345.00	160.00
Hy-160	Vase, bud	165.00	200.00	85.00

HYDRANGEA (BLACK)

This pattern is the alternate colourway to **Hydrangea** but it is not popular with North American collectors. According to the James Kent pattern books, the pattern number is 2742 suggesting this pattern was introduced around 1933-1934.

Cat. No.	Shape	U.S $	Can. $	U.K. £
HyB-04	Bonbon dish	35.00	45.00	25.00
HyB-10	Bowl, 6"	40.00	50.00	30.00
HyB-15	Bowl, 9"	90.00	110.00	65.00
HyB-23	Breakfast set	500.00	600.00	395.00
HyB-28	Butter dish	90.00	110.00	80.00
HyB-36	Cake plate, square, 11"	135.00	165.00	65.00
HyB-55	Coffee pot, 4 cup	425.00	510.00	375.00
HyB-60	Compote, footed	70.00	85.00	65.00
HyB-65	Condiment set on tray	115.00	140.00	90.00
HyB-70	Cream and sugar	90.00	110.00	60.00
HyB-71	Cream and sugar on tray	145.00	175.00	95.00
HyB-75	Demi-tasse	60.00	75.00	45.00
HyB-85	Jam pot	110.00	135.00	80.00

Cat. No.	Shape	U.S. $	Can. $	U.K. £
HyB-97	Nut dish	40.00	50.00	30.00
HyB-103	Plate, 6 1/2"	40.00	50.00	30.00
HyB-106	Plate, 9"	85.00	105.00	50.00
HyB-112	Relish dish	75.00	90.00	55.00
HyB-117	Salt and pepper	75.00	90.00	50.00
HyB-118	Salt and pepper on tray	120.00	145.00	95.00
HyB-120	Sandwich tray	85.00	105.00	45.00
HyB-130	Teacup and saucer	85.00	105.00	50.00
HyB-136	Teapot, 4 cup	325.00	390.00	275.00
HyB-137	Teapot, 6 cup	400.00	480.00	325.00
HyB-150	Toast rack, 4 slice	155.00	190.00	90.00
HyB-160	Vase, bud	100.00	120.00	50.00

LICHFIELD

This pattern is mentioned in the column *Around the London Showrooms* in May 1938: "two designs…are the **Lichfield** and **Du Barry**, renderings of all-over chintz, with a bright colour play." Although not considered a chintz by many American collectors, Miss Ruth Kent said in a letter dated April 15, 1996 that this was definitely considered one of the Kent chintz patterns. The pattern number 1973 suggests that this is one of the earlier of the modern Kent chintzes. The Dutch firm Société Céramique also used this pattern on their chintz ware.

Cat. No.	Shape	U.S $	Can. $	U.K. £
L-04	Bonbon dish	35.00	45.00	30.00
L-10	Bowl, 6"	35.00	45.00	35.00
L-15	Bowl, 9"	80.00	100.00	70.00
L-23	Breakfast set	400.00	480.00	350.00
L-28	Butter dish	75.00	90.00	70.00
L-36	Cake plate, square, 11"	90.00	110.00	70.00
L-55	Coffee pot, 4 cup	350.00	420.00	325.00
L-60	Compote, footed	60.00	75.00	55.00
L-65	Condiment set on tray	100.00	120.00	65.00
L-70	Cream and sugar	65.00	80.00	50.00
L-71	Cream and sugar on tray	105.00	125.00	85.00
L-75	Demi-tasse	40.00	50.00	40.00
L-85	Jam pot	75.00	90.00	65.00

Cat. No.	Shape	U.S. $	Can. $	U.K. £
L-97	Nut dish	35.00	45.00	30.00
L-103	Plate, 6 1/2"	35.00	45.00	30.00
L-106	Plate, 9"	55.00	70.00	40.00
L-112	Relish dish	65.00	80.00	55.00
L-117	Salt and pepper	55.00	70.00	40.00
L-118	Salt and pepper on tray	85.00	105.00	80.00
L-120	Sandwich tray	65.00	80.00	50.00
L-130	Teacup and saucer	45.00	55.00	35.00
L-136	Teapot, 4 cup	275.00	330.00	250.00
L-137	Teapot, 6 cup	325.00	390.00	300.00
L-150	Toast rack, 4 slice	135.00	165.00	95.00
L-160	Vase, bud	65.00	80.00	45.00

MARIGOLD

According to the James Kent pattern books, this is pattern 8901 from a Rataud pattern book. The number James Kent assigned to **Marigold** is pattern number 3047.

Cat. No.	Shape	U.S $	Can. $	U.K. £
Mg-04	Bonbon dish	35.00	45.00	25.00
Mg-10	Bowl, 6"	40.00	50.00	30.00
Mg-15	Bowl, 9"	90.00	110.00	65.00
Mg-23	Breakfast set	500.00	600.00	325.00
Mg-28	Butter dish	90.00	110.00	85.00
Mg-36	Cake plate, square, 11"	135.00	165.00	65.00
Mg-55	Coffee pot, 4 cup	425.00	510.00	325.00
Mg-60	Compote, footed	70.00	85.00	65.00
Mg-65	Condiment set on tray	115.00	135.00	90.00
Mg-70	Cream and sugar	90.00	110.00	45.00
Mg-71	Cream and sugar on tray	145.00	175.00	80.00
Mg-75	Demi-tasse	60.00	75.00	40.00
Mg-85	Jam pot	110.00	135.00	70.00

Cat. No.	Shape	U.S. $	Can. $	U.K. £
Mg-97	Nut dish	40.00	50.00	30.00
Mg-103	Plate, 6 1/2"	40.00	50.00	30.00
Mg-106	Plate, 9"	85.00	105.00	50.00
Mg-112	Relish dish	95.00	115.00	65.00
Mg-117	Salt and pepper	65.00	80.00	50.00
Mg-118	Salt and pepper on tray	100.00	120.00	95.00
Mg-120	Sandwich tray	85.00	105.00	55.00
Mg-130	Teacup and saucer	85.00	105.00	50.00
Mg-136	Teapot, 4 cup	325.00	390.00	275.00
Mg-137	Teapot, 6 cup	400.00	480.00	325.00
Mg-150	Toast rack, 4 slice	155.00	190.00	95.00
Mg-160	Vase, bud	100.00	120.00	50.00

MILLE FLEURS

This pattern was an uncontrolled pattern and was used by a number of companies, including A.G. Richardson pattern number 5007 and Elijah Cotton, who called it **Marigold**. It was also produced in Czechoslovakia and Holland. A 1941 American advertisement by Bullocks of Los Angeles offered **Mille Fleurs** cups and saucers for sale at 75¢ each.

Cat. No.	Shape	U.S $	Can. $	U.K. £
MF-04	Bonbon dish	50.00	60.00	35.00
MF-10	Bowl, 6"	50.00	60.00	35.00
MF-15	Bowl, 9"	115.00	140.00	90.00
MF-23	Breakfast set	650.00	750.00	425.00
MF-28	Butter dish	125.00	150.00	95.00
MF-36	Cake plate, square, 11"	135.00	165.00	90.00
MF-55	Coffee pot, 4 cup	550.00	635.00	390.00
MF-60	Compote, footed	100.00	120.00	75.00
MF-65	Condiment set on tray	175.00	210.00	105.00
MF-70	Cream and sugar	95.00	115.00	65.00
MF-71	Cream and sugar on tray	150.00	180.00	90.00
MF-75	Demi-tasse	85.00	105.00	45.00
MF-85	Jam pot	110.00	135.00	70.00

Cat. No.	Shape	U.S. $	Can. $	U.K. £
MF-97	Nut dish	45.00	55.00	35.00
MF-103	Plate, 6 1/2"	50.00	60.00	35.00
MF-106	Plate, 9"	95.00	115.00	65.00
MF-112	Relish dish	100.00	120.00	70.00
MF-117	Salt and pepper	75.00	90.00	50.00
MF-118	Salt and pepper on tray	135.00	165.00	95.00
MF-120	Sandwich tray	85.00	105.00	50.00
MF-130	Teacup and saucer	85.00	105.00	45.00
MF-136	Teapot, 4 cup	450.00	540.00	325.00
MF-137	Teapot, 6 cup	550.00	635.00	375.00
MF-150	Toast rack, 4 slice	175.00	210.00	120.00
MF-160	Vase, bud	95.00	115.00	50.00

PRIMULA

This pattern has become more popular in the last year.

Cat. No.	Shape	U.S $	Can. $	U.K. £
Pr-04	Bonbon dish	50.00	60.00	45.00
Pr-10	Bowl, 6"	50.00	60.00	45.00
Pr-15	Bowl, 9"	150.00	180.00	125.00
Pr-23	Breakfast set	800.00	920.00	495.00
Pr-28	Butter dish	150.00	180.00	120.00
Pr-36	Cake plate, square, 11"	175.00	210.00	130.00
Pr-55	Coffee pot, 4 cup	750.00	865.00	450.00
Pr-60	Compote, footed	115.00	140.00	125.00
Pr-65	Condiment set on tray	200.00	240.00	165.00
Pr-70	Cream and sugar	150.00	180.00	105.00
Pr-71	Cream and sugar on tray	225.00	270.00	145.00
Pr-75	Demi-tasse	95.00	115.00	70.00
Pr-85	Jam pot	150.00	180.00	125.00

Cat. No.	Shape	U.S. $	Can. $	U.K. £
Pr-97	Nut dish	50.00	60.00	40.00
Pr-103	Plate, 6 1/2"	75.00	90.00	55.00
Pr-106	Plate, 9"	125.00	150.00	95.00
Pr-112	Relish dish	145.00	175.00	120.00
Pr-117	Salt and pepper	120.00	145.00	75.00
Pr-118	Salt and pepper on tray	175.00	210.00	130.00
Pr-120	Sandwich tray	135.00	165.00	95.00
Pr-130	Teacup and saucer	110.00	135.00	75.00
Pr-136	Teapot, 4 cup	595.00	685.00	395.00
Pr-137	Teapot, 6 cup	695.00	800.00	500.00
Pr-150	Toast rack, 4 slice	250.00	300.00	165.00
Pr-160	Vase, bud	150.00	180.00	90.00

RAPTURE

According to the James Kent pattern books **Rapture** and **Pearl De Light** are the same pattern with the pattern number 3007. This would explain why there are no references to **Rapture** in the American trade catalogues.

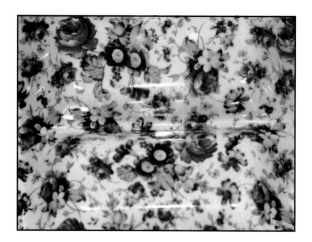

Cat. No.	Shape	U.S $	Can. $	U.K. £
Ra-04	Bonbon dish	50.00	60.00	40.00
Ra-10	Bowl, 6"	50.00	60.00	55.00
Ra-15	Bowl, 9"	115.00	140.00	80.00
Ra-23	Breakfast set	650.00	750.00	450.00
Ra-28	Butter dish	125.00	150.00	95.00
Ra-36	Cake plate, square, 11"	135.00	165.00	95.00
Ra-55	Coffee pot, 4 cup	550.00	635.00	350.00
Ra-60	Compote, footed	100.00	120.00	85.00
Ra-65	Condiment set on tray	175.00	210.00	100.00
Ra-70	Cream and sugar	95.00	115.00	60.00
Ra-71	Cream and sugar on tray	150.00	180.00	90.00
Ra-75	Demi-tasse	85.00	105.00	55.00
Ra-85	Jam pot	110.00	135.00	90.00

Cat. No.	Shape	U.S. $	Can. $	U.K. £
Ra-97	Nut dish	45.00	55.00	45.00
Ra-103	Plate, 6 1/2"	50.00	60.00	40.00
-Ra-106	Plate, 9"	95.00	115.00	65.00
Ra-112	Relish dish	100.00	120.00	60.00
Ra-117	Salt and pepper	75.00	90.00	50.00
Ra-118	Salt and pepper on tray	135.00	165.00	85.00
Ra-120	Sandwich tray	85.00	105.00	60.00
Ra-130	Teacup and saucer	85.00	105.00	45.00
Ra-136	Teapot, 4 cup	450.00	540.00	265.00
Ra-137	Teapot, 6 cup	550.00	635.00	325.00
Ra-150	Toast rack, 4 slice	175.00	210.00	95.00
Ra-160	Vase, bud	95.00	115.00	50.00

ROCHELLE

This pattern has also been found on ware produced by H.J. Wood & Sons.

Cat. No.	Shape	U.S $	Can. $	U.K. £
Roc-04	Bonbon dish	50.00	60.00	35.00
Roc-10	Bowl, 6"	50.00	60.00	35.00
Roc-15	Bowl, 9"	115.00	140.00	80.00
Roc-23	Breakfast set	650.00	750.00	390.00
Roc-28	Butter dish	125.00	150.00	95.00
Roc-36	Cake plate, square, 11"	135.00	165.00	85.00
Roc-55	Coffee pot, 4 cup	550.00	635.00	350.00
Roc-60	Compote, footed	100.00	120.00	70.00
Roc-65	Condiment set on tray	175.00	210.00	100.00
Roc-70	Cream and sugar	95.00	115.00	60.00
Roc-71	Cream and sugar on tray	150.00	180.00	115.00
Roc-75	Demi-tasse	85.00	105.00	55.00
Roc-85	Jam pot	110.00	135.00	80.00

Cat. No.	Shape	U.S. $	Can. $	U.K. £
Roc-97	Nut dish	45.00	55.00	35.00
Roc-103	Plate, 6 1/2"	50.00	60.00	40.00
Roc-106	Plate, 9"	95.00	115.00	55.00
Roc-112	Relish dish	100.00	120.00	60.00
Roc-117	Salt and pepper	75.00	90.00	55.00
Roc-118	Salt and pepper on tray	135.00	165.00	95.00
Roc-120	Sandwich tray	85.00	105.00	60.00
Roc-130	Teacup and saucer	85.00	105.00	50.00
Roc-136	Teapot, 4 cup	450.00	540.00	295.00
Roc-137	Teapot, 6 cup	550.00	635.00	350.00
Roc-150	Toast rack, 4 slice	175.00	210.00	105.00
Roc-160	Vase, bud	95.00	115.00	60.00

ROSALYNDE

The pattern number is 2662. This pattern was introduced around 1933 and exported in quantity to North America before and after the war. Complete dinner services still turn up occasionally in North America. Miss Ruth Kent remembers **Rosalynde** as one of the most popular patterns produced by her factory. In 1999, James Kent created a new yellow colourway of **Rosalynde** — the **Ruth Kent** chintz (see the section on new chintz). **Rosalynde** is also being reproduced by James Kent.

Cat. No.	Shape	U.S $	Can. $	U.K. £
Ro-04	Bonbon dish	65.00	80.00	45.00
Ro-10	Bowl, 6"	65.00	80.00	45.00
Ro-15	Bowl, 9"	175.00	210.00	120.00
Ro-23	Breakfast set	800.00	920.00	650.00
Ro-28	Butter dish	150.00	180.00	120.00
Ro-36	Cake plate, square, 11"	175.00	210.00	120.00
Ro-55	Coffee pot, 4 cup	750.00	865.00	450.00
Ro-60	Compote, footed	135.00	165.00	90.00
Ro-65	Condiment set on tray	245.00	295.00	165.00
Ro-70	Cream and sugar	150.00	180.00	95.00
Ro-71	Cream and sugar on tray	225.00	270.00	150.00
Ro-75	Demi-tasse	95.00	115.00	65.00
Ro-85	Jam pot	165.00	200.00	95.00

Cat. No.	Shape	U.S. $	Can. $	U.K. £
Ro-97	Nut dish	55.00	70.00	40.00
Ro-103	Plate, 6 1/2"	75.00	90.00	45.00
Ro-106	Plate, 9"	125.00	150.00	75.00
Ro-112	Relish dish	145.00	175.00	95.00
Ro-117	Salt and pepper	120.00	145.00	65.00
Ro-118	Salt and pepper on tray	195.00	235.00	115.00
Ro-120	Sandwich tray	125.00	150.00	75.00
Ro-130	Teacup and saucer	110.00	135.00	65.00
Ro-136	Teapot, 4 cup	650.00	750.00	425.00
Ro-137	Teapot, 6 cup	750.00	865.00	500.00
Ro-150	Toast rack, 4 slice	250.00	300.00	150.00
Ro-160	Vase, bud	150.00	180.00	75.00

SILVERDALE

The James Kent pattern number is 1097, but this pattern has also been found with a Royal Winton backstamp. The early pattern number suggests this may have been the first modern Kent chintz.

Cat. No.	Shape	U.S $	Can. $	U.K. £
S-04	Bonbon dish	35.00	45.00	30.00
S-10	Bowl, 6"	40.00	50.00	30.00
S-15	Bowl, 9"	90.00	110.00	60.00
S-23	Breakfast set	450.00	540.00	350.00
S-28	Butter dish	90.00	110.00	80.00
S-36	Cake plate, square, 11"	95.00	115.00	50.00
S-55	Coffee pot, 4 cup	400.00	480.00	265.00
S-60	Compote, footed	75.00	90.00	60.00
S-65	Condiment set on tray	135.00	165.00	90.00
S-70	Cream and sugar	75.00	90.00	50.00
S-71	Cream and sugar on tray	125.00	150.00	90.00
S-75	Demi-tasse	60.00	75.00	40.00
S-85	Jam pot	95.00	115.00	65.00

Cat. No.	Shape	U.S. $	Can. $	U.K. £
S-97	Nut dish	40.00	50.00	30.00
S-103	Plate, 6 1/2"	40.00	50.00	35.00
S-106	Plate, 9"	85.00	105.00	60.00
S-112	Relish dish	75.00	90.00	65.00
S-117	Salt and pepper	65.00	80.00	50.00
S-118	Salt and pepper on tray	100.00	120.00	75.00
S-120	Sandwich tray	65.00	80.00	50.00
S-130	Teacup and saucer	65.00	80.00	50.00
S-136	Teapot, 4 cup	300.00	360.00	250.00
S-137	Teapot, 6 cup	375.00	450.00	275.00
S-150	Toast rack, 4 slice	135.00	165.00	85.00
S-160	Vase, bud	100.00	120.00	70.00

TAPESTRY

The pattern number is 5615, and the pattern was introduced at the gift show in Blackpool in 1958. This pattern was used by a number of factories in the 1950s including Rosina on bone china.

Cat. No.	Shape	U.S $	Can. $	U.K. £
Tp-04	Bonbon dish	50.00	60.00	35.00
Tp-10	Bowl, 6"	50.00	60.00	35.00
Tp-15	Bowl, 9"	125.00	150.00	90.00
Tp-23	Breakfast set	650.00	750.00	490.00
Tp-28	Butter dish	125.00	150.00	90.00
Tp-36	Cake plate, square, 11"	145.00	175.00	90.00
Tp-55	Coffee pot, 4 cup	550.00	635.00	375.00
Tp-60	Compote, footed	120.00	145.00	80.00
Tp-65	Condiment set on tray	185.00	225.00	115.00
Tp-70	Cream and sugar	115.00	140.00	80.00
Tp-71	Cream and sugar on tray	165.00	200.00	105.00
Tp-75	Demi-tasse	85.00	105.00	50.00
Tp-85	Jam pot	135.00	165.00	75.00

Cat. No.	Shape	U.S $	Can. $	U.K. £
Tp-97	Nut dish	50.00	60.00	35.00
Tp-103	Plate, 6 1/2"	55.00	70.00	45.00
Tp-106	Plate, 9"	95.00	115.00	65.00
Tp-112	Relish dish	110.00	135.00	70.00
Tp-117	Salt and pepper	85.00	105.00	60.00
Tp-118	Salt and pepper on tray	135.00	165.00	95.00
Tp-120	Sandwich tray	95.00	115.00	65.00
Tp-130	Teacup and saucer	85.00	105.00	50.00
Tp-136	Teapot, 4 cup	450.00	540.00	325.00
Tp-137	Teapot, 6 cup	550.00	635.00	375.00
Tp-150	Toast rack, 4 slice	225.00	270.00	140.00
Tp-160	Vase, bud	125.00	150.00	70.00

JOHNSON BROTHERS LTD.

Johnson Brothers opened their factory in Hanley in 1883 to produce earthenwares. They became much praised in design books and articles in the 1920s and 1930s for the very plain, often undecorated wares they produced. Johnsons Brothers were not interested in handpainted wares which Clarice Cliff was making a name with or all over transfers such as Royal Winton was becoming known for. In a survey of the pottery industry published in *The Studio* in 1936, Johnsons Brothers are commended: their aim is to produce earthenware bodies of fine texture and colour and to encourage decoration in printing, lithography and stamping which will show a real appreciation of these more mechanized techniques and enable the artist to produce honest work in the particular idiom and not the mass production travesties of hand-painting to which one is accustomed." Interestingly, it was Gordon Forsyth who later went to work for Royal Winton as a designer who praised the firm of Johnson Brothers as an outstanding example of excellent cheap production.

Johnson Brothers produced several charming chintz patterns including the popular **Victorian Chintz**. Since most chintz collectors do not collect Johnson Brothers, the only pattern I have included in this edition is still the **Rose Chintz** sold in great quanties in North America for many years. Advertisements in the 1950s *Crockery and Glass Journal* talk of the delightful fabric inspired pattern which is a permanent favourite with hostesses. Fifty-piece sets retailed for $29.95 in the United States. Perhaps because of the quality of the production and the popularity of this pattern for so many years, this pattern is still easily found throughout North America.

Collectors interested in Johnson Brothers patterns should look for Mary Finegan's book, *Directory of Johnson Brothers Dinnerware*.

ROSE CHINTZ

This is not considered a chintz pattern by many chintz collectors but it is bought by them for use as opposed to display and has developed a growing market among this group. This charming informal chintz pattern was advertised widely in the *Crockery and Glass Journal* as intended "for use in every American home."

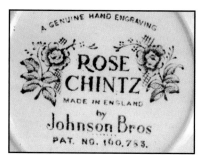

Cat. No.	Shape	U.S $	Can. $	U.K. £
RC-09	Bowl, 5"	25.00	30.00	20.00
RC-10	Bowl, 6"	30.00	40.00	35.00
RC-55	Coffee Pot, 6 cup	275.00	330.00	125.00
RC-70	Cream and Sugar	75.00	90.00	45.00
RC-103	Plate, 6 1/2"	25.00	30.00	20.00

Cat. No.	Shape	U.S. $	Can. $	U.K. £
RC-106	Plate, 9"	35.00	45.00	25.00
RC-107	Plate, 10"	40.00	50.00	30.00
RC-130	Teacup and saucer	35.00	45.00	25.00
RC-137	Teapot, 6 cup	250.00	300.00	105.00

W.R. MIDWINTER LTD.

William Robinson Midwinter spent 18 years working for the head of Royal Doulton and selling seconds at night and on weekends. By 1910 he had saved 50 pounds and was ready to set up his own business at Bournes Bank Pottery in Burslem. The factory turned out very much the same product lines as every other small pottery in Staffordshire, and it prospered. After buying up the Albion Pottery and Stewart Maddock Ltd., Midwinter increased production and began to produce tablewares in addition to teawares and toiletwares. For the most part the patterns were the traditional florals produced by the other factories.

According to Allan Peat, author of *Midwinter: A Collectors Guide,* the Midwinter factory worked on the basis of one new pattern a week and Roy Midwinter, William's son, set off for North America in 1952 with a number of recent designs. Colonel Keene, the legendary buyer for Eatons of Canada, is reported to have said, "Get that. . . stuff out of here," and his colleague at Robert Simpson of Canada, Maurice Pickles, concurred. Asked for advice, Colonel Keene directed Roy Midwinter to the American West Coast and designers like Eva Zeisal. Roy shipped samples home from California and helped to change the design direction not only of Midwinter but of the Potteries as well.

Midwinter became renowned for their risk taking in leading the way in modern design in Staffordshire. Their designs by Jessie Tait, Terence Conran, Sir Hugh Casson and David Queensberry have found their way into most museums of modern design. Roy Midwinter never lost sight of the traditional markets, however, and he was careful to continue to cater to them. The Midwinter chintzes are part of this traditional market and they warrant exactly one line in Allan Peat's book on Midwinter.

Although the whole factory was modernized and a decorating department opened, the printing shop was still used principally for traditional printed patterns such as **Springtime.** Several Midwinter advertisements from the mid 1940s feature **Springtime** as a controlled Midwinter chintz. The only other reference to **Springtime** is in the pattern information from *The Midwinter Trade Price Book*, which states that the pattern was discontinued in 1974 on the Fine shape. Since this shape is chunky and seemingly unsuited to chintz, one wonders if **Springtime** was now a different pattern. This could account for chintz pieces with the name **Brama** clearly marked on **Springtime** chintz and for backstamps which date to the late 1940s and the 1950s.

An advertisement appeared in May 1949 for a new Wilkinson production of "superb colour and charm ". . . and the pattern was called **Lorna Doone**. This identical pattern appears frequently with the Midwinter Stylecraft backstamp. In fact, Midwinter bought Wilkinson from Clarice Cliff in 1964 and presumably took over the pattern. It is an excellent example of a transitional period in design. The Midwinter **Lorna Doone** range is a strange amalgam of traditional decoration and modern styling. Most of the line was in some way fitted with chrome handles or chrome bases. Neither the shapes nor the fittings were particularly well-suited to chintz. Some pieces have a Midwinter backstamp with the name **Bird Chintz** underneath so perhaps at some point the factory renamed their patterns.

In 1968 Midwinter merged with J & G Meakin Ltd., and in 1970 the combined company was taken over by the Wedgwood Group.

BRAMA

This was a pattern controlled to Midwinter as **Springtime** and advertised as such before and after the Second World War. It is unclear when and why the name was changed to **Brama**.

Cat. No.	Shape	U.S. $	Can. $	U.K. £
Br-170	Biscuit barrel	550.00	635.00	295.00
Br-04	Bonbon dish	60.00	75.00	50.00
Br-40	Cake plate, 2 tier	125.00	150.00	90.00
Br-41	Cake plate, 3 tier	175.00	210.00	145.00
Br-42	Cake plate, with server	175.00	210.00	145.00
Br-43	Cake stand, chrome handle	100.00	120.00	80.00
Br-44	Cake stand, chrome base	100.00	120.00	80.00

Cat. No.	Shape	U.S. $	Can. $	U.K. £
Br-65	Condiment set on tray	200.00	240.00	140.00
Br-85	Jam pot with liner	125.00	150.00	90.00
Br-103	Plate, 6"	75.00	90.00	55.00
Br-106	Plate, 9"	155.00	190.00	85.00
Br-120	Sandwich tray	175.00	210.00	95.00
Br-169	Sugar shaker	425.00	510.00	250.00
Br-130	Teacup and saucer	100.00	120.00	60.00

CORAL

We currently have no information available on this pattern.

Cat. No.	Shape	U.S. $	Can. $	U.K. £
C-170	Biscuit barrel	550.00	635.00	295.00
C-04	Bonbon dish	50.00	60.00	45.00
C-40	Cake plate, 2 tier	125.00	150.00	90.00
C-41	Cake plate, 3 tier	175.00	210.00	140.00
C-42	Cake plate, with server	175.00	210.00	165.00
C-43	Cake stand, chrome handle	100.00	120.00	75.00
C-44	Cake stand, chrome base	85.00	105.00	65.00

Cat. No.	Shape	U.S. $	Can. $	U.K. £
C-65	Condiment set on tray	175.00	210.00	150.00
C-85	Jam pot with liner	115.00	140.00	85.00
C-103	Plate, 6"	60.00	75.00	45.00
C-106	Plate, 9"	145.00	175.00	90.00
C-120	Sandwich tray	175.00	210.00	95.00
C-169	Sugar shaker	400.00	480.00	225.00
C-130	Teacup and saucer	100.00	120.00	65.00

LORNA DOONE

This pattern can be found in the A.J. Wilkinson Clarice Cliff archive from the late 1940s. Some pieces have been found with a Royal Staffordshire Ceramics by Clarice Cliff backstamp. We assume that any piece of **Lorna Doone** with a Midwinter backstamp must have been produced after the 1964 takeover of Wilkinsons. At some point Midwinter changed the name and pieces appear with the backstamp pattern name **Bird Chintz**. This pattern was also produced by a number of Staffordshire factories including Barker Brothers and Brexton (pattern 7219). Arklow Pottery in Ireland also used this pattern on their ware.

Cat. No.	Shape	U.S. $	Can. $	U.K. £
LD-170	Biscuit barrel	500.00	600.00	275.00
LD-04	Bonbon dish	55.00	70.00	35.00
LD-40	Cake plate, 2 tier	115.00	140.00	80.00
LD-41	Cake plate, 3 tier	160.00	195.00	120.00
LD-42	Cake plate, with server	160.00	195.00	125.00
LD-43	Cake stand, chrome handle	75.00	90.00	60.00
LD-44	Cake stand, chrome base	75.00	90.00	55.00

Cat. No.	Shape	U.S. $	Can. $	U.K. £
LD-65	Condiment set on tray	175.00	210.00	115.00
LD-85	Jam pot with liner	105.00	125.00	70.00
LD-103	Plate, 6"	60.00	75.00	40.00
LD-106	Plate, 9"	85.00	105.00	70.00
LD-120	Sandwich tray	135.00	165.00	80.00
LD-169	Sugar shaker	375.00	450.00	200.00
LD-130	Teacup and saucer	85.00	105.00	60.00

MYOTT SON & COMPANY

Although the original pottery was established in the early nineteenth century, when Ashley Myott inherited the chairmanship at 19 years of age, he and his brother Sydney built up the business into a worldwide concern. The factory tried to produce a little of everything in earthenware. They produced some extreme shapes with vivid handpainting during the 1920s and 1930s in competition with Newport Pottery. They produced art pottery in the Carlton ware mould but not of the same quality. They used a wide variety of prints and enamels on their tablewares during the 1930s, and the company registered almost 500 different patterns between the years 1933 and 1935. In April 1933 the *Pottery Gazette* reported Myott, Son & Company to be "extensive producers of a reputable brand of semi-porcelain, with which they cater for the whole of the worlds markets. It is perhaps, hardly necessary for us to add that this firm, in the semi-procelain trade, ranks as a first grade house, and that in this special field they count amongst The Big Five." Myott were not known for their chintzes, but obviously did not want to let a potential market go completely unaddressed. A couple of Myott chintzes have come to light, but there may well be others. The **Summer Flower** pattern seems to date from the 1930s. **Bermuda** was a very popular chintz pattern produced by Myott in the 1930s.

The factory passed out of family hands some years after the war and eventually amalgamated with Alfred Meakin Pottery. There was a dreadful fire in 1949 and all the records and pattern books from the Myott factory were destroyed. The Churchill Group took over the combined company in 1991.

BERMUDA

Complete dinner services were produced in both a brown and a blue colourway in the 1930s. In their great fall sale of 1941, B. Altman & Company offered an 84-piece service in **Bermuda by Myott Staffordshire** for $19.50. "You'll take a second look at any table set with **Bermuda** it's so stunning. And you'll thank Altman for this sale which makes it easy to entertain so beautifully for very little."

Cat. No.	Shape	U.S. $	Can. $	U.K. £
Ber-55	Coffee pot, 6 cup	275.00	330.00	125.00
Ber-70	Cream and sugar	75.00	90.00	35.00
Ber-95	Jug, 7" straight-sided	150.00	180.00	95.00
-Ber103	Plate, 6"	45.00	55.00	25.00

Cat. No.	Shape	U.S. $	Can. $	U.K. £
Ber-104	Plate, 7"	65.00	80.00	30.00
Ber-106	Plate, 9"	95.00	115.00	45.00
Ber-130	Teacup and saucer	55.00	70.00	25.00
Ber-137	Teapot, 6 cup	275.00	330.00	160.00

"SPRING FLOWER"

The pattern number is 3005. This pattern appears to have been used for complete dinner services. The handles of the teapots and coffee pots are painted bright orange and black.

Cat. No.	Shape	U.S. $	Can. $	U.K. £
SF-55	Coffee pot, 6 cup	700.00	805.00	400.00
SF-70	Cream and sugar	165.00	200.00	95.00
SF-95	Jug, 7" straight-sided	450.00	540.00	220.00
SF-103	Plate, 6"	85.00	105.00	45.00

Cat. No.	Shape	U.S. $	Can. $	U.K. £
SF-104	Plate, 7"	110.00	135.00	50.00
SF-106	Plate, 9"	165.00	200.00	80.00
SF-130	Teacup and saucer	110.00	135.00	65.00
SF-137	Teapot, 6 cup	550.00	635.00	350.00

SUMMER FLOWER

This pattern is difficult to find particularly in North America.

Cat. No.	Shape	U.S. $	Can. $	U.K. £
SuF-55	Coffee pot, 6 cup	500.00	600.00	385.00
SuF-70	Cream and sugar	135.00	165.00	95.00
SuF-95	Jug, 7" straight-sided	300.00	360.00	220.00
SuF-103	Plate, 6"	60.00	75.00	45.00

Cat. No.	Shape	U.S. $	Can. $	U.K. £
SuF-104	Plate, 7"	75.00	90.00	60.00
SuF-106	Plate, 9"	125.00	150.00	90.00
SuF-130	Teacup and saucer	85.00	105.00	65.00
SuF-137	Teapot, 6 cup	450.00	540.00	350.00

A.G. RICHARDSON & CO. LTD.
(CROWN DUCAL)

In 1915 at the Gordon Pottery, Tunstall, Albert Goodwin Richardson formed A.G. Richardson & Co. Ltd. with the stated intention of producing good quality earthenware under the trade name Crown Ducal. The early production included Victorian silver luster ware and black groundlay decoration. The first chintz pattern produced by Richardson was in 1918 and was numbered A500. The pattern book started at A1 and by 1931 had reached A2000, when the A was dropped. In 1919 *The Pottery and Glass Record* noted two new Ducal chintzes, **Rose and Motifs** A601 and **Delhi** A617. According to this report, vases were made from 4 1/2 inches up to 12 inches and the flower pots came in four sizes.

In 1919 Albert Richardson left Richardsons, and Harry Taylor, owner of Universal Transfer Company, Burslem, bought a major interest in the company. Universal, Rataud, and the Chromo Transfer Company supplied most of Richardsons lithographs.

Maddock & Miller, the New York importers, agreed to represent Richardsons in the United States and sales grew rapidly. Crown Ducal is mentioned in *The Pottery Glass & Brass Salesman* in June 1920 and frequently thereafter. Chintzware was particularly popular with the American public, and Richardsons expanded the line to include teaware in 1921. Again with the urging of America, Richardsons expanded their line in 1925 to include dinnerware for the first time. All-over patterns like **Blue Chintz** A1185 and **Florida** A1257 (known to many American collectors as **Mauve Crown Ducal**) were advertised in 1926 and much admired. In 1928 they offered six delightful new chintz patterns on square or octagonal plates, tea and breakfast sets, full dinner services, fancy pieces and salad sets. According to the American *Crockery & Glass Journal* these lines were planned to harmonize with the trend of interior decoration today.

By 1929 the *Brass Salesman* had published a two-page story on the success of A.G. Richardson in America. They said "the thrifty American housewife loved Crown Ducal, which duplicated bone china in terms of quality but cost $100 compared to $500 for a china service of equal charm. Richardsons led the way in adapting designs which had previously been reserved for fine china to earthenware. The great success of the Crown Ducal ware surely proves that people of moderate means as well as the wealthier class prefer to have good-looking belongings in table service, even if the price is necessarily slightly higher than that of uninspired thick potteries." They were praised in English publications as well. The 1932 *Pottery Gazette* commented that "they were reliable

without being high-priced and exclusive" and noted their ability to lead rather than follow the other potteries. *The Pottery and Glass Record* made a similar point in 1935: "In these days when the artistic standard of the people is high, it is comforting to know that by dealing with Messrs. A. G. Richardson, a smart and well equipped table does not depend on whether or not one has a big income."

The company purchased a second potbank, Britannia Pottery at Cobridge, to cope with increased production. Although Harold Holdcroft joined the design staff in 1928 and is said to be responsible for many of the firms lithographic patterns, most of the exotic chintzes were already in production by that time and he was gone by 1934. Charlotte Rhead joined them as a designer in 1931 and stayed for the next eleven years. Many wonderful designs were produced over the next few years but there seems to be a gap of close to ten years before the next group of chintz designs were produced at Richardson. **Primrose**, **Peony**, **Pansy**, and **Priscilla** were all designed late in the 1930s, but none achieved the popularity of the earlier chintzes. The deep ivory glaze base colour which was developed at Richardsons in 1931 was used for all the later chintzes. Richardsons were still producing chintzes in 1940 but wartime restrictions drastically reduced the output of decorated ware.

Although there is no mention of Crown Ducal chintzes in the American trade magazines after the war, a reporter for *The Pottery and Glass Record*, on a visit to the works at Cobridge in 1955 commended the earthenware as being of very fine quality ". . . an all-over engraving of a conventionalized bird and flowers in blue, mauve or pink is a magnificent reminder of Victorian plenitude." This would suggest that Crown Ducal chintzes were still being produced in the 1950s.

Like all too many potteries during these years, A.G. Richardson could not survive alone and they were acquired by Enoch Wedgwood (Tunstall) Ltd. in 1974 which in turn were taken over by the Wedgwood Group in 1980 and renamed the Unicorn Pottery.

Thanks in part to the detective work and perseverance of Gerrard Shaw, who completed his manuscript on the A. G. Richardson factory, some of the pattern books have been located in the City Museum in Stoke-on-Trent. Gerrard, Dora Shaw and Ivy Mayer went through the pattern books for us and recorded and photographed any chintz patterns they could find. Interestingly only five or six of the patterns were in the pattern books including **Peony** pattern number 5008, and **Spring Blossom,** pattern number 3271.

ASCOT

The March 1926 *Pottery Gazette* mentions the introduction of a new design called the **Ascot** at the British Industries Fair. The Gazette described "a new litho pattern of the sheet type, that is to say, a covering pattern which is to be known as the **Ascot**." They went on to say that **Ascot** came in for the attention of a number of responsible buyers. This pattern was introduced into the United States later in 1926.

Cat. No.	Shape	U.S. $	Can. $	U.K. £
As-17	Bowl, lily 12"	100.00	120.00	75.00
As-22	Bowl, octagonal, 7"	255.00	310.00	190.00
As-24	Bowl, octagonal, 8"	300.00	360.00	200.00
As-53	Coffee pot, 3 cup	550.00	635.00	375.00
As-65	Condiment set	165.00	200.00	120.00
As-70	Cream and sugar	125.00	150.00	85.00
As-75	Demi-tasse	65.00	80.00	50.00
As-85	Jam pot	125.00	150.00	85.00
As-95	Jug, 5"	250.00	300.00	160.00
As-96	Jug, 7"	325.00	390.00	180.00

Cat. No.	Shape	U.S. $	Can. $	U.K. £
As-402	Plate, octagonal, 5"	65.00	80.00	45.00
As-406	Plate, octagonal, 9"	100.00	120.00	70.00
As-407	Plate, octagonal, 10"	125.00	150.00	90.00
As-130	Teacup and saucer	75.00	90.00	50.00
As-135	Teapot, 2 cup	375.00	450.00	260.00
As-136	Teapot, 4 cup	475.00	570.00	315.00
As-160	Vase, bud	125.00	150.00	80.00
As-163	Vase, spill, 8"	175.00	210.00	110.00
As-162	Vase, trumpet 6"	145.00	175.00	95.00
As-165	Vase, 9"	225.00	270.00	165.00

BLUE CHINTZ

The pattern number is 1185. This chintz pattern was introduced in the United States in 1926 and continued in production for many years. We have named the identical pattern without the bird **Spring Blossom** (see page 168) because it tends to sell for less than the **Blue Chintz**.

Cat. No.	Shape	U.S. $	Can. $	U.K. £
BC-17	Bowl, lily 12"	150.00	180.00	90.00
BC-22	Bowl, octagonal, 7"	300.00	360.00	225.00
BC-24	Bowl, octagonal, 8"	350.00	420.00	275.00
BC-53	Coffee pot, 3 cup	700.00	805.00	450.00
BC-65	Condiment set	295.00	355.00	135.00
BC-70	Cream and sugar	175.00	210.00	95.00
BC-75	Demi-tasse	125.00	150.00	60.00
BC-85	Jam pot	165.00	200.00	80.00
BC-95	Jug, 5"	375.00	450.00	160.00
BC-96	Jug, 7"	500.00	600.00	185.00

Cat. No.	Shape	U.S. $	Can. $	U.K. £
BC-402	Plate, octagonal, 5"	75.00	90.00	50.00
BC-406	Plate, octagonal, 9"	150.00	180.00	85.00
BC-407	Plate, octagonal, 10"	185.00	225.00	115.00
BC-130	Teacup and saucer	125.00	150.00	65.00
BC-135	Teapot, 2 cup	500.00	600.00	320.00
BC-136	Teapot, 4 cup	600.00	690.00	360.00
BC-160	Vase, bud	185.00	225.00	95.00
BC-163	Vase, spill, 8"	250.00	300.00	135.00
BC-162	Vase, trumpet 6"	210.00	255.00	125.00
BC-165	Vase, 9"	395.00	475.00	195.00

CANTON

The March 1926 *Pottery & Glass Record* describes a new pattern introduced by Crown Ducal at the British Industries Fair as "an oriental design called the **Canton** — Chinese lanterns with a fir tree and finished up with royal blue and a black border." This chintz-like pattern could not have been exclusive to Crown Ducal, however, since a number of other Staffordshire factories used it on their wares.

Cat. No.	Shape	U.S. $	Can. $	U.K. £
C-17	Bowl, lily 12"	90.00	110.00	85.00
C-22	Bowl, octagonal, 7"	175.00	210.00	165.00
C-24	Bowl, octagonal, 8"	195.00	235.00	185.00
C-53	Coffee pot, 3 cup	350.00	420.00	325.00
C-65	Condiment set	125.00	150.00	115.00
C-70	Cream and sugar	75.00	90.00	75.00
C-75	Demi-tasse	45.00	55.00	45.00
C-85	Jam pot	90.00	110.00	75.00
C-95	Jug, 5"	125.00	150.00	85.00
C-96	Jug, 7"	150.00	180.00	100.00

Cat. No.	Shape	U.S. $	Can. $	U.K. £
C-402	Plate, octagonal, 5"	45.00	55.00	35.00
C-406	Plate, octagonal, 9"	75.00	90.00	65.00
C-407	Plate, octagonal, 10"	95.00	115.00	75.00
C-130	Teacup and saucer	55.00	70.00	45.00
C-135	Teapot, 2 cup	250.00	300.00	235.00
C-136	Teapot, 4 cup	300.00	360.00	275.00
C-160	Vase, bud	90.00	110.00	75.00
C-163	Vase, spill, 8"	135.00	165.00	90.00
C-162	Vase, trumpet 6"	115.00	140.00	85.00
C-165	Vase, 9"	150.00	180.00	150.00

DELHI

This was one of the earlier of the Crown Ducal chintzes, pattern number A617 and was introduced in 1918. It has been found on a limited range of vases and toiletware as well as plates and teapots.

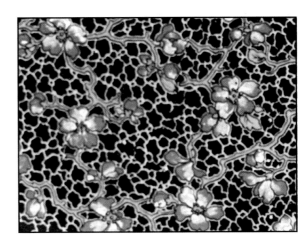

Cat. No.	Shape	U.S. $	Can. $	U.K. £
Dh-95	Jug, 5"	100.00	120.00	85.00
Dh-96	Jug, 7"	125.00	150.00	110.00
Dh-406	Plate, octagonal, 9"	75.00	90.00	65.00
Dh-135	Teapot, 2 cup	245.00	295.00	195.00

Cat. No.	Shape	U.S. $	Can. $	U.K. £
Dh-160	Vase, bud	75.00	90.00	75.00
Dh-163	Vase, spill, 8"	110.00	135.00	85.00
Dh-162	Vase, trumpet 6"	95.00	115.00	85.00
Dh-165	Vase, 9"	150.00	180.00	145.00

FESTIVAL

This pattern was introduced in the United States around 1926.

Cat. No.	Shape	U.S. $	Can. $	U.K. £
Fe-17	Bowl, lily 12"	100.00	120.00	75.00
Fe-22	Bowl, octagonal, 7"	250.00	300.00	195.00
Fe-24	Bowl, octagonal, 8"	300.00	360.00	225.00
Fe-53	Coffee pot, 3 cup	550.00	635.00	395.00
Fe-65	Condiment set	165.00	200.00	145.00
Fe-70	Cream and sugar	115.00	140.00	115.00
Fe-75	Demi-tasse	65.00	80.00	60.00
Fe-85	Jam pot	100.00	120.00	75.00
Fe-95	Jug, 5"	250.00	300.00	145.00
Fe-96	Jug, 7"	325.00	390.00	175.00

Cat. No.	Shape	U.S. $	Can. $	U.K. £
Fe-402	Plate, octagonal, 5"	65.00	80.00	50.00
Fe-406	Plate, octagonal, 9"	100.00	120.00	75.00
Fe-407	Plate, octagonal, 10"	125.00	150.00	85.00
Fe-130	Teacup and saucer	75.00	90.00	55.00
Fe-135	Teapot, 2 cup	375.00	450.00	275.00
Fe-136	Teapot, 4 cup	475.00	570.00	325.00
Fe-160	Vase, bud	100.00	120.00	75.00
Fe-163	Vase, spill, 8"	165.00	200.00	100.00
Fe-162	Vase, trumpet 6"	135.00	165.00	85.00
Fe-165	Vase, 9"	250.00	300.00	150.00

FLORIDA

The pattern number for **Florida** is A1257. This pattern was mentioned in 1925 in the column Around the London Showrooms as "another new chintz pattern called the **Florida,** the colours being notably soft and the pattern including a pheasant and flower design." This chintz pattern was advertised in the United States in 1925 and was described as "a wordless song of the tropics." American collectors know this pattern as **Mauve Crown Ducal** and it is the most popular Crown Ducal pattern in the United States.

Cat. No.	Shape	U.S. $	Can. $	U.K. £
Fd-17	Bowl, lily 12"	200.00	240.00	150.00
Fd-22	Bowl, octagonal, 7"	450.00	540.00	325.00
Fd-24	Bowl, octagonal, 8"	550.00	635.00	350.00
Fd-53	Coffee pot, 3 cup	1,000.00	1,150.00	650.00
Fd-65	Condiment set	350.00	420.00	225.00
Fd-70	Cream and sugar	250.00	300.00	150.00
Fd-75	Demi-tasse	175.00	210.00	95.00
Fd-85	Jam pot	215.00	260.00	150.00
Fd-95	Jug, 5"	495.00	595.00	250.00
Fd-96	Jug, 7"	695.00	800.00	275.00

Cat. No.	Shape	U.S. $	Can. $	U.K. £
Fd-402	Plate, octagonal, 5"	100.00	120.00	75.00
Fd-406	Plate, octagonal, 9"	185.00	225.00	150.00
Fd-407	Plate, octagonal, 10"	245.00	295.00	200.00
Fd-130	Teacup and saucer	175.00	210.00	85.00
Fd-135	Teapot, 2 cup	700.00	805.00	450.00
Fd-136	Teapot, 4 cup	1,200.00	1,320.00	575.00
Fd-160	Vase, bud	195.00	235.00	150.00
Fd-163	Vase, spill, 8"	295.00	355.00	220.00
Fd-162	Vase, trumpet 6"	235.00	285.00	175.00
Fd-165	Vase, 9"	500.00	600.00	300.00

"GREY FRUIT"

The pattern number for **Grey Fruit** is A1106 dating it to around 1925.

Cat. No.	Shape	U.S. $	Can. $	U.K. £
GF-17	Bowl, lily 12"	100.00	120.00	85.00
GF-22	Bowl, octagonal, 7"	255.00	310.00	175.00
GF-24	Bowl, octagonal, 8"	300.00	360.00	225.00
GF-53	Coffee pot, 3 cup	550.00	635.00	350.00
GF-65	Condiment set	165.00	200.00	120.00
GF-70	Cream and sugar	115.00	140.00	75.00
GF-75	Demi-tasse	65.00	80.00	45.00
GF-85	Jam pot	100.00	120.00	100.00
GF-95	Jug, 5"	225.00	270.00	110.00
GF-96	Jug, 7"	300.00	360.00	120.00

Cat. No.	Shape	U.S. $	Can. $	U.K. £
GF-402	Plate, octagonal, 5"	65.00	80.00	45.00
GF-406	Plate, octagonal, 9"	100.00	120.00	75.00
GF-407	Plate, octagonal, 10"	125.00	150.00	80.00
GF-130	Teacup and saucer	75.00	90.00	55.00
GF-135	Teapot, 2 cup	375.00	450.00	250.00
GF-136	Teapot, 4 cup	475.00	570.00	325.00
GF-160	Vase, bud	100.00	120.00	85.00
GF-163	Vase, spill, 8"	165.00	200.00	105.00
GF-162	Vase, trumpet 6"	135.00	165.00	95.00
GF-165	Vase, 9"	225.00	270.00	160.00

IVORY CHINTZ

The pattern number is A500 for the all chintz pattern and A559 for the **Ivory Chintz** centre and the black border. This is considered the first Crown Ducal chintz and was designed in 1918. This chintz pattern was introduced into the United States early in the 1920s and is found on a very wide variety of shapes and sizes of vases and bowls. The version with the **Ivory Chintz** centre and the black border with large pink roses is called **Roseland** according to an article in *The Pottery, Glass & Brass Salesman* on December 16, 1926.

Cat. No.	Shape	U.S. $	Can. $	U.K. £
IC-17	Bowl, lily 12"	125.00	150.00	115.00
IC-22	Bowl, octagonal, 7"	300.00	360.00	225.00
IC-24	Bowl, octagonal, 8"	350.00	420.00	275.00
IC-53	Coffee pot, 3 cup	650.00	750.00	450.00
IC-65	Condiment set	200.00	240.00	160.00
IC-70	Cream and sugar	135.00	165.00	95.00
IC-75	Demi-tasse	100.00	120.00	65.00
IC-85	Jam pot	125.00	150.00	85.00
IC-95	Jug, 5"	275.00	330.00	190.00
IC-96	Jug, 7"	350.00	420.00	195.00

Cat. No.	Shape	U.S. $	Can. $	U.K. £
IC-402	Plate, octagonal, 5"	75.00	90.00	50.00
IC-406	Plate, octagonal, 9"	125.00	150.00	80.00
IC-407	Plate, octagonal, 10"	150.00	180.00	85.00
IC-130	Teacup and saucer	125.00	150.00	65.00
IC-135	Teapot, 2 cup	450.00	540.00	320.00
IC-136	Teapot, 4 cup	550.00	635.00	360.00
IC-160	Vase, bud	135.00	165.00	90.00
IC-163	Vase, spill, 8"	200.00	240.00	165.00
IC-162	Vase, trumpet 6"	165.00	200.00	140.00
IC-165	Vase, 9"	350.00	420.00	185.00

"IVORY FRUIT"

This must have been an uncontrolled pattern since it appeared on Dutch ware produced by the Société Céramique in 1926.

Cat. No.	Shape	U.S. $	Can. $	U.K. £	Cat. No.	Shape	U.S. $	Can. $	U.K. £
IF-17	Bowl, lily 12"	100.00	120.00	75.00	IF-402	Plate, octagonal, 5"	65.00	80.00	40.00
IF-22	Bowl, octagonal, 7"	255.00	310.00	160.00	IF-406	Plate, octagonal, 9"	100.00	120.00	70.00
IF-24	Bowl, octagonal, 8"	300.00	360.00	175.00	IF-407	Plate, octagonal, 10"	125.00	150.00	80.00
IF-53	Coffee pot, 3 cup	550.00	635.00	320.00	IF-130	Teacup and saucer	75.00	90.00	55.00
IF-65	Condiment set	165.00	200.00	95.00	IF-135	Teapot, 2 cup	375.00	450.00	240.00
IF-70	Cream and sugar	115.00	140.00	70.00	IF-136	Teapot, 4 cup	475.00	570.00	290.00
IF-75	Demi-tasse	65.00	80.00	45.00	IF-160	Vase, bud	100.00	120.00	75.00
IF-85	Jam pot	100.00	120.00	75.00	IF-163	Vase, spill, 8"	165.00	200.00	110.00
IF-95	Jug, 5"	250.00	300.00	95.00	IF-162	Vase, trumpet 6"	135.00	165.00	95.00
IF-96	Jug, 7"	325.00	390.00	115.00	IF-165	Vase, 9"	225.00	270.00	150.00

MARIGOLD

This pattern is most often found on vases and rose bowls. The pattern number A1063 indicates that it was probably produced around 1924-25. This pattern has become more popular in the United States in the past year and prices have risen accordingly.

Cat. No.	Shape	U.S. $	Can. $	U.K. £
MgR-17	Bowl, lily 12"	150.00	180.00	80.00
MgR-22	Bowl, octagonal, 7"	300.00	360.00	190.00
MgR-24	Bowl, octagonal, 8"	350.00	420.00	225.00
MgR-53	Coffee pot, 3 cup	650.00	750.00	365.00
MgR-65	Condiment set	275.00	330.00	120.00
MgR-70	Cream and sugar	165.00	200.00	90.00
MgR-75	Demi-tasse	115.00	140.00	80.00
MgR-85	Jam pot	150.00	180.00	95.00
MgR-95	Jug, 5"	375.00	450.00	165.00
MgR-96	Jug, 7"	550.00	635.00	175.00

Cat. No.	Shape	U.S. $	Can. $	U.K. £
MgR-402	Plate, octagonal, 5"	75.00	90.00	45.00
MgR-406	Plate, octagonal, 9"	140.00	170.00	80.00
MgR-407	Plate, octagonal, 10"	165.00	200.00	90.00
MgR-130	Teacup and saucer	115.00	140.00	60.00
MgR-135	Teapot, 2 cup	450.00	540.00	300.00
MgR-136	Teapot, 4 cup	550.00	635.00	400.00
MgR-160	Vase, bud	160.00	195.00	80.00
MgR-163	Vase, spill, 8"	225.00	270.00	120.00
MgR-162	Vase, trumpet 6"	195.00	235.00	95.00
MgR-165	Vase, 9"	325.00	390.00	165.00

"MAUVE CHINTZ"

This pattern was not a controlled pattern and was used by a number of companies. Baker & Company Ltd. used this transfer on plates, bowls and candlesticks but the pattern often appears on pieces without any backstamp. **Mauve Chintz** has never been particularly popular with collectors in North America but has become quite popular in England.

Cat. No.	Shape	U.S. $	Can. $	U.K. £
MC-17	Bowl, lily 12"	100.00	120.00	115.00
MC-22	Bowl, octagonal, 7"	225.00	270.00	165.00
MC-24	Bowl, octagonal, 8"	250.00	300.00	185.00
MC-53	Coffee pot, 3 cup	475.00	570.00	325.00
MC-65	Condiment set	150.00	180.00	125.00
MC-70	Cream and sugar	100.00	120.00	75.00
MC-75	Demi-tasse	50.00	60.00	45.00
MC-85	Jam pot	100.00	120.00	75.00
MC-95	Jug, 5"	150.00	180.00	95.00
MC-96	Jug, 7"	175.00	210.00	135.00

Cat. No.	Shape	U.S. $	Can. $	U.K. £
MC-402	Plate, octagonal, 5"	50.00	60.00	45.00
MC-406	Plate, octagonal, 9"	100.00	120.00	75.00
MC-407	Plate, octagonal, 10"	100.00	120.00	85.00
MC-130	Teacup and saucer	65.00	80.00	50.00
MC-135	Teapot, 2 cup	325.00	390.00	250.00
MC-136	Teapot, 4 cup	400.00	480.00	350.00
MC-160	Vase, bud	100.00	120.00	85.00
MC-163	Vase, spill, 8"	150.00	180.00	110.00
MC-162	Vase, trumpet 6"	125.00	150.00	95.00
MC-165	Vase, 9"	200.00	240.00	150.00

PANSY

This pattern is difficult to find in the United States but more common in Australia and New Zealand. According to the *Pottery Gazette,* November 1938, this pattern was introduced earlier that year. In the A.G. Richardson pattern books, this pattern is recorded as number 6153.

Cat. No.	Shape	U.S. $	Can. $	U.K. £	Cat. No.	Shape	U.S. $	Can. $	U.K. £
PaR-17	Bowl, lily 12"	150.00	180.00	90.00	PaR-402	Plate, octagonal, 5"	75.00	90.00	55.00
PaR-22	Bowl, octagonal, 7"	300.00	360.00	225.00	PaR-406	Plate, octagonal, 9"	150.00	180.00	80.00
PaR-24	Bowl, octagonal, 8"	350.00	420.00	250.00	PaR-407	Plate, octagonal, 10"	185.00	225.00	105.00
PaR-53	Coffee pot, 3 cup	700.00	805.00	380.00	PaR-130	Teacup and saucer	125.00	150.00	65.00
PaR-65	Condiment set	295.00	355.00	150.00	PaR-135	Teapot, 2 cup	500.00	600.00	275.00
PaR-70	Cream and sugar	175.00	210.00	100.00	PaR-136	Teapot, 4 cup	600.00	690.00	350.00
PaR-75	Demi-tasse	125.00	150.00	55.00	PaR-160	Vase, bud	185.00	225.00	85.00
PaR-85	Jam pot	165.00	200.00	80.00	PaR-163	Vase, spill, 8"	250.00	300.00	135.00
PaR-95	Jug, 5"	375.00	450.00	165.00	PaR-162	Vase, trumpet 6"	210.00	255.00	125.00
PaR-96	Jug, 7"	500.00	600.00	195.00	PaR-165	Vase, 9"	395.00	475.00	195.00

PEONY

The pattern number is 5008 and can be dated to 1937. *The Pottery & Glass Record* described the pattern in January 1938: "a very warm colour ensemble in a new chintz engraved pattern, schemed as an all-over pattern of massed roses, with orange dominant, and also reds and yellows softened by shades of greens and greys; stronger combination than the older type of chintz patterns. The pattern was used on "a newly designed bedside set of very good value and acceptable design." This pattern has become very popular in North America.

Cat. No.	Shape	U.S. $	Can. $	U.K. £		Cat. No.	Shape	U.S. $	Can. $	U.K. £
Py-17	Bowl, lily 12"	150.00	180.00	125.00		Py-402	Plate, octagonal, 5"	75.00	90.00	55.00
Py-22	Bowl, octagonal, 7"	350.00	420.00	225.00		Py-406	Plate, octagonal, 9"	155.00	190.00	85.00
Py-24	Bowl, octagonal, 8"	450.00	540.00	290.00		Py-407	Plate, octagonal, 10"	225.00	270.00	125.00
Py-53	Coffee pot, 3 cup	850.00	980.00	450.00		Py-130	Teacup and saucer	165.00	200.00	65.00
Py-65	Condiment set	250.00	300.00	165.00		Py-135	Teapot, 2 cup	500.00	600.00	320.00
Py-70	Cream and sugar	175.00	210.00	120.00		Py-136	Teapot, 4 cup	950.00	1,095.00	375.00
Py-75	Demi-tasse	135.00	165.00	65.00		Py-160	Vase, bud	195.00	235.00	95.00
Py-85	Jam pot	165.00	200.00	90.00		Py-163	Vase, spill, 8"	235.00	285.00	135.00
Py-95	Jug, 5"	450.00	540.00	165.00		Py-162	Vase, trumpet 6"	205.00	250.00	125.00
Py-96	Jug, 7"	550.00	635.00	200.00		Py-165	Vase, 9"	475.00	570.00	195.00

"PINK CHINTZ"

Although little is known about this pattern, **Pink Chintz** appears to have been introduced into the United States in the late 1920s. This pattern has become very popular in North America in the past year.

Cat. No.	Shape	U.S. $	Can. $	U.K. £
PC-17	Bowl, lily 12"	150.00	180.00	95.00
PC-22	Bowl, octagonal, 7"	350.00	420.00	225.00
PC-24	Bowl, octagonal, 8"	450.00	540.00	240.00
PC-53	Coffee pot, 3 cup	800.00	920.00	390.00
PC-65	Condiment set	250.00	300.00	175.00
PC-70	Cream and sugar	175.00	210.00	100.00
PC-75	Demi-tasse	135.00	165.00	65.00
PC-85	Jam pot	165.00	200.00	90.00
PC-95	Jug, 5"	450.00	540.00	165.00
PC-96	Jug, 7"	550.00	635.00	225.00

Cat. No.	Shape	U.S. $	Can. $	U.K. £
PC-402	Plate, octagonal, 5"	75.00	90.00	55.00
PC-406	Plate, octagonal, 9"	155.00	190.00	85.00
PC-407	Plate, octagonal, 10"	225.00	270.00	105.00
PC-130	Teacup and saucer	165.00	200.00	60.00
PC-135	Teapot, 2 cup	500.00	600.00	275.00
PC-136	Teapot, 4 cup	950.00	1,095.00	385.00
PC-160	Vase, bud	195.00	235.00	95.00
PC-163	Vase, spill, 8"	235.00	285.00	150.00
PC-162	Vase, trumpet 6"	205.00	250.00	115.00
PC-165	Vase, 9"	475.00	570.00	195.0 0

PRIMULA

The Pottery & Glass Record describes the 1936 British Industries Fair: "among the newest designs was…a chintz pattern, a soft yet warm note in green and yellow flowers on ivory ground available ensuite." This pattern seems to have been called **Primrose Chintz** as well as **Primula**. This pattern has become popular in England in the past year.

Cat. No.	Shape	U.S. $	Can. $	U.K. £	Cat. No.	Shape	U.S. $	Can. $	U.K. £
PrR-17	Bowl, lily 12"	120.00	145.00	95.00	PrR-402	Plate, octagonal, 5"	65.00	80.00	50.00
PrR-22	Bowl, octagonal, 7"	250.00	300.00	225.00	PrR-406	Plate, octagonal, 9"	100.00	120.00	75.00
PrR-24	Bowl, octagonal, 8"	300.00	360.00	250.00	PrR-407	Plate, octagonal, 10"	125.00	150.00	95.00
PrR-53	Coffee pot, 3 cup	550.00	635.00	375.00	PrR-130	Teacup and saucer	75.00	90.00	75.00
PrR-65	Condiment set	165.00	200.00	150.00	PrR-135	Teapot, 2 cup	375.00	450.00	275.00
PrR-70	Cream and sugar	135.00	165.00	120.00	PrR-136	Teapot, 4 cup	475.00	570.00	375.00
PrR-75	Demi-tasse	95.00	115.00	75.00	PrR-160	Vase, bud	135.00	165.00	80.00
PrR-85	Jam pot	135.00	165.00	95.00	PrR-163	Vase, spill, 8"	165.00	200.00	120.00
PrR-95	Jug, 5"	225.00	270.00	150.00	PrR-162	Vase, trumpet 6"	145.00	175.00	90.00
PrR-96	Jug, 7"	250.00	300.00	175.00	PrR-165	Vase, 9"	225.00	270.00	165.00

PRISCILLA

In the A.G. Richardson pattern books this pattern is recorded in June 1940 as pattern number 6150. It is favorably mentioned in the *Pottery Gazette* in April, 1941 and described as "an all-over chintz in pink apple blossom applied to a delicate buff ground, and broken up by small white speedwell flower heads."

Cat. No.	Shape	U.S. $	Can. $	U.K. £
Ps-17	Bowl, lily 12"	100.00	120.00	75.00
Ps-22	Bowl, octagonal, 7"	250.00	300.00	165.00
Ps-24	Bowl, octagonal, 8"	300.00	360.00	190.00
Ps-53	Coffee pot, 3 cup	525.00	605.00	325.00
Ps-65	Condiment set	150.00	180.00	100.00
Ps-70	Cream and sugar	115.00	140.00	75.00
Ps-75	Demi-tasse	75.00	90.00	60.00
Ps-85	Jam pot	115.00	140.00	85.00
Ps-95	Jug, 5"	200.00	240.00	95.00
Ps-96	Jug, 7"	250.00	300.00	115.00

Cat. No.	Shape	U.S. $	Can. $	U.K. £
Ps-402	Plate, octagonal, 5"	65.00	80.00	45.00
Ps-406	Plate, octagonal, 9"	100.00	120.00	65.00
Ps-407	Plate, octagonal, 10"	125.00	150.00	75.00
Ps-130	Teacup and saucer	75.00	90.00	55.00
Ps-135	Teapot, 2 cup	375.00	450.00	250.00
Ps-136	Teapot, 4 cup	450.00	540.00	275.00
Ps-160	Vase, bud	125.00	150.00	85.00
Ps-163	Vase, spill, 8"	165.00	200.00	115.00
Ps-162	Vase, trumpet 6"	135.00	165.00	90.00
Ps-165	Vase, 9"	225.00	270.00	175.00

"PURPLE CHINTZ"

This is one of the most popular Crown Ducal chintzes in the United States.

Cat. No.	Shape	U.S. $	Can. $	U.K. £
PuC-17	Bowl, lily 12"	150.00	180.00	125.00
PuC-22	Bowl, octagonal, 7"	375.00	450.00	275.00
PuC-24	Bowl, octagonal, 8"	425.00	510.00	295.00
PuC-53	Coffee pot, 3 cup	800.00	920.00	600.00
PuC-65	Condiment set	295.00	355.00	195.00
PuC-70	Cream and sugar	175.00	210.00	140.00
PuC-75	Demi-tasse	125.00	150.00	85.00
PuC-85	Jam pot	165.00	200.00	95.00
PuC-95	Jug, 5"	375.00	450.00	195.00
PuC-96	Jug, 7"	475.00	570.00	250.00

Cat. No.	Shape	U.S. $	Can. $	U.K. £
PuC-402	Plate, octagonal, 5"	100.00	120.00	75.00
PuC-406	Plate, octagonal, 9"	150.00	180.00	95.00
PuC-407	Plate, octagonal, 10"	175.00	210.00	145.00
PuC-130	Teacup and saucer	125.00	150.00	85.00
PuC-135	Teapot, 2 cup	550.00	635.00	375.00
PuC-136	Teapot, 4 cup	650.00	750.00	475.00
PuC-160	Vase, bud	195.00	235.00	120.00
PuC-163	Vase, spill, 8"	250.00	300.00	195.00
PuC-162	Vase, trumpet 6"	220.00	265.00	150.00
PuC-165	Vase, 9"	400.00	480.00	250.00

ROSE & MOTIFS

This was one of the earliest Crown Ducal chintzes and was introduced in 1918. It has been found on vases and toiletware only and rarely in North America.

Cat. No.	Shape	U.S. $	Can. $	U.K. £
RM-95	Jug, 5"	275.00	330.00	225.00
RM-96	Jug, 7"	325.00	390.00	240.00
RM-160	Vase, bud	150.00	180.00	125.00

Cat. No.	Shape	U.S. $	Can. $	U.K. £
RM-163	Vase, spill, 8"	250.00	300.00	225.00
RM-162	Vase, trumpet 6"	225.00	270.00	185.00
RM-165	Vase, 9"	350.00	420.00	275.00

"SPRING BLOSSOM"

This pattern is in the A.G. Richardson pattern books as pattern number 3271 with a note to see 1185 (**Blue Chintz**). Looking at the sequence of pattern numbers would suggest that this pattern dates to 1933. We have named this pattern without the bird **Spring Blossom**. It tends to sell for less than the **Blue Chintz**. Other manufacturers, including Elijah Cotton, used this pattern.

Cat. No.	Shape	U.S. $	Can. $	U.K. £
SB-17	Bowl, lily 12"	135.00	165.00	85.00
SB-22	Bowl, octagonal, 7"	250.00	300.00	195.00
SB-24	Bowl, octagonal, 8"	300.00	360.00	225.00
SB-53	Coffee pot, 3 cup	550.00	635.00	375.00
SB-65	Condiment set	175.00	210.00	140.00
SB-70	Cream and sugar	115.00	140.00	90.00
SB-75	Demi-tasse	85.00	105.00	60.00
SB-85	Jam pot	110.00	135.00	95.00
SB-95	Jug, 5"	225.00	270.00	165.00
SB-96	Jug, 7"	300.00	360.00	175.00

Cat. No.	Shape	U.S. $	Can. $	U.K. £
SB-402	Plate, octagonal, 5"	65.00	80.00	45.00
SB-406	Plate, octagonal, 9"	105.00	125.00	75.00
SB-407	Plate, octagonal, 10"	125.00	150.00	85.00
SB-130	Teacup and saucer	95.00	115.00	55.00
SB-135	Teapot, 2 cup	375.00	450.00	275.00
SB-136	Teapot, 4 cup	475.00	570.00	350.00
SB-160	Vase, bud	135.00	165.00	90.00
SB-163	Vase, spill, 8"	175.00	210.00	120.00
SB-162	Vase, trumpet 6"	150.00	180.00	115.00
SB-165	Vase, 9"	235.00	285.00	150.00

Laurie's Glories

Dealer in Rare Chintz

*We specialize
in those
hard-to-find
chintzware
pieces*

*Antiques
& Collectibles*

LAURIE'S GLORIES
P.O. Box 853, McLean
Virginia, 22101, U.S.A
Tel.: 703-790-5377

RIDGWAY POTTERIES LTD.

The firm was founded in 1866 at the Bedford Works in Shelton by Edward John Ridgway and produced both fine and utility earthenwares. The firm had a variety of names and partnerships through the first half of the twentieth century and by 1955 the firm had eight different works in Staffordshire, including Colcloughs and Booths. Ridgway Potteries Ltd. now operates under the Royal Doulton umbrella.

UNKNOWN

In 1953 Portland Pottery, Cobridge was taken over by Ridgway and this chintz pattern sometimes appears with a Portland Pottery, Cobridge backstamp.

Cat. No.	Shape	U.S. $	Can. $	U.K. £
RP-78	Egg cup, large	95.00	115.00	65.00
RP-93	Jug, 6"	300.00	360.00	225.00

Cat. No.	Shape	U.S. $	Can. $	U.K. £
RP-106	Plate, 9"	150.00	180.00	115.00

ROYAL DOULTON LTD.

Doulton & Company manufactured drainpipes in the mid-nineteenth century, and from that beginning a huge company has grown which today encompasses Royal Crown Derby, Minton, Shelley, Beswick, Royal Albert and many more. The firm opened their present-day works on Nile Street in Burslem in 1882. The only all-over transfer which might be of interest to chintz collectors was produced in several versions by Royal Doulton around 1913 and was called **Persian**. It was a forerunner of the patterns produced by A.G. Richardson some five years later. The pattern was used on a wide variety of pieces including candle sticks, octagon shape tea set, rack plates and cabinet pieces. The pattern continued in production until approximately 1940.

PERSIAN

This is an early chintz-type pattern and not yet collected by enough chintz collectors to establish a market. This pattern also came in another colourway called **Blue Persian**.

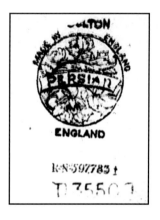

Cat. No.	Shape	U.S. $	Can. $	U.K. £
Per-107	Plate, 10"	145.00	175.00	95.00

Cat. No.	Shape	U.S. $	Can. $	U.K. £
Per-145	Tennis Set	135.00	165.00	110.00

SHELLEY POTTERIES LTD.

In 1853 Henry Wileman became a partner in Foley Potteries and three years later built Foley China Works. Joseph Shelley became a partner in 1872, and the name changed to Wileman & Co. By 1884 Wileman had gone and the firm became a Shelley family business. Although the Shelley backstamp was introduced as early as 1910 it was not until 1925 that Wileman & Co. became Shelley Potteries.

Shelley produced an extraordinary range of teawares in a range of shapes and decorative techniques. Although Colley Shorter and Clarice Cliff were excellent at self promotion, Shelley Potteries are the outstanding example of a firm who not only survived but thrived in the desperate 1930s through the skillful use of advertising. They not only produced remarkable advertisements, they printed large numbers of beautifully illustrated catalogues which were supplied free-of-charge to retailers for distribution to customers. Mr. Norman Shelley, in a 1938 interview with *The Pottery & Glass Record,* suggested that other potteries could increase sales by doing the same.

According to Susan Hill's book, some of the all-over transfers such as **Cloisonne** were used by Shelley as seconds patterns and applied to ware which did not meet the factory's high standards. Patterns like **Maytime** and **Melody** however, were offered on a wide range of wares and were advertised first in the 1930s. These patterns were produced on earthenware before the second world war and on bone china following the war. Shelley stopped producing earthenware after the war and as a result the other Shelley chintz patterns appear only on bone china. . The rarest of the Shelley chintzes is

the black or multi chintz and closely resembles the Royal Winton black background chintzes.The pattern numbers for most of these chintzes range from 13300 to 14300 which means they were sold from about 1942 until 1962. Chris Davenport, a researcher on-post-war Shelley, told us that the last chintz pattern was 14341 and was produced on the 18th of May,1964. The chintz patterns were used particularly on teacups and the variations of pattern are endless. Some cups have pattern inside, some outside, some have pattern only on the center of the saucer, some just around the outside. I am told by Curt Leiser of the National Shelley Club that a Shelley pattern is a combination of the litho, portion of the piece over which the litho was applied, the edge trim, handle colour and cup shape. Shelley chintz collectors sometimes specialize in different shapes of cup and variations of pattern. Since collectors will pay a premium for a chintz Ripon shape cup and saucer I have added this as well as the Oleander to the shapes. I have also added a 6 inch plate since many Shelley collectors buy trios cup, saucer and 6 inch plate. There is page after page of chintz in the Shelley pattern books and it is amazing that so little has been written about them. Chris Davenport's book on post war Shelley has added greatly to the information available to Shelley chintz collectors and I am told Kelly Moran's book on Shelley Chintz is in process.

The Shelley family remained in the business until 1966, when the company was taken over by Allied English Potteries. The owners of Allied acquired Doulton & Company in 1971, and the companies merged to form Royal Doulton Tableware Ltd.

BLACK CHINTZ

This pattern is the most difficult of all the Shelley chintzes to find. Shelley collectors tell me they have only seen this pattern on a cup and saucer. I have included it here so that collectors will know what they have if they are lucky enough to happen on a piece.

Cat. No.	Shape	U.S. $	Can. $	U.K. £
BD-130	Teacup and saucer		RARE	

Cat. No.	Shape	U.S. $	Can. $	U.K. £

BLUE DAISY

This pattern is one of the most common of the Shelley chintzes with at least twelve different patterns known to have this litho applied. A Shelley pattern is a combination of the litho, portion of the piece over which the litho was applied, the edge trim, handle colour and cup shape.. This pattern was also produced with a green background. See **Green Daisy.**

Cat. No.	Shape	U.S. $	Can. $	U.K. £
BD-01	Ashtray, small	60.00	75.00	50.00
BD-02	Ashtray, large	85.00	105.00	80.00
BD-04	Bonbon dish	55.00	70.00	50.00
BD-05	Bonbon dish, tab handles	55.00	70.00	50.00
BD-36	Cake plate	160.00	195.00	120.00
BD-55	Coffee pot, 6 cup	210.00	255.00	195.00
BD-70	Cream and sugar	105.00	125.00	80.00

Cat. No.	Shape	U.S. $	Can. $	U.K. £
BD-98	Pin tray, small	65.00	80.00	65.00
BD-102	Plate, 6"	60.00	75.00	50.00
BD-105	Plate, 8"	70.00	85.00	55.00
BD-130	Teacup and saucer	90.00	110.00	75.00
BD-131	Teacup/saucer, Oleander	110.00	135.00	85.00
BD-132	Teacup and saucer, Ripon	100.00	120.00	80.00
BD-137	Teapot, 6 cup	315.00	380.00	250.00

CLOISONNE

According to Susan Hill's book on Shelley, **Cloisonne** was a seconds pattern, used to disguise imperfect china but Shelley collectors say they have seen it on Shelley Ideal china as well. This pattern also comes with a bright blue background but the blue ground has been seen only on pottery vases, bowls, pots and the like. This litho was used by other companies including John Shaw & Sons Burlington Ware.

Cat. No.	Shape	U.S. $	Can. $	U.K. £
Clo-01	Ashtray, small	60.00	75.00	55.00
Clo-02	Ashtray, large	90.00	110.00	80.00
Clo-04	Bonbon dish	55.00	70.00	55.00
Clo-05	Bonbon dish, tab handles	55.00	70.00	45.00
Clo-36	Cake plate	160.00	195.00	120.00
Clo-55	Coffee pot, 6 cup	220.00	265.00	175.00

Cat. No.	Shape	U.S. $	Can. $	U.K. £
Clo-70	Cream and sugar	105.00	125.00	65.00
Clo-98	Pin tray, small	65.00	80.00	55.00
Clo-102	Plate, 6"	60.00	75.00	45.00
Clo-104	Plate, 8"	70.00	85.00	55.00
Clo-130	Teacup and saucer	85.00	105.00	70.00
Clo-137	Teapot, 6 cup	330.00	400.00	250.00

COUNTRYSIDE

This pattern is listed as produced on four different Shelley shapes but it is rare in North America.

Cat. No.	Shape	U.S. $	Can. $	U.K. £
Cs-01	Ashtray, small	105.00	125.00	75.00
Cs-02	Ashtray, large	115.00	140.00	95.00
Cs-04	Bonbon dish	85.00	105.00	85.00
Cs-05	Bonbon dish, tab handles	85.00	105.00	75.00
Cs-36	Cake plate	230.00	280.00	160.00
Cs-55	Coffee pot, 6 cup	495.00	595.00	375.00
Cs-70	Cream and sugar	165.00	200.00	120.00

Cat. No.	Shape	U.S. $	Can. $	U.K. £
Cs-98	Pin tray, small	100.00	120.00	80.00
Cs-102	Plate, 6"	95.00	115.00	65.00
Cs-105	Plate, 8"	105.00	125.00	75.00
Cs-130	Teacup and saucer	135.00	165.00	115.00
Cs-131	Teacup/saucer, Oleander	165.00	200.00	135.00
Cs-132	Teacup and saucer, Ripon	150.00	180.00	125.00
Cs-137	Teapot, 6 cup	525.00	605.00	395.00

GREEN DAISY

This pattern does not appear as often in North America as the other colourway **Blue Daisy** and it is sometimes confused with **Marguerite**.

Cat. No.	Shape	U.S. $	Can. $	U.K. £
GD-01	Ashtray, small	60.00	75.00	50.00
GD-02	Ashtray, large	85.00	105.00	65.00
GD-04	Bonbon dish	55.00	70.00	60.00
GD-05	Bonbon dish, tab handles	55.00	70.00	60.00
GD-36	Cake plate	160.00	195.00	120.00
GD-55	Coffee pot, 6 cup	210.00	255.00	175.00
GD-70	Cream and sugar	105.00	125.00	85.00

Cat. No.	Shape	U.S. $	Can. $	U.K. £
GD-98	Pin tray, small	65.00	80.00	65.00
GD-102	Plate, 6"	60.00	75.00	55.00
GD-105	Plate, 8"	70.00	85.00	65.00
GD-130	Teacup and saucer	90.00	110.00	85.00
GD-131	Teacup/saucer, Oleander	110.00	135.00	120.00
GD-132	Teacup and saucer, Ripon	100.00	120.00	110.00
GD-137	Teapot, 6 cup	325.00	390.00	250.00

MARGUERITE

This pattern was available on five different shapes but it is still difficult to find in North America.

Cat. No.	Shape	U.S. $	Can. $	U.K. £
MS-01	Ashtray, small	65.00	80.00	55.00
MS-02	Ashtray, large	95.00	115.00	85.00
MS-04	Bonbon dish	60.00	75.00	65.00
MS-05	Bonbon dish, tab handles	60.00	75.00	65.00
MS-36	Cake plate	175.00	210.00	150.00
MS-55	Coffee pot, 6 cup	300.00	360.00	275.00
MS-70	Cream and sugar	120.00	145.00	85.00

Cat. No.	Shape	U.S. $	Can. $	U.K. £
MS-98	Pin tray, small	70.00	85.00	65.00
MS-102	Plate, 6"	70.00	85.00	55.00
MS-105	Plate, 8"	80.00	100.00	65.00
MS-130	Teacup and saucer	100.00	120.00	80.00
MS-131	Teacup/saucer, Oleander	120.00	145.00	115.00
MS-132	Teacup and saucer, Ripon	110.00	135.00	105.00
MS-137	Teapot, 6 cup	385.00	465.00	250.00

MAYTIME

This pattern was very popular and appears on a great variety of shapes produced in earthenware prior to the Second World War. **Maytime** is mentioned in a report on Shelley in the September 1938 *Pottery & Glass Record*: "Another very good selling line is **Maytime**, which is a bright May Blossom decoration and gives a chintz effect which harmonizes perfectly with soft furnishings. It might be mentioned that the **Maytime** decoration is now being applied with great success to fancy lines…it also looks bright and cheerful on such necessities as toast racks, biscuit barrels, triple trays and cruet sets." **Maytime** was produced only in bone china following the war.

Cat. No.	Shape	U.S. $	Can. $	U.K. £	Cat. No.	Shape	U.S. $	Can. $	U.K. £
Mat-01	Ashtray, small	90.00	110.00	70.00	Mat-98	Pin tray, small	85.00	105.00	80.00
Mat-02	Ashtray, large	100.00	120.00	85.00	Mat-102	Plate, 6"	80.00	100.00	75.00
Mat-04	Bonbon dish	75.00	90.00	70.00	Mat-105	Plate, 8"	95.00	115.00	85.00
Mat-05	Bonbon dish, tab handles	75.00	90.00	75.00	Mat-130	Teacup and saucer	125.00	150.00	95.00
Mat-36	Cake plate	210.00	255.00	135.00	Mat-131	Teacup/saucer, Oleander	145.00	175.00	125.00
Mat-55	Coffee pot, 6 cup	475.00	570.00	395.00	Mat-132	Teacup and saucer, Ripon	135.00	165.00	115.00
Mat-70	Cream and sugar	150.00	180.00	115.00	Mat-137	Teapot, 6 cup	425.00	510.00	300.00

MELODY

"The colouring and pattern makes an instant appeal and gives a pleasure that increases on its daily appearance."(*Pottery Gazette*, 1940). This pattern appears on more shapes than any other Shelley chintz and it is the most popular in North America. **Melody** was produced in earthenware prior to the Second World War and in bone china following the war.

Cat. No.	Shape	U.S. $	Can. $	U.K. £
Me-01	Ashtray, small	105.00	125.00	80.00
Me-02	Ashtray, large	115.00	140.00	85.00
Me-04	Bonbon dish	80.00	100.00	65.00
Me-05	Bonbon dish, tab handles	80.00	100.00	70.00
Me-36	Cake plate	210.00	255.00	165.00
Me-55	Coffee pot, 6 cup	475.00	570.00	425.00
Me-70	Cream and sugar	160.00	195.00	125.00

Cat. No.	Shape	U.S. $	Can. $	U.K. £
Me-98	Pin tray, small	95.00	115.00	65.00
Me-102	Plate, 6"	95.00	115.00	65.00
Me-105	Plate, 8"	105.00	125.00	75.00
Me-130	Teacup and saucer	135.00	165.00	115.00
Me-131	Teacup/ saucer, Oleander	165.00	200.00	165.00
Me-132	Teacup and saucer, Ripon	150.00	180.00	150.00
Me-137	Teapot, 6 cup	525.00	605.00	400.00

PINK SUMMER GLORY

This pattern is the pink colourway of **Summer Glory** and is found with that back stamp, although a 1964 Edward Walker Company sales catalogue calls the pattern **Pink Clover**. (I am now calling the pattern **Pink Summer Glory** at the request of a number of Shelley chintz collectors) This is one of the most popular Shelley chintzes in North America and found more often than the other colourway. See **Summer Glory.**

Cat. No.	Shape	U.S. $	Can. $	U.K. £
PiSG-01	Ashtray, small	100.00	120.00	75.00
PiSG-02	Ashtray, large	105.00	125.00	75.00
PiSG-04	Bonbon dish	80.00	100.00	65.00
PiSG-05	Bonbon dish, tab handles	80.00	100.00	65.00
PiSG-36	Cake plate	235.00	285.00	175.00
PiSG-55	Coffee pot, 6 cup	525.00	605.00	375.00
PiSG-70	Cream and sugar	160.00	195.00	125.00

Cat. No.	Shape	U.S. $	Can. $	U.K. £
PiSG-98	Pin tray, small	100.00	120.00	75.00
PiSG-102	Plate, 6"	95.00	115.00	65.00
PiSG-105	Plate, 8"	105.00	125.00	75.00
PiSG-130	Teacup and saucer	135.00	165.00	95.00
PiSG-131	Teacup/saucer, Oleander	160.00	195.00	125.00
PiSG-132	Teacup and saucer, Ripon	145.00	175.00	115.00
PiSG-137	Teapot, 6 cup	550.00	635.00	400.00

PRIMROSE

This pattern appears on more cup shapes than any other Shelley chintz but is not particularly popular with American collectors. The cup typically has a pink handle and a light yellow interior.

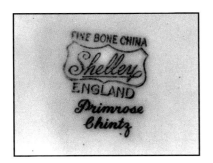

Cat. No.	Shape	U.S. $	Can. $	U.K. £
Pri-01	Ashtray, small	70.00	85.00	55.00
Pri-02	Ashtray, large	90.00	110.00	75.00
Pri-04	Bonbon dish	65.00	80.00	65.00
Pri-05	Bonbon dish, tab handles	65.00	80.00	65.00
Pri-36	Cake plate	175.00	210.00	125.00
Pri-55	Coffee pot, 6 cup	350.00	420.00	295.00
Pri-70	Cream and sugar	135.00	165.00	95.00

Cat. No.	Shape	U.S. $	Can. $	U.K. £
Pri-98	Pin tray, small	80.00	100.00	65.00
Pri-102	Plate, 6"	70.00	85.00	55.00
Pri-105	Plate, 8"	80.00	100.00	65.00
Pri-130	Teacup and saucer	100.00	120.00	85.00
Pri-131	Teacup/ saucer, Oleander	135.00	165.00	120.00
Pri-132	Teacup and saucer, Ripon	120.00	145.00	110.00
Pri-137	Teapot, 6 cup	400.00	480.00	295.00

ROCK GARDEN

This pattern is difficult to find in England and it is considered one of the most desirable chintz patterns to Shelley collectors.

Cat. No.	Shape	U.S. $	Can. $	U.K. £
RG-01	Ashtray, small	105.00	125.00	75.00
RG-02	Ashtray, large	125.00	150.00	85.00
RG-04	Bonbon dish	85.00	105.00	75.00
RG-05	Bonbon dish, tab handles	85.00	105.00	75.00
RG-36	Cake plate	215.00	260.00	150.00
RG-55	Coffee pot, 6 cup	475.00	570.00	350.00
RG-70	Cream and sugar	160.00	195.00	125.00

Cat. No.	Shape	U.S. $	Can. $	U.K. £
RG-98	Pin tray, small	105.00	125.00	85.00
RG-102	Plate, 6"	105.00	125.00	80.00
RG-105	Plate, 8"	115.00	140.00	90.00
RG-130	Teacup and saucer	135.00	165.00	125.00
RG-131	Teacup/saucer, Oleander	160.00	195.00	140.00
RG-132	Teacup and saucer, Ripon	145.00	175.00	125.00
RG-137	Teapot, 6 cup	575.00	665.00	395.00

SUMMER GLORY

This pattern is very popular with North American Shelley chintz collectors. See **Pink Summer Glory** for the alternate colourway.

Cat. No.	Shape	U.S. $	Can. $	U.K. £
SuG-01	Ashtray, small	90.00	110.00	60.00
SuG-02	Ashtray, large	100.00	120.00	75.00
SuG-04	Bonbon dish	75.00	90.00	55.00
SuG-05	Bonbon dish, tab handles	75.00	90.00	65.00
SuG-36	Cake plate	195.00	235.00	140.00
SuG-55	Coffee pot, 6 cup	475.00	570.00	350.00
SuG-70	Cream and sugar	150.00	180.00	90.00

Cat. No.	Shape	U.S. $	Can. $	U.K. £
SuG-98	Pin tray, small	90.00	110.00	65.00
SuG-102	Plate, 6"	85.00	105.00	65.00
SuG-105	Plate, 8"	95.00	115.00	75.00
SuG-130	Teacup and saucer	125.00	150.00	85.00
SuG-131	Teacup/saucer, Oleander	155.00	190.00	125.00
SuG-132	Teacup and saucer, Ripon	140.00	170.00	115.00
SuG-137	Teapot, 6 cup	500.00	600.00	375.00

TAPESTRY ROSE

This pattern is one of the later Shelley chintzes and does not appear to have been widely used on different shapes. The pattern came in two colourways, burgundy and yellow. The burgundy colourway has gone up dramatically in the past two years. The yellow background sells for about 20% less than the burgundy.

Cat. No.	Shape	U.S. $	Can. $	U.K. £
TR-01	Ashtray, small	95.00	115.00	40.00
TR-02	Ashtray, large	140.00	170.00	55.00
TR-04	Bonbon dish	70.00	85.00	55.00
TR-05	Bonbon dish, tab handles	70.00	85.00	55.00
TR-36	Cake plate	250.00	300.00	125.00
TR-55	Coffee pot, 6 cup	350.00	420.00	140.00
TR-70	Cream and sugar	175.00	210.00	70.00

Cat. No.	Shape	U.S. $	Can. $	U.K. £
TR-98	Pin tray, small	135.00	165.00	60.00
TR-102	Plate, 6"	105.00	125.00	45.00
TR-105	Plate, 8"	115.00	140.00	50.00
TR-130	Teacup and saucer	135.00	165.00	75.00
TR-131	Teacup/ saucer, Oleander	175.00	210.00	120.00
TR-132	Teacup and saucer, Ripon	150.00	180.00	110.00
TR-137	Teapot, 6 cup	540.00	625.00	225.00

WADE CERAMICS LTD.

The original company was founded in 1810 and made pottery fittings for shuttles and textile machinery. The firm was bought by George Wade just after the turn of the century. In 1938 the Wade Heath & Company was moved to a new location at Royal Victoria Pottery in Burslem. The Wade Group of Potteries came into existence in the mid 1950s; prior to that time there were a number of individually owned companies with members of the Wade family or their friends in control. At the Wade factories, there was a book of rules; it quoted their belief that efficiency and happiness went hand in hand. The only all-over pattern that Wade appears to have done in the 1920s was the open stock **Paisley** pattern used by many other companies, including Grimwades. In the 1950s the Wade Group offered two chintz patterns among a group of 18 transfer-type patterns available in tea ware and dinnerware on the Orb shape.

The Wade Groups combination of giftwares and industrial products, such as gas refactories and high alumina bodies used in micro-electronic and nuclear fields, have helped them to survive through several recessions in the pottery industry. The Wade Potteries were renamed in the late 1980s and they are still in production today under the name Wade Ceramics.

BUTTERFLY CHINTZ

This pattern was one of two chintz patterns available on a complete range of tablewares in the mid 1950s. This pattern is not easily found but has become more popular in the last couple of years.

Cat. No.	Shape	U.S. $	Can. $	U.K. £
Bu-70	Cream and sugar	100.00	120.00	65.00
Bu-103	Plate, 6"	75.00	90.00	45.00

Cat. No.	Shape	U.S. $	Can. $	U.K. £
Bu-104	Plate, 7"	95.00	115.00	55.00
Bu-130	Teacup and saucer	100.00	120.00	65.00

PAISLEY

This pattern was also produced by Grimwades Ltd. **Paisley** is often sought after by Wade collectors rather than Chintz collectors.

Cat. No.	Shape	U.S. $	Can. $	U.K. £	Cat. No.	Shape	U.S. $	Can. $	U.K. £
Pai-103	Plate, 6"	60.00	75.00	45.00	Pai-130	Teacup and saucer	75.00	90.00	65.00
Pai-104	Plate, 7"	75.00	90.00	60.00					

THISTLE CHINTZ

This pattern was one of two chintz patterns available on a complete range of tablewares in the mid 1950s.

Cat. No.	Shape	U.S. $	Can. $	U.K. £
Th-103	Plate, 6"	60.00	75.00	45.00
Th-104	Plate, 7"	75.00	90.00	55.00

Cat. No.	Shape	U.S. $	Can. $	U.K. £
Th-130	Teacup and saucer	85.00	105.00	60.00

WEDGWOOD & COMPANY LTD.

The firm was formerly Podmore, Walker & Co. but renamed Wedgwood & Company in 1860. They were housed at the Unicorn and Pinnox Works in Tunstall and as a result, a number of the backstamps over the years have included a unicorn. They were an undistinguished firm who produced a broad range of domestic earthenware. In 1932 they launched a new shape called Farnol which was almost an exact copy of the Shelley's Eve shape. In similar fashion they produced several chintzes in the thirties, several years after the leading firms had established the market. The firm was renamed Enoch Wedgwood (Tunstall) Ltd. in 1965. Ironically they acquired A.G. Richardson & Company in 1974 only to be taken over in their turn by the Wedgwood Group in 1980 and renamed the Unicorn Pottery.

UNKNOWN

This pattern probably dates to about 1936 since both the Wedgwood chintzes were found on the same page in the Capper Rataud pattern books along with several of the Royal Winton chintzes dating to the middle of the 1930s.

Cat. No.	Shape	U.S. $	Can. $	U.K. £
WC1-120	Sandwich Tray	165.00	200.00	120.00
WC1-130	Teacup and saucer	75.00	90.00	60.00

Cat. No.	Shape	U.S. $	Can. $	U.K. £
WC1-205	Plate, 8"	110.00	135.00	80.00

UNKNOWN

This pattern probably dates to about 1936 since both the Wedgwood chintzes were found on the same page in the Capper Rataud pattern books along with several of the Royal Winton chintzes dating to the middle of the 1930s.

Cat. No.	Shape	U.S. $	Can. $	U.K. £
WC2-120	Sandwich Tray	165.00	200.00	120.00
WC2-130	Teacup and saucer	75.00	90.00	55.00

Cat. No.	Shape	U.S. $	Can. $	U.K. £
WC2-205	Plate, 8"	105.00	125.00	75.00

"Lorna Doone"

A New Wilkinson production of
superb colour and charm . . .

A. J. WILKINSON LTD

ROYAL STAFFORDSHIRE POTTERY : NEWPORT POTTERY : BURSLEM

A. J. WILKINSON, LTD.

Arthur J. Wilkinson set up his earthenware factory in Burslem in 1885. His brother-in-law Arthur Shorter had some years before started a factory in Stoke-upon-Trent. When, six years later, Wilkinson fell to his death while on holiday in Switzerland, Shorter was appointed to manage the Burslem factory. Three years later he bought the firm of A. J. Wilkinson. Around the turn of the century, his son Colley was sent to Wilkinsons and shortly thereafter his second son Guy went to Shorter & Sons. Wilkinsons became known for medium priced earthenwares which were marketed under the name of Royal Staffordshire and included a full range of tablewares, toilet ware and ornamental lines. An early mention of the firm in *The Pottery Gazette* April 2, 1917 commended them for their enterprise and concluded that A.J. Wilkinson have been successful in securing some superior specimens of litho work for their dinnerware. They show several pictures of an early chintz called **Rose and Trellis** which is very like the A.G. Richardson and Grimwades chintzes of the same period. In 1919 Wilkinson are mentioned in the *Glass Trade Review* as "makers of a grade of earthenware which plays a very definite part in the middle-class trade, not only of our own country merely, but in the majority of the leading export markets of the world."

In 1926 Wilkinson were reported to claim to have one of the most representative ranges in the trade of useful and decorative earthenware. At the same time as Clarice Cliff was beginning to handpaint visible brush strokes of orange and blue paint on a warehouse full of abandoned ware at the Newport Pottery (bought by Wilkinson in 1920), *The Gazette* was commending the firm for "the **Mayflower** chintz which we should regard as a good provincial or suburban line. We do not suggest that it will sell briskly in the city, though one never knows." As the twenties continued and Clarice's work was eagerly sought around the country, more and more of the resources of the firm went in the direction of handpainted deco ceramics. Whenever one thinks of Wilkinsons today it is immediately Clarice Cliff who comes to mind, although they produced a number of interesting chintzes as part of their overall line.

The strangest designs are the combination of the very modern Clarice shape like the cup on the artists palette tray with a traditional chintz although **Modern Mayflower** is clearly an attempt to update the 1920s **Mayflower.** The 1950s versions of some of the chintzes are a startling attempt to find a new way to attract buyers once it became clear that post-war housewives were looking for something different.

In 1964 Clarice Cliff sold A.J. Wilkinson and Newport Pottery to W.R. Midwinter and in 1970 the combined firm was taken over by the Wedgwood Group.

MAYFLOWER

The first appearance of this pattern was numbered 7929. The September 1, 1926 Gazette reported that, "one of the finest lithographic patterns which has been put on the market for some time as regards effect and colouring is probably the Mayflower pattern, which the firm under notice brought out last spring . . . the effect of the lithograph itself is to portray a feeling of brushwork and extension, the design being intended to create an impression of a meadow in Maytime." This pattern was also used by Grimwades on a patented cube teapot, also around 1926, and the pattern name **Mayflower** was actually in the backstamp. This is the first example I have seen of the same litho being given the same name by two different factories. The Paragon China Company also used this pattern on bone china and called it **Springtime**.

Cat. No.	Shape	U.S. $	Can. $	U.K. £
Maf-405	Plate, 8" octagonal	125.00	150.00	55.00
Maf-120	Sandwich Tray	175.00	210.00	90.00

Cat. No.	Shape	U.S. $	Can. $	U.K. £
Maf-145	Tennis Set	110.00	135.00	75.00

MODERN MAYFLOWER

Although little is known about this pattern to date, it seems to be an updated version of **Mayflower** and it appears on modern 1950s shapes and has a Royal Staffordshire Ceramics backstamp associated with the 1950s. The bright oranges and modern look make it unpopular with traditional chintz collectors.

Cat. No.	Shape	U.S. $	Can. $	U.K. £
MM-405	Plate, 8" octagonal	65.00	80.00	45.00
MM-120	Sandwich Tray	115.00	140.00	75.00

Cat. No.	Shape	U.S. $	Can. $	U.K. £
MM-145	Tennis Set	85.00	105.00	65.00

GRIMWADES LTD. :: STOKE-ON-TRENT

(Incorporating Rubian Art Pottery & Atlas China)

Royal Winton
"Gera"
No. 2209.

A most attractive adaptation in strong relief of the popular Geranium Foliage and Flower in natural colours with an appropriate Rustic background.

This design is made in three distinct colourings other than the illustration. It is impossible to describe them, but small sample pieces can be supplied.

PRICE LIST.

Item No.		Price
1.	Cheese	21/- per doz.
2.	Toast-Rack, 3 bar	12/6 ,, ,,
	Also 5 bar	16/- ,, ,,
3.	Sugar, 4" diameter	16/- per doz. pairs.
4.	Cream, 6½ ozs. capacity	
5.	Covered Butter	21/- per doz.
6.	Mint Boat and Stand	12/- ,, ,,
7.	Marmalade and Stand	21/- ,, ,,
8.	Cup and Saucer, tea size	12/- ,, ,,
	Also Tea Plate (See Illustration No. 14)	6/6 ,, ,,
9.	Cake Comport, 8¾" diameter, 2" high ...	33/- ,, ,,
10.	3 Compartment Tray	33/- ,, ,,
11.	Twin Tray	18/- ,, ,,
12.	Sweet, 6" diameter	10/- ,, ,,
	,, 7" ,, ...	12/- ,, ,,
	,, 8" ,, ...	15/- ,, ,,
	Shallow Fruit (same shape as illustration No. 12, but 9½" diameter)	24/- ,, ,,
13.	Dessert Plate, 8" diameter	14/- ,, ,,
14.	Tea or Sandwich Plate, 6½" diameter ...	6/6 ,, ,,

Item No.		Price
15.	Covered Jug, 23 ozs. capacity	24/- per doz.
16.	Teapot, 33 ozs. capacity	33/- ,, ,,
	Also Teapot Stand	10/- ,, ,,
17.	Condiment Set (Salt and Pepper on Tray) ...	15/- ,, ,,
18.	Salad Bowl, 9½" diameter	33/- ,, ,,
	And Salad Servers	15/- doz. pairs
19.	Cruet Set, 3 pieces on Tray	21/- per doz.
20.	Sandwich Tray, 12½" × 7"	30/- ,, ,,
	Sandwich Set, 7 pieces	5/9 per set
	Comprising :—1 Tray as No. 20	
	6 Plates as No. 14	
21.	Sugar Sifter	15/- per doz.
22.	Cake Plate, handled	24/- ,, ,,
	Also made :—	
	Jug, 30's. 42 ozs. capacity	21/- ,, ,,
	,, 36's. 34 ,, ,, ...	18/- ,, ,,
	,, 42's. 26 ,, ,, ...	15/- ,, ,,
	,, 48's. 19 ,, ,, ...	14/- ,, ,,
	,, 54's. 14 ,, ,, ...	13/- ,, ,,
	Shape as Illustration No. 15, but without cover.	

Sherwin & Co. (Hanley), Ltd., Printers.

WOOD & SONS LTD.

The name of Wood stretches back seven generations in the pottery industry in Staffordshire. In 1865 Thomas Wood established the present firm of Wood and Sons and he built it into one of the largest manufacturers of earthenwares and ironstones in the area. H.J. Wood joined the firm in 1889 and he was an outstanding businessman. He had working relationships with many of the leading designers of the day. He brought Frederick Rhead into the firm in 1912 as art director and Rhead's daughter Charlotte joined him and worked for Wood and Sons until the mid twenties. The company produced such good quality whiteware that a number of firms including A.E. Gray and subsequently Susie Cooper bought in their wares.

As early as 1931 the firm was experimenting with colourful lithograph patterns for their Ivory Ware and may have produced several all-over florals around this time. The association with Susie Cooper and her very different approach to the use of lithos probably steered Wood & Sons away from any involvement in the production of chintz ware. The factory finally passed out of the family in the early 1980s but the name was retained.

UNKNOWN

This pattern is rarely found in North America and eagerly sought by collectors.

Cat. No.	Shape	U.S. $	Can. $	U.K. £		Cat. No.	Shape	U.S. $	Can. $	U.K. £
WS-103	Plate, 6"	75.00	90.00	45.00		WS-130	Teacup and saucer	125.00	150.00	75.00

NEW CHINTZ

CLEMENTINE RUSK
COLLECT IT!
COMPTON & WOODHOUSE
FRANCIS JOSEPH
GRIMWADES LTD. (ROYAL WINTON)
HOUSE OF CLARIDGE
JAMES KENT LTD.
(Mikasa)
(Next Interiors)
MAGNOLIA ANTIQUES
OLD CHINTZ COMPANY (THE)
VICTORIA COLLECTION

HOUSE OF CLARIDGE

NEW CHINTZ INTRODUCTION

In the late 1950s and early 1960s, with ever-increasing costs and a demand for a very different style, most Staffordshire factories ceased to produce chintz. The 1990s have been very hard times in the Potteries and every factory has searched for new markets. It was inevitable that the wild prices paid by collectors for English chintz ware would come to the attention of works managers as well as business people. Gail Claridge, from the House of Claridge, decided to sell a line of chintz starting with Summertime. Unable to reach agreement with Royal Winton, she arranged for Wedgwood to produce her ware. Royal Winton then looked at the potential of this market and produced their first piece in 1997, an 11-inch high Florence vase in a limited edition of 2,000 pieces. At the same time, The Old Chintz Company commissioned Royal Winton to produce a stacking teapot in Julia in a limited edition of 1,000. They followed with three wallpockets in the Nita shape in a limited edition of 500 each. All these pieces are numbered and backstamped "Limited Edition." The Old Chintz Company next commissioned James Kent to produce 250 tea sets in Du Barry and Hydrangea with a special "100th Year Anniversary" backstamp. The teaset consists of six cups and saucers with matching spoons in a presentation box. In mid-1998, a round Diamond shape teapot, cream and sugar were made in the same limited edition of 250. Late in 1997 Royal Winton brought out a line of giftwares with a new backstamp which was easily confused with the Deco stamp of the earlier chintzware. A number of pieces appeared at antique fairs and on the Internet. New collectors, assuming they had a vintage piece of chintz, paid over the top for pieces they could have ordered new from the factory. The Australian, American, and English Collectors Groups all sent letters to the factory pointing out what an adverse effect this confusion was having on the collecting market. The pieces from the boxed giftware line produced for several months before February 1998, still create confusion among inexperienced collectors. As of February, 1998, Royal Winton agreed to add 1995 under the backstamp. Royal Winton chose this date because that is when the factory was bought by Taylor Tunnicliffe. Unfortunately, new dealers are sometimes under the impression that this means the chintz was made in 1995. The limited edition pieces do not have the date because they could be in production for more than one year depending on how long the edition takes to sell out. For example, the Summertime mantel clock (limited edition of 1,000) and the Florence/Summertime/Welbeck Ascot candlesticks (limited edition of 500) are not yet sold out. In July 1998 Victoria magazine offered a Welbeck teapot in the Ascot shape — there were 1,000 of them and they were numbered and exclusive to Victoria. Collectors assumed that this was a limited edition. Although the first 1,000 sold are numbered, thousands more have been made since. When I was at the factory in the summer of 1998 making my own Welbeck teapot, there were Welbeck teapots everywhere, on shelves, on benches and on the floor. Since that first success Victoria has continued to offer Welbeck in cups and saucers, cream and sugars, various sizes of plates, and a Christmas bell and later, a breakfast set. Royal Winton has offered a limited edition Welbeck stacking teapot through the factory. Just as Royal Winton produced lines for Wright, Tyndal & van Roden in the 1930s, for Jay Willfred in the 1940s and 1950s, they have produced several pieces with special backstamps for English and American companies. *Collect It!* magazine in England commissioned a covered box in Welbeck in a limited edition of 1,000 which was offered to their readers. A California company, Clementine Rusk, ordered Julia teasets with special backstamps "Clementine Rusk For The Home." They now offer platters and breakfast sets with the same backstamp. Magnolia Antique Mall in El Cajon commissioned a limited edition of 1,000 stacking teapots, breakfast sets, and a teapot and hot water pot on a tray set, in the post-war Joyce-Lynn pattern. The first 25 sets are signed by Bill Hansen, owner of the Magnolia Antique Mall, and they have a special backstamp "Presented by Magnolia Pottery." While Royal Winton were producing Welbeck, Florence and Summertime, James Kent continued to supply the Old Chintz Company with a wide variety of goods. They created a new pattern Lydia, the black background version of Du Barry. Sugar shakers and toast racks were offered in Hydrangea, Du Barry and Lydia in limited editions. Stacking teapots, cruet sets, breakfast sets and a whole range of giftware were offered in what was called a limited supply and were to be discontinued December 1998. It is not clear if these will still be produced simply omitting the 100th Year Anniversary backstamp. Although originally, James Kent only produced chintz on behalf of the Old Chintz Company, they are now producing chintz on their own behalf. It is interesting that Hadida halted the production of Chintz when they took over the factory in the late 1980s — too labour-intensive and not cost-effective. In the late 1990s, the story is completely different. Clare Hadida, owner of the factory, is very interested in the history of the James Kent company and has been exploring some of the archival material in search of possible patterns. The factory has created a yellow version of Rosalynde they are calling Ruth Kent to honour the former owner. They intend to produce a whole range of chintz ware using the original moulds they found when they bought the factory. In the last year, both giftwares and tablewares have been pouring out of Royal Winton and James Kent. The Wedgwood version of Summertime, made for the House of Claridge, is now being sold through various specialty publications of *Better Homes and Gardens* in the United States. Production will continue to expand as long as there is a market for chintz. Long time collectors either dislike this new chintz or, sometimes, buy it for use, while still collecting the vintage pieces. Some new collectors have discovered chintz through these reproductions and, having begun by buying new chintz, are now in the market for the vintage pieces. This seems to have kept the market for old chintz relatively high. Although new versions of Julia, Florence and Welbeck, were introduced, this did not have much of an impact on the prices for the vintage pieces especially of Welbeck. Royal Winton have now introduced Marion and plan to introduce Stratford, Royalty, Majestic and Richmond in the next year. What impact this will have remains to be seen. The Old Chintz Company now owns the Elijah Cotton (Lord Nelson) trademark. It seems likely that some of the popular Nelson patterns will soon be back on the market. I have tried to illustrate backstamps and as many shapes of the new chintz as I could to show collectors what is currently in production or recently made. With limited editions I have included the edition size.

CLEMENTINE RUSK

1998 Royal Winton Special Editions

Clementine Rusk is a California company owned by two sisters who were initially given exclusive rights to Julia sold in the United States. "Clementine Rusk For The Home 1998" has been used on all pieces regardless of which year they were produced.

Shape	Pattern	Retail Price	Shape	Pattern	Retail Price
Breakfast set	Julia	$421.00	Plate (salad), 8"	Julia	$31.00
Cake plate		145.00	Plate (dinner), 10"		38.00
Candy dish		57.00	Platter, 18"		143.00
Creamer		47.00	Saucer		19.00
Cup		26.00	Sugar bowl (open)		40.00
Plate, 6"		23.00	Teapot (6-cup)		125.00

Note: Retail prices quoted are in U.S. dollars.

COLLECT IT!

1998 Candy Box, Royal Winton in a limited edition of 1,000

Collect It! magazine in England started to commission limited edition pieces from the factories featured in their articles. In June 1998, the magazine offered the readers a Welbeck footed candy box in a limited edition of 1,000 pieces, with a special Collect It! Backstamp.

Shape	Pattern	Retail Price
Candy box, footed	Welbeck	£62.95

Note: Retail price quoted is in U.K. pounds.

COMPTON & WOODHOUSE

1998 The Chintz Plate Collection Royal Winton Limited Edition

Commissioned exclusively by Compton & Woodhouse in association with Royal Winton, there were 9,500 sets of three plates produced.

Shape	Pattern	Retail Price
Plate, 9"	Florence	£24.50
Plate, 9"	Julia	24.50
Plate, 9"	Summertime	24.50

Note: Retail prices quoted are in U.K. pounds.

FRANCIS JOSEPH

1998 "The Chintz Girl," Royal Winton in a limited edition of 999.

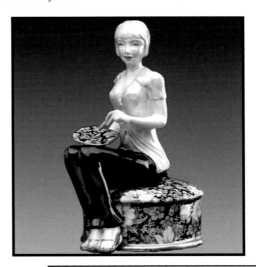

Shape	Pattern	Retail Price
The Chintz Girl	Florence	£165.00

1998 "A Celebration of Chintz," Royal Winton in a limited edition of 1,000.

Shape	Pattern	Retail Price
A Celebration of Chintz	Welbeck	£165.00

Note: Retail prices quoted are in U.K. pounds.

GRIMWADES LTD. (ROYAL WINTON)

1998 Tableware

Florence

Marion

Summertime

Welbeck

Shape	Pattern	Retail Price		Shape	Pattern	Retail Price
Beaker, 240 ml	Florence	£15.98		Platter, 18"	Florence	£79.90
Bread/butter plate, 11 1/2"	Marion	35.00		Rimmed soup, 7"	Marion	18.78
Breakfast set, 10 1/2"	Summertime	258.50		Salad/Vegtable open 8 1/2"	Summertime	44.65
Cake comport, 10 1/2"	Welbeck	75.20		Sauce boat	Welbeck	45.43
Cream, 3 1/2"		28.41		Sauce boat stand, 7 1/2"		22.72
Cup, 170 ml		15.98		Saucer, 6"		11.99
Plate, 10 1/2"		22.75		Sugar, 5 1/2"		24.44
Plate, 8"		18.78		Teapot, 1000 ml		77.08
Plate, 6"		13.35		Vegtable dish covered, 9 1/2"		93.41

Note: Retail prices quoted are in U.K. pounds.

GRIMWADES LTD. (ROYAL WINTON)

1998 Giftware

Florence

Marion

Summertime

Welbeck

Shape	Pattern	Retail Price	Shape	Pattern	Retail Price
Basket, 5"	Florence	£30.55	Shoe, 5"	Florence	£19.97
Broach (oval), 1 1/2"	Marion	9.85	Square tray, 4 1/2"	Marion	19.97
Candlestick, 3"	Summertime	30.55	Sweet comport, 5 1/2"	Summertime	35.25
Canoe, 11 1/2"	Welbeck	49.35	Table bell, 4"	Welbeck	24.67
Display stand, 3 1/2"		19.95	Thimble		7.05
Necklace (oval), 1 1/2"		9.85	Trinket box, round 4 1/2"		30.55
Oblong tray, 9"		30.55	Trinket box, round 3 1/2"		24.68
Posy pot, 3 1/2"		19.97	Trinket box, round 2 1/2"		18.80

Note: Retail prices quoted are in U.K. pounds.

GRIMWADES LTD. (ROYAL WINTON)

1998 "Candlesticks," Royal Winton in a limited edition of 500

Shape	Pattern	Retail Price
Candlesticks (pair)	Florence	£112.00
	Summertime	112.00
	Welbeck	112.00

1998 "Mantle Clock," Royal Winton in a limited edition of 1,000

Shape	Pattern	Retail Price
Mantle Clock	Summertime	£120.00

Note: Retail prices quoted are in U.K. pounds.

GRIMWADES LTD. (ROYAL WINTON)

1998 "Octagonal Vase," Royal Winton in a limited edition of 2,000

Shape	Pattern	Retail Price
Vase	Florence	£120.00

"Display Signs," Royal Winton

Naturally, the display signs do not carry backstamps

Shape	Pattern	Retail Price
Display Sign	Florence	£19.95
	Summertime	
	Welbeck	

Note: Retail prices quoted are in U.K. pounds.

GRIMWADES LTD. (ROYAL WINTON)

1998 Stacking Teapot, Royal Winton in a limited edition of 1,000 sets

Shape	Pattern	Retail Price
Stacking teapot	Welbeck	£195.00

1999 "Breakfast Set," Royal Winton

Shape	Pattern	Retail Price
Breakfast set (6-piece)	Florence	£259.00
	Julia	259.00
	Marion	259.00
	Summertime	259.00
	Welbeck	259.00

Note: Retail prices quoted are in U.K. pounds.

HOUSE OF CLARIDGE

1997 Tableware

Shape	Pattern	Retail Price
Cup	Summertime	$39.50
Plate (dinner)		55.50
Plate (salad/dessert)		42.50
Plate (Bread and butter)		32.50
Saucer		29.50
5pc. place setting		199.50

Shape	Pattern	Retail Price
Cake stand (3-tiered)	Summertime	$219.50
Creamer		79.50
Sugar with cover		99.50
Teapot		199.50

Note: Retail prices quoted are in U.S. dollars.

JAMES KENT LTD.

1988 Tableware

It has been very difficult to unravel the mystery of James Kent production in the late 1980s. The company was in financial difficulties and clearly tried everything to stay afloat. Clare Hadida gave me advertising flyers from 1988 for both the tableware and the giftware lines. According to the *Weekend Telegraph* newspaper August 15, 1987, Next Interiors offered teawares in Du Barry on the square Diamond shape.

Shape	Pattern	Retail Price
Cereal/oatmeal bowl	Du Barry	Retail
Cream jug, 8oz		prices
Oval dish, 13" (actual)		not
Oval dish, 11" (actual)		available
Place setting, 5-piece		at
Plate, 10" (actual)		press
Plate, 8" (actual)		time
Plate, 6 ½" (actual)		

Shape	Pattern	Retail Price
Soup plate	Du Barry	Retail
Stone rim fruit dish		prices
Sugar box, covered		not
Tea cup, 5oz		available
Tea saucer		at
Teapot, 4-cup		press
Teapot, 6-cup		time
Tea set, 18-piece		
Tea set, 22-piece		

JAMES KENT LTD.

1988 Giftware

I have not been able to find a price list for the giftware made in Du Barry. I know that a number of these shapes were made with a MIKASA backstamp, I have seen both flat and tall covered boxes stamped MIKASA. The Old Foley backstamp was used around the same time. I have certainly seen the bud vase and the pie server and plate marked with the 1988 Old Foley backstamp. Clare Hadida thinks the MIKASA Du Barry was the last but she is not sure. In the first edition of the Chintz guide we showed a James Kent Du Barry shaving mug in the shape section. I found this shape in a James Kent giftware flyer from the 1980s and I suspect it dates to that time, not earlier. If you are buying Du Barry, spend some time studying the backstamps as the differences are quite small and you could easily make a mistake.

Shape	Pattern	Retail Price
Bud vase	Cathay	Retail
Canterbury tray		prices
Coaster		not
Comport, large		available
Comport, small		at
Devon sweet tray		press
Flat box		time
Henley tray		
Oval box		
Pie server		
Sandwich tray, 12"		
Spice box		
Square sweet tray		
Surrey tray		
Tall box		

Shape	Pattern	Retail Price
Bud vase	Du Barry	Retail
Canterbury tray		prices
Coaster		not
Comport, large		available
Comport, small		at
Devon sweet tray		press
Flat box		time
Henley tray		
Oval box		
Pie server		
Sandwich tray, 12"		
Spice box		
Square sweet tray		
Surrey tray		
Tall box		

JAMES KENT LTD.

1999 Tableware

James Kent has been making changes in their chintz lines; they are now selling directly to the consumer as well as through the Old Chintz Company. For their own pieces they are using a backstamp with Old Foley across the globe and James Kent in the ribbon below. I have attached a list of the more-than-sixty items which Hadida intends to produce in Du Barry, Hydrangea, Lydia, (Du Barry black colourway), Ruth Kent (Rosalynde yellow colourway), Rosalynde and two older-type chintzes called Rosarie and 18th Century. Some of the items issued earlier in Du Barry and Hydrangea as limited editions will only be available in the other patterns. Other shapes such as most of the Granville line will not be in stock items but special order. Retail prices quoted are in U.S. dollars.

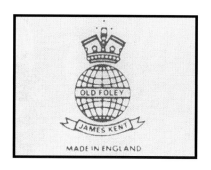

Shape	Pattern	Retail Price
Antique jug/bowl	Available	$550.00
Butter dish, covered	in	110.00
Breakfast set	18th Century	365.00
Chamber pot	Du Barry	110.00
Comport, small	Hydrangea	65.00
Cup	Lydia	45.00
Cosy stacking teapot set	Rosalynde	170.00
Cheese dish, covered	Rosarie	130.00
Corn dish	Ruth Kent	55.00
Cruet, 3-piece		190.00
Devon sweet, small		20.00
Dolphin jug/bowl, medium		245.00
Dolphin jug/bowl, small		150.00
Double egg cup		65.00
Dove tray		45.00
Duchess tray		115.00
Four egg cups/stand		130.00
Flower pocket		60.00
Granville, 3-piece cruet		195.00
Granville comport, large		125.00
Granville coffee pot		180.00
Granville tea pot		130.00
Granville round stand		30.00
Granville gravy boat/stand		125.00
Granville sugar (base/lid)		115.00
Granville milk jug		65.00
Granville breakfast cup		65.00
Granville breakfast saucer		35.00
Granville cup		50.00
Granville saucer		30.00
Granville plate, 7"		35.00
Granville plate, 9"		40.00
Grapefruit dish		70.00

Shape	Pattern	Retail Price
Handle tray	Available	$55.00
Morning set	in	395.00
Mayonnaise bowl	18th Century	50.00
Mayonnaise spoon	Du Barry	35.00
Mayonnaise stand	Hydrangea	50.00
Majestic plate, 8"	Lydia	50.00
Majestic plate, 9"	Rosalynde	50.00
Oval mirror with glass	Roasrie	245.00
Oval pill box, small	Ruth Kent	15.00
Powder bowl, covered		80.00
Plate, plain 4 ½"		20.00
Plate, fluted 4 ½"		20.00
Pill box, small round (deep)		20.00
Pill box, small round		15,00
Round diamond teapot		165.00
Round diamond teapot stand		30.00
Round diamond milk		70.00
Round diamond sugar		100.00
Saucer		25.00
Square plate, 6"		30.00
Square nut tray		65.00
Square nut scope		35.00
Square diamond teapot		180.00
Square diamond teapot stand		40.00
Square diamond milk		75.00
Square diamond sugar		100.00
Temple jar		190.00
Tray, 10"		80.00
Toast rack		110.00
Tennis set, medium		80.00
Tennis set, large		90.00
Triple tray		85.00
Twin tray		65.00

MAGNOLIA ANTIQUES

1999 "Stacking Teapot," Royal Winton in a limited edition of 1,000

Bill Hansen of the Magnolia Antique Mall went to England in 1988 and met with Royal Winton. He ordered 1,000 limited edition stacking teapots in the 1950s pattern Joyce-Lynn. He then found a teapot and hot water pot on a tray made originally by Soho Pottery in the 1940s and asked Royal Winton to duplicate the shapes. He ordered 1,000 sets again in Joyce-Lynn. He recently ordered a limited edition Joyce-Lynn breakfast set which is in production now. The first 25 of each edition has a special backstamp and is signed by Bill Hansen, but the issue price is the same.

Shape	Pattern	Retail Price
Stacking teapot	Joyce-Lynn	$295.00

1998 "Tea/Hot Water Set," Royal Winton in a limited edition of 1,000

Shape	Pattern	Retail Price
3-piece set Teapot Water pot Tray	Joyce-Lynn	$295.00

Note: Retail prices quoted are in U.S. dollars.

THE OLD CHINTZ COMPANY

1998 "Sugar Shakers," James Kent in a limited edition 250 each.

Shape	Pattern	Retail Price
Sugar shaker	Du Barry	£75.00
	Hydrangea	75.00
	Lydia	75.00

1998 "Teapot, Cream and Sugar," James Kent in a limited edition of 250 each.

Shape	Pattern	Retail Price
Set	Du Barry	£175.00
Teapot	Hydrangea	
Creamer		
Sugar		

Note: Retail prices quoted are in U.K. pounds.

THE OLD CHINTZ COMPANY

1998 "Teasets," James Kent in a limited edition 250 of each pattern.

These tea sets comprise 6 cups and saucers with 6 matching teaspoons.

Shape	Pattern	Retail Price
Teaset	Du Barry	£195.00
	Hydrangea	195.00

1998 "Toast Rack," James Kent in a limited edition of 75 each pattern

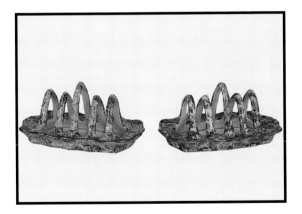

Shape	Pattern	Retail Price
Toast rack	Du Barry	£59.00
	Hydrangea	59.00

Note: Retail prices quoted are in U.K. pounds.

THE OLD CHINTZ COMPANY

1998 "Cruet Set," James Kent in a Special Edition

Shape	Pattern	Retail Price
Cruet set (4-piece)	Du Barry	£95.00
	Hydrangea	95.00

1998 "Stacking Teapot," James Kent in a Special Edition

Shape	Pattern	Retail Price
Stacking teapot	Du Barry	£95.00
	Hydrangea	95.00

Note: Retail prices quoted are in U.K. pounds

THE OLD CHINTZ COMPANY

1998 James Kent Special Editions

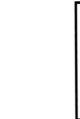

Shape	Pattern	Retail Price
Antique jug/bowl	Du Barry	£225.00
Dolphin jug/bowl, medium		95.00
Dolphin jug/bowl, small		70.00
Royal jug/bowl		95.00
Chamber pot, 7" dia.		65.00
Temple jar with cover, 11"		85.00
Cheese dish with cover, 7"		65.00
Sugar bowl with cover, 4 ½" dia.		35.00
Butter dish with cover		50.00
Powder bowl with cover		30.00
Regal tray, 10"		35.00
Tray, two handled, 6 ½"		15.00
Devon pin tray, 3 ½"		10.00
Double egg cup, 4"		35.00
Four-egg cruet set, 6 ½" sq.		70.00
Cosy stacking teaset, 7"		95.00

Shape	Pattern	Retail Price
Antique jug/bowl	Hydrangea	£225.00
Dolphin jug/bowl, medium		95.00
Dolphin jug/bowl, small		70.00
Royal jug/bowl		95.00
Chamber pot, 7" dia.		65.00
Temple jar with cover, 11"		85.00
Cheese dish with cover, 7"		65.00
Sugar bowl with cover, 4 ½" dia.		35.00
Butter dish with cover		50.00
Powder bowl with cover		30.00
Regal tray, 10"		35.00
Tray, two handled, 6 "½		15.00
Devon pin tray, 3 ½"		10.00
Double egg cup, 4"		35.00
Four-egg cruet set, 6 ½" sq.		70.00
Cosy stacking teaset, 7"		95.00

Note: Retail prices quoted are in U.K. pounds.

THE OLD CHINTZ COMPANY

1997 "Stacking Teapot," Royal Winton in a limited edition of 1,000

Shape	Pattern	Retail Price
Stacking teapot	Julia	£195.00

"Wall Pockets," Royal Winton in a limited edition of 500

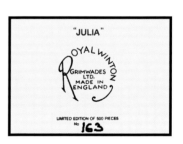

Shape	Pattern	Retail Price
Wall Pocket	Florence	£65.00
	Julia	65.00
	Summertime	65.00

Note: Retail prices quoted are in U.K. pounds.

VICTORIA COLLECTION

Victoria Magazine was given the exclusive right to market Welbeck in the U.S. The first 1,000 Welbeck teapots sold by Victoria are numbered, but this was not a limited edition and thousands more have been sold. The starter set consists of 4 pieces each of the cup and saucer and three plates, a 6-inch bread plate, an 8-inch salad/dessert plate and a 10-inch dinner plate.

Breakfast Set

Bell

Shape	Pattern	Retail Price
Tea service/Breakfast set	Welbeck	$495.00
Teapot		150.00
Cream and Sugar Set		80.00
Cup and saucer, set of four		195.00
Dinner plates, set of four		165.00
Salad/dessert plates, set of four		135.00
Bread plates, set of four		110.00
Bell		29.95
Bells, set of three		85.95
Bells, set of six		170.00
Starter set		170.00

Note: Retail prices quoted are in U.S. dollars.

PHOTOGRAPH LUCIANA PAMPALONE

We Bring Back a Treasured Collectible
TEA SERVICE FOR ONE

There's hardly a better time than this—our tribute-to-England issue—to reacquaint you with our stunning collection of chintzware. In addition to the beautiful stock of "Welbeck"-pattern pieces still available (all made in England by Royal Winton for us alone) we are making an exciting new addition: a classic chintz breakfast set, destined to be one of the most endearing collectibles you'll ever own.

Who wouldn't love to indulge themselves with this exquisite set of chintz pottery? Like the once-popular, but today-rare, chintz breakfast sets of decades past, this service has all the makings of a sought-after collectible. Each piece in the set is perfectly sized for one serving and rests in a sculpted niche on the serving plate. Note the lovely, gold line that rims the inside of the sugar bowl, creamer, and cup.

(Please note these dimensions are approximate):

Teacup	standard size
Teapot	4" high
Sugar bowl	1¼" high
Creamer	2¼" high
Toast rack	2" high
Tray	9" in diameter

Whether you make this set a gift to yourself or a special person, it will turn an ordinary day into an extraordinary occasion.

A Resonant Collectible

In making your chintzware selections, don't overlook this wonderful bell. Use it as a dinner bell, a decoration for your mantel, or a gift for a hostess. Or buy several as gifts for bridal attendants.

PHOTOGRAPHS JIM BASTARDO

SHAPES

ELIJAH COTTON (LORD NELSON)
GRIMWADES LTD. (ROYAL WINTON)
JAMES KENT LTD.
A. G. RICHARDSON (CROWN DUCAL)
SHELLEY

As you can see the shape section has been greatly expanded. Clare Hadida, owner of James Kent, Ltd. allowed me to go through all the cupboards in her office when I was in Stoke-on-Trent in the summer of 1998. I found all these shape pages and she kindly allowed me to take them for this third edition. I have tried to set this section up so that you will be able to find the shape you are looking for as quickly as possible. I put all the 1930s catalogue pages from Royal Winton and from James Kent together so that you can study them easily. I still haven't stumbled onto a Crown Ducal or a Lord Nelson catalogue. I did find references to the Nelson jug names in the *Pottery & Glass Record.* Although the shape name is not impressed into the jugs, Elijah Cotton named each jug shape Dart, Leda, Cecil, Holborn and Bute. Most chintz patterns appear on the tankard shape BUTE, introduced in 1925 and the wide-bellied shape BELL. Every time I thought I was finished organizing the different shapes, a letter would arrive with a new and interesting shape — the Sweet Pea cigarette box with the ashtray lid, the Summertime Ajax shape cream and sugar, the Crown Ducal Peony and Pink Chintz toast racks. I did not add these rare shapes to the price guide part of this book. Pieces which turn up once or twice in a lifetime of collecting are impossible to price. Collectors often ask me why I don't price

baskets and lamp bases. These pieces really don't turn up often enough to establish a market. They vary widely in what they sell for when they do turn up.

I included a wide variety of jug shapes, teapots, coffee pots, bowls, cream and sugar shapes, eggcups and so on to help you in recognizing what you find. These are not individually priced either. If you have found a very rare shape jug in a great pattern, obviously it will be more expensive than the price in the book.

This is a collector's guide and I have tried to create a shape section to help you to avoid errors. Any of you who have the second edition of this book should look at page 198 and study the Julia Albans shape coffee pot. You will see that the lid to this coffee pot is from a Chelsea jampot! I must have looked at that picture hundreds of times without noticing the lid. The owner of this pot realized recently that it was the wrong lid and called me about it. I once bought a Susie Cooper teapot with a sugar bowl lid. Pay very close attention to shapes especially on breakfast sets, eggcup sets, salt and peppers and anything with a lid. Lots of married pieces fit together perfectly. You just want to be sure they are the right pieces. Don't buy two salts, or a mustard without a lid or an Albans shape cup on a Norman saucer.

ELIJAH COTTON (LORD NELSON) SHAPES

Sauce boat

Stacking teapot (white spout)

Tennis set

Stacking teapot with demi tasse cups and saucers

ELIJAH COTTON (LORD NELSON) SHAPES

Bute jug

Cake plate and server

Bell jugs in three sizes

Bud vase   Bud vase   Bud vase

Bud vase   Bud vase   Bud vase

GRIMWADES LTD. (ROYAL WINTON)
CATALOGUE OF 1936

GRIMWADES LTD., STOKE-ON-TRENT.   Supplement "C"

All articles on this list can be supplied in decorations illustrated
on sheets C/1, C/2, C/3, and any similar styles of decoration.

021. "CANOE" TRAY
022. BUTTER "TREFU"
023. TRAY "FIFE"
024. TRIPLE DISH "STAFFORD"
025. CONDIMENT SET (2PCE ON TRAY) "ACME"
026. TWIN DISH "STAFFORD."
027. TENNIS SET 2PCE "ASCOT"
028. TOAST, BUTTER & MARMALADE "SAVILLE"
029. TRIPLE TRAY VIOLA.
030. EGG SET 4 CUP "SAVILLE"
031. INDIVIDUAL BREAKFAST SET 6 PCE "ATHENA"
032. CRUET SET EGG & CLOVER LEAF.
033. EGG - CRUET SET 5 PCE "ASCOT"
034. TRIPLE TRAY "GEM"
035. EGG - CRUET SET 7 PCE "YORK"
036. CRUET SET "FIFE"
037. BEDSIDE SET 6 PCE "COUNTESS"
038. BEDSIDE SET 7 PCE "ASCOT"
039. BEDSIDE SET 7 PCE "YORK".

"ROYAL WINTON" IVORY TABLEWARE.

Sherwin & Co. (Hanley), Ltd., Printers

GRIMWADES LTD. (ROYAL WINTON)
CATALOGUE OF 1936

GRIMWADES LTD. (ROYAL WINTON)
CATALOGUE OF 1936

040. SWEET "HOLBORN"
041. SWEET "BOW"
042. OATMEAL
043. MINT BOAT & STAND "ERA"
044. LOW COMPORT "ASCOT"
045. CHOCOLATE COMPORT "LILY"
046. FOOTED NUT "BOW"
047. JUG "CAMBRIDGE"
048. JUG "GLOBE"
049. COFFEEPOT "PERTH"
050. CHOCOLATE COMPORT "GREEK"
051. CHOCOLATE COMPORT "ETON"
052. JUG "DUVAL"
053. JUG "GRAFTON"
054. CAKE PLATE HANDLED "ASCOT"
055. COFFEEPOT "NORMAN"
056. COFFEEPOT "GREEK"
057. BOWL "FIFE"
058. PLATE "ASCOT"
059. BOWL "KING"

GRIMWADES LTD. (ROYAL WINTON)
CATALOGUE OF 1936

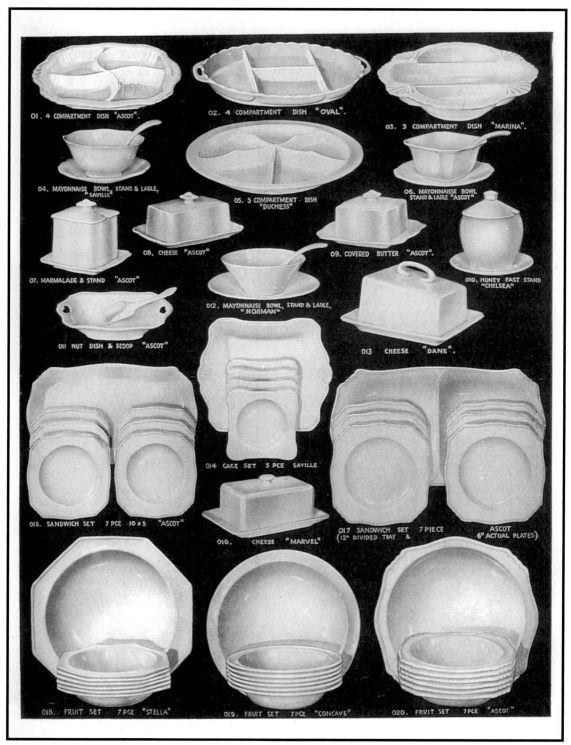

O1. 4 COMPARTMENT DISH "ASCOT".

O2. 4 COMPARTMENT DISH "OVAL".

O3. 3 COMPARTMENT DISH "MARINA".

O4. MAYONNAISE BOWL, STAND & LADLE, "SAVILLE"

O5. 5 COMPARTMENT - DISH "DUCHESS"

O6. MAYONNAISSE BOWL STAND & LADLE "ASCOT"

O7. MARMALADE & STAND "ASCOT"

O8. CHEESE "ASCOT"

O9. COVERED BUTTER "ASCOT".

O10. HONEY FAST STAND "CHELSEA"

O11 NUT DISH & SCOOP "ASCOT"

O12. MAYONNAISE BOWL, STAND & LADLE, "NORMAN"

O13 CHEESE "DANE".

O14 CAKE SET 5 PCE SAVILLE

O15. SANDWICH SET 7 PCE 10 x 5 "ASCOT"

O16. CHEESE "MARVEL"

O17 SANDWICH SET 7 PIECE (12" DIVIDED TRAY & ASCOT 6" ACTUAL PLATES)

O18. FRUIT SET 7 PCE "STELLA"

O19. FRUIT SET 7 PCE "CONCAVE"

O20. FRUIT SET 7 PCE "ASCOT"

GRIMWADES LTD. (ROYAL WINTON)
CATALOGUE OF 1936

"ASCOT" SHAPE (Reg. No. 768985).   Decoration 3459.

Covered
Sugar

Fruit Saucer

Individual
Butter Pad

Cream

Bowl

3"

4"

5"

6"

7"

8"

Coupe Soup

Cream, Soup & Stand

Plate

Teacup and Saucer
(Tall)

Sauce Boat

Oatmeal

Pickle or
Boat Stand

Covered
Vegetable Dish

Low Comport

Dish

"ROYAL WINTON"
IVORY.

Scollop

GRIMWADES LTD. (ROYAL WINTON)
CATALOGUE OF 1936

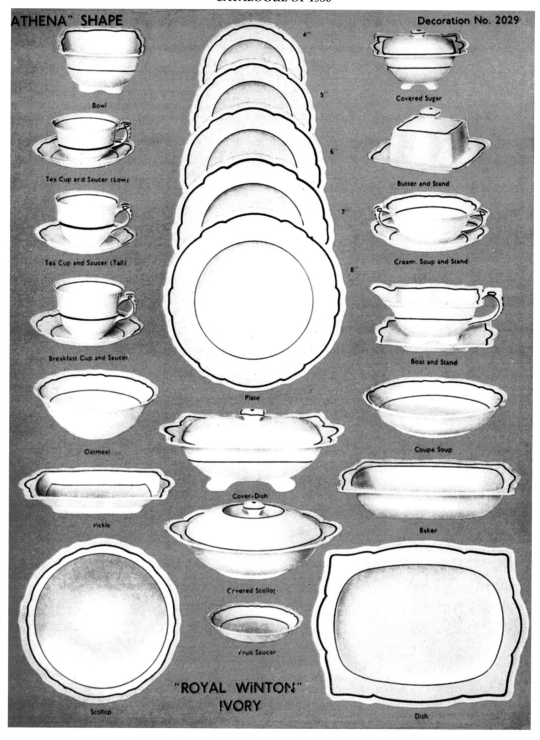

"ATHENA" SHAPE

Decoration No. 2029

Bowl

Tea Cup and Saucer (Low)

Tea Cup and Saucer (Tall)

Breakfast Cup and Saucer

Oatmeal

Pickle

Plate

Cover-Dish

Covered Scollop

Fruit Saucer

Covered Sugar

Butter and Stand

Cream. Soup and Stand

Boat and Stand

Coupe Soup

Baker

Scollop

"ROYAL WINTON"
IVORY

Dish

GRIMWADES LTD. (ROYAL WINTON)
BREAKFAST SETS

Ascot

Honeymoon

Unknown

Lily

Unknown

York

Countess

Sexta teapot and hot water pot

GRIMWADES LTD. (ROYAL WINTON)
TEAPOTS

Unknown

Later Athena

Globe

Albans

Elite

Ascot

Ascot

Ascot

GRIMWADES LTD. (ROYAL WINTON)
TEAPOTS

Unknown

Sexta

Lily

Cube

Unknown

Norman

Rosebud

Athena

GRIMWADES LTD. (ROYAL WINTON)
TEA and COFFEE POTS

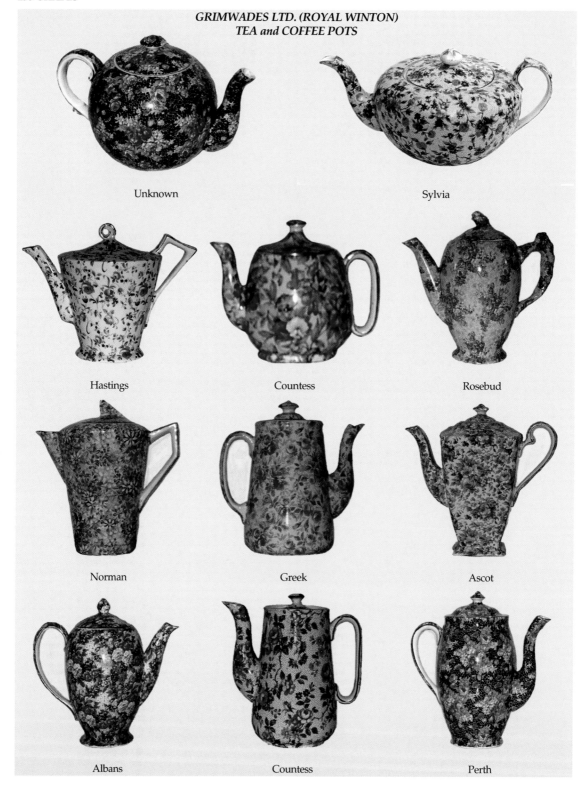

Unknown

Sylvia

Hastings

Countess

Rosebud

Norman

Greek

Ascot

Albans

Countess

Perth

GRIMWADES LTD. (ROYAL WINTON)
CREAM and SUGAR

Ascot, covered sugar

York cream and sugar on tray

Ascot covered sugar

Ascot open sugar

Ascot cream jug

Ascot alternate open sugar

Norman open sugar

Norman cream jug

Countess, breakfast cream and sugar

Stafford cream and sugar

GRIMWADES LTD. (ROYAL WINTON)
CREAM, SUGAR and HOT WATER POTS

Grecian cream and sugar

Stuart cream and sugar

Jacobean cream jug

Jacobean open sugar

Countess hot water pot

Albans cream jug

Albans open sugar

Sexta hot water pot variation

Countess cream jug

Countess open sugar

Rustic hot water pot

GRIMWADES LTD. (ROYAL WINTON)
CREAM, SUGAR and HOT WATER POTS

Countess breakfast cream jug

Countess breakfast sugar

Countess sugar variation

Athena cream jug

Athena open sugar

Sexta hot water pot

Elite cream jug

Elite covered sugar

Countess hot water pot

Albans cream jug

Albans covered sugar

Albans hot water pot

GRIMWADES LTD. (ROYAL WINTON)
CREAM, SUGAR, HOT WATER POTS and CAKE STANDS

Later Athena cream jug   Athena open sugar   Countess hot water pot

Winton cream jug   Huntsmere open sugar   Athena hot water pot

Ajax cream jug   Ajax open sugar   Cake stand variation

Ventnor cream jug   Ventnor open sugar   Cake stand

GRIMWADES LTD. (ROYAL WINTON)
JUGS

Albans

Dutch

Lily

Globe

Dutch

Diamond

Duval

Ventnor

Ronda

Athena

Delius

GRIMWADES LTD. (ROYAL WINTON)
JUGS and PLATES

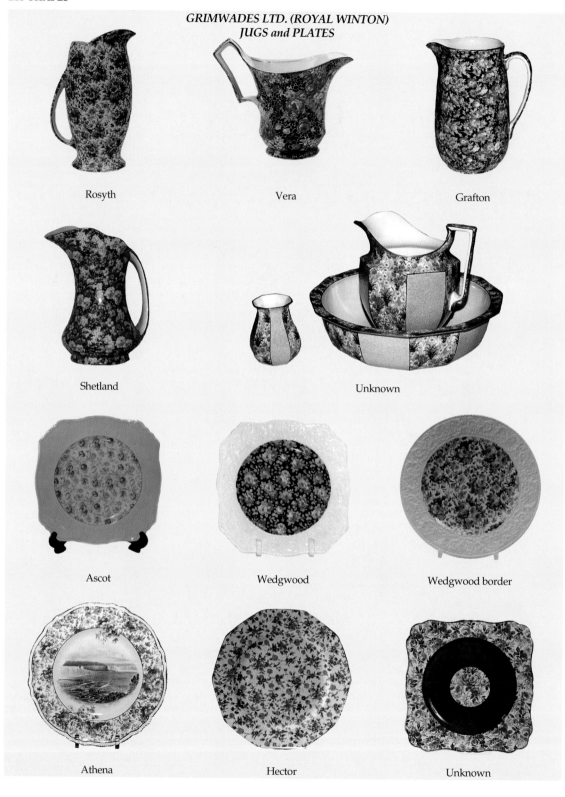

Rosyth

Vera

Grafton

Shetland

Unknown

Ascot

Wedgwood

Wedgwood border

Athena

Hector

Unknown

GRIMWADES LTD. (ROYAL WINTON)
JAM POTS (PRESERVES)

Ninevah

Low Rheims (missing liner)

Unknown

Chelsea (missing liner)

Later Rosebud

Athena

Ascot

Rheims (tall)

Rosebud

Rheims ('mini' tall)

Norman

Unknown

GRIMWADES LTD. (ROYAL WINTON)
TOAST RACKS, EGG and BREAKFAST SETS

Stafford toast rack

Saville, toast, butter and marmalade

Lily toast rack

Unknown

Queen, 3-bar toast rack

Queen, 5-bar toast rack

Saville egg set

Athena individual breakfast set

GRIMWADES LTD. (ROYAL WINTON)
EGG CUPS and TRAYS

York egg set

Regina egg set

Unknown, egg cup fast-stand

Ascot egg-cruet set

Ascot egg cup

Egg cup, footed

Egg cup, bucket

Egg cup, double

Egg cup, footed, square

Egg cup, footed, round

GRIMWADES LTD. (ROYAL WINTON)
CRUETS and SUGAR SHAKERS

Acme salt and pepper on tray

Fife cruet

Lily salt and pepper on tray

Fife salt and pepper on tray

Cloverleaf cruet

Unknown

Rosebud sugar shaker

Fife sugar shaker

Unknown

GRIMWADES LTD. (ROYAL WINTON)
SAUCE BOATS and JUGS

Rosebud sauce boat

Era sauce boat

Unknown

Duchess sauce boat

Later Athena gravy boat

Era sauce boat

Later Athena jug

Raleigh jug

Isis jug

Etona

Doreen jug

Cambridge jug

GRIMWADES LTD. (ROYAL WINTON)
BISCUIT BARRELS, CHEESE AND BUTTER DISHES

Unknown

Ascot rectangular butter dish

Dane cheese

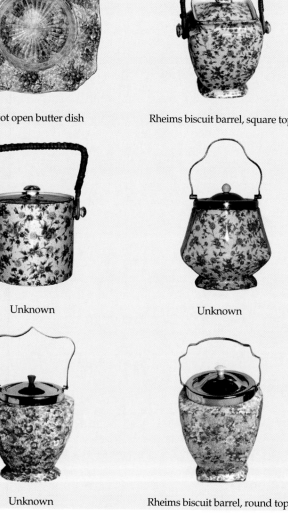

Ajax butter dish

Ascot open butter dish

Rheims biscuit barrel, square top

Unknown

Unknown

Unknown

Athena biscuit barrel

Unknown

Rheims biscuit barrel, round top

GRIMWADES LTD. (ROYAL WINTON)
VASES and COVERED VEGETABLE DISHES

Ascot

Unknown

Unknown

Delphic

Tiber

Unknown

Unknown

GRIMWADES LTD. (ROYAL WINTON)
VASES

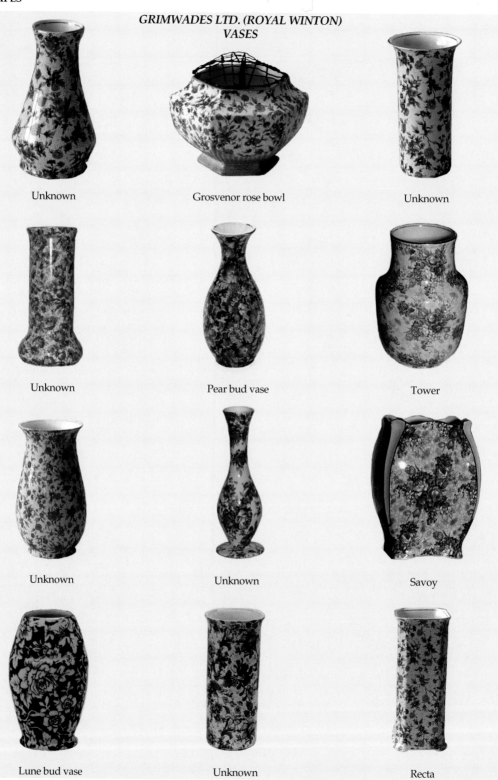

Unknown

Grosvenor rose bowl

Unknown

Unknown

Pear bud vase

Tower

Unknown

Unknown

Savoy

Lune bud vase

Unknown

Recta

GRIMWADES LTD. (ROYAL WINTON)
VASES

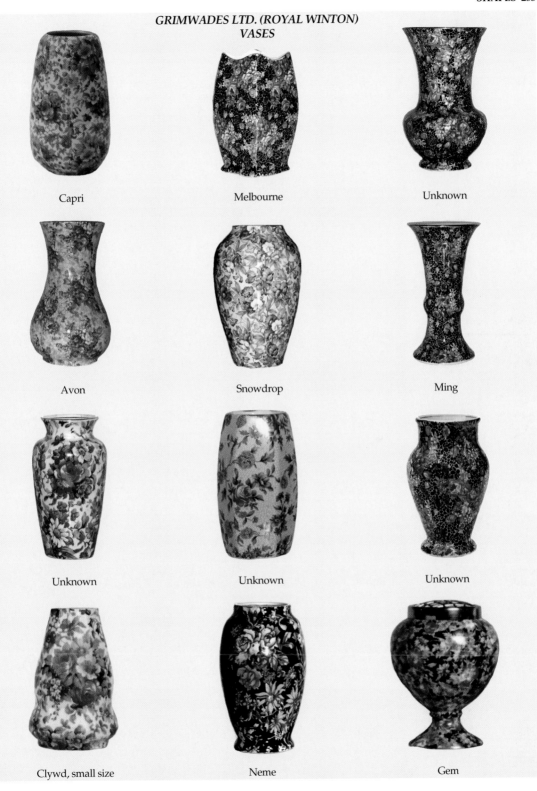

Capri

Melbourne

Unknown

Avon

Snowdrop

Ming

Unknown

Unknown

Unknown

Clywd, small size

Neme

Gem

GRIMWADES LTD. (ROYAL WINTON)
BUD VASES

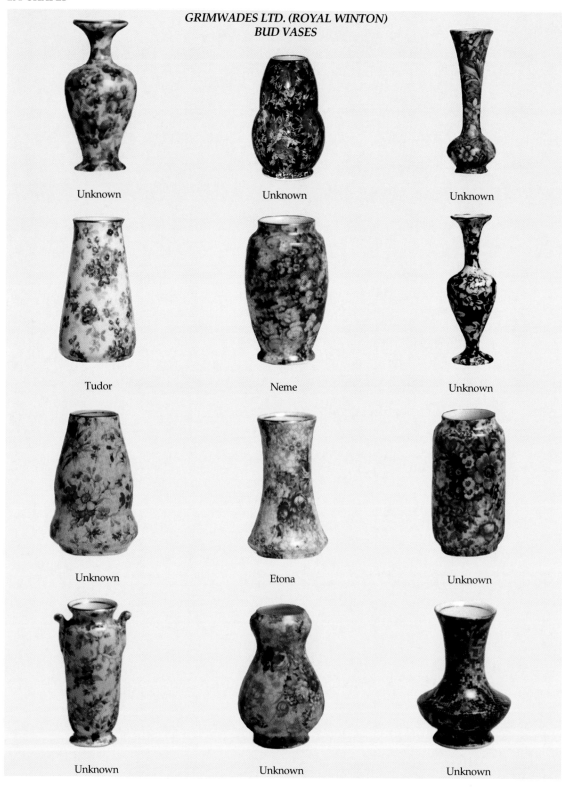

Unknown   Unknown   Unknown

Tudor   Neme   Unknown

Unknown   Etona   Unknown

Unknown   Unknown   Unknown

GRIMWADES LTD. (ROYAL WINTON)
COVERED CANDY DISHES

Chinese pot pourri jar

Gordon

Unknown

Olympic

Richmond

GRIMWADES LTD. (ROYAL WINTON)
BOWLS

Sexta

Unknown

King

Crown

Ely

Fife

Corfe

Unknown

GRIMWADES LTD. (ROYAL WINTON)
BOWLS and COMPORTS

Unknown

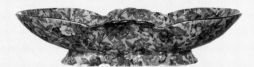

Unknown

Unknown

Unknown salad bowl

Octagon

Ascot high cake stand

Ascot cake plate, chrome base

Bonbon dish, bakelite base

GRIMWADES LTD. (ROYAL WINTON)
BASKETS and BOWLS

Rowsley

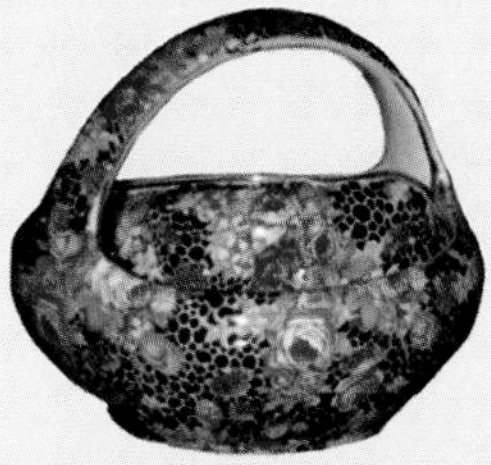

Hampton

Kew

Unknown

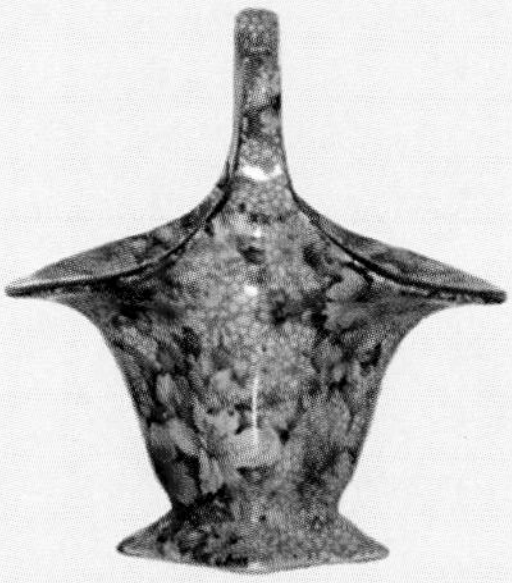

Dudley

Unknown

Rheims

Flora

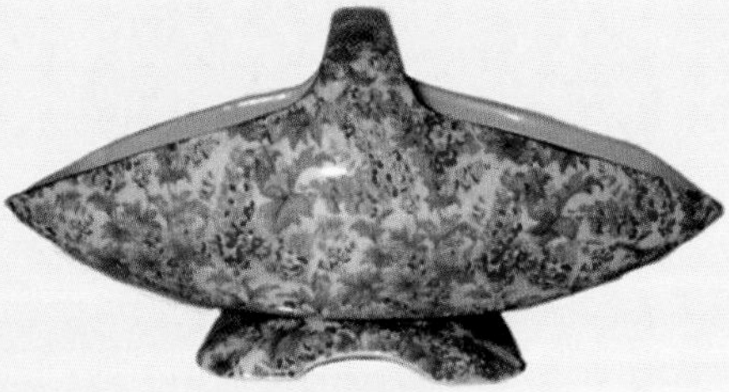

Unknown

Rosebud

GRIMWADES LTD. (ROYAL WINTON)
CANDLESTICKS, LAMPS and LIGHTER

Greek   Octron

Unknown   Lighter

Eden   Unknown   Unknown

Unknown   Unknown   Unknown

GRIMWADES LTD. (ROYAL WINTON)
BOXES

Burke

Lotus

Unknown

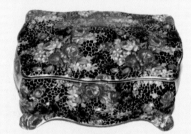

Candy box

Candy box

Covered box

Music box

Cigarette box, ashtray lid

Covered box

GRIMWADES LTD. (ROYAL WINTON)
MISCELLANEOUS ITEMS

Norman Mayonnaise bowl and stand

Saville Mayonnaise bowl, stand and ladle

Unknown

Countess mug

Doreen

Beaker

Unknown

Shaving mug

Cigarette holder

Ash box

Bell

GRIMWADES LTD. (ROYAL WINTON)
CUPS and SAUCERS

Athena

Unknown

Raleigh

Raleigh breakfast

Unknown

Ajax

Hastings

Can

Albans demi-tasse

Norman

Ascot breakfast

Ascot tea

JAMES KENT LTD., THE OLD FOLEY POTTERY

GRANVILLE SHAPE

2 SIZES
42s. – 1/2 PT.
36s. – 3/4 PT.

4 OZS.

2 SIZES
3 1/2" x 9"
3" x 6"

2 SIZES
3/4 PT.
1 PT.

1/2 PT.

JEWEL SHAPE

QUEEN

RICHMOND

TUDOR

STOKE-ON-TRENT, ENGLAND.

Printed in England

MAJESTIC SHAPE

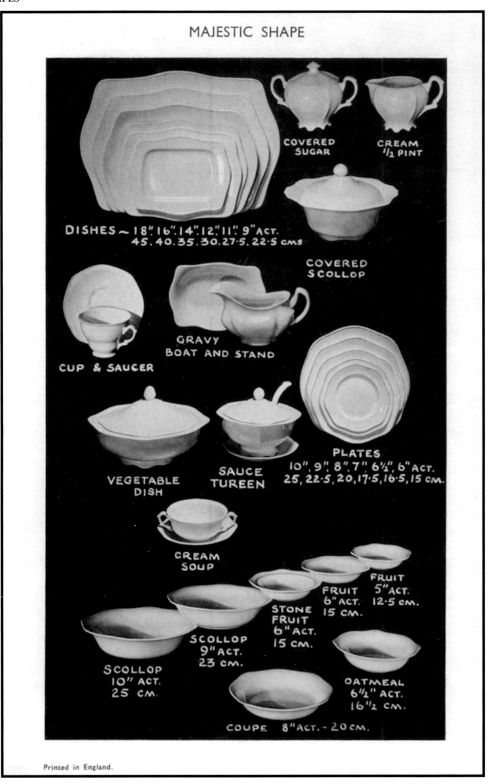

COVERED
SUGAR

CREAM
½ PINT

DISHES ~ 18". 16". 14". 12". 11". 9" ACT.
45. 40. 35. 30. 27·5. 22·5 cms

COVERED
SCOLLOP

GRAVY
BOAT AND STAND

CUP & SAUCER

VEGETABLE
DISH

SAUCE
TUREEN

PLATES
10", 9", 8", 7", 6½", 6" ACT.
25, 22·5, 20, 17·5, 16·5, 15 cm.

CREAM
SOUP

FRUIT
5" ACT.
12·5 cm.

FRUIT
6" ACT.
15 cm.

STONE
FRUIT
6" ACT.
15 cm.

SCOLLOP
9" ACT.
23 cm.

SCOLLOP
10" ACT.
25 cm.

OATMEAL
6½" ACT.
16½ cm.

COUPE 8" ACT. – 20 cm.

Printed in England.

TEA-POTS, COFFEE-POTS, JUGS, Etc.

DIAMOND MILK-JUG ¾ PT.

BUTE TEA-POT 1¼ – 2 – 2½ PINTS

TUDOR TEA-POT ¾ PT

DIAMOND COFFEE-POT 1 PT.

DIAMOND ROUND TEA-POT 1 – 1¾ PINTS

ROYAL COFFEE-POT 2 PT.

JEWEL TEA-POT 1 – 1½ – 2 PINTS

SQ. DIAMOND TEA-POT 1 – 1¾ – 2 PINT.

MELROSE TEA-POT 1 – 1¾ PINTS

JEWEL JUG 1 – 1¼ – 1¾ PT.

DIAMOND JUG ¾ – 1½ – 2 PINTS

MELROSE JUG 1 – 1½ – 1¾ – 2½ PINT

DUTCH JUG ¾ – 1 – 1¼ 1¾ – 2¼ PINTS

REGENT JUG 1 – 1½ – 2 – 3 PINTS

YORK JUG ¼ – ½ – ¾ – 1 PT.

TANKARD JUG ½ – 1 – 1½ – 2 PT.

MELROSE TEA-POT STAND

DIAMOND TEA-POT STAND

Printed in England.

SUGARS AND CREAMS

OCTAGON SUGAR CREAM ¼ PT. & TRAY

MAJESTIC SUGAR

MAJESTIC CREAM ½ PT.

ROYAL SUGAR

ROYAL CREAM ½ PT.

JEWEL SUGAR 36's

JEWEL CREAM ½ PT.

CHESTER SUGAR 36's

CHESTER CREAM ⅓ PT.

OCTAGON COVERED SUGAR

OCTAGON CREAM ½ PT.

ESSEX SUGAR

TANKARD CREAM ½ PT.

JEWEL SUGAR S/S

JEWEL CREAM ¼ PT.

KENT SUGAR. KENT CREAM ¼ PT.

MELROSE INDIVIDUAL SUGAR CREAM ¼ PT.

HARROW CREAM ½ PT.

DIAMOND SQUAT CREAM ½ PT.

KENT CREAM ¼ PT. & STAND

TUDOR SUGAR TUDOR CREAM ⅕ PT.

MELROSE CREAM ½ PT.

GRANVILLE SUGAR, CREAM ⅕ PT. & TRAY

JAMES KENT LTD., THE OLD FOLEY POTTERY

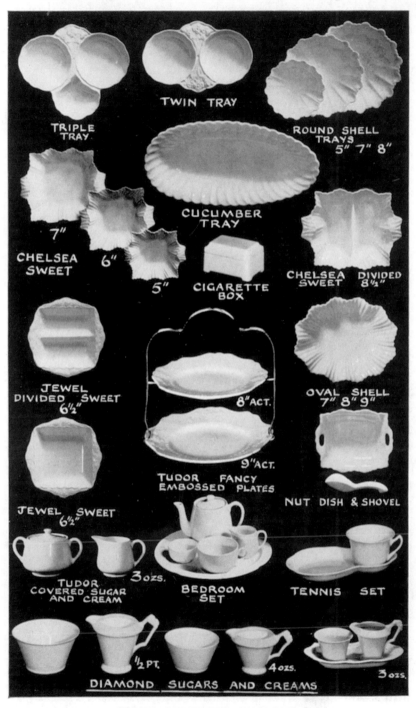

STOKE-ON-TRENT, ENGLAND.

CUPS AND SAUCERS

JUMBO.

SILVER TEA.

GRANVILLE TEA.

WORCESTER TEA.

JEWEL TEA.

CANADA TEA.

DEVON TEA.

ROYAL TEA.

EATON TEA.

MINTON TEA.

HARROW TEA. BREAKFAST.

MELROSE BREAKFAST. TEA.

MAJESTIC TEA. BREAKFAST.

CLARENCE CAFÉ.

PARIS TEA.

CARLTON TEA.

COFFEE CAN.

DIAMOND COFFEE.

MAJESTIC COFFEE.

GRANVILLE COFFEE.

Printed in England.

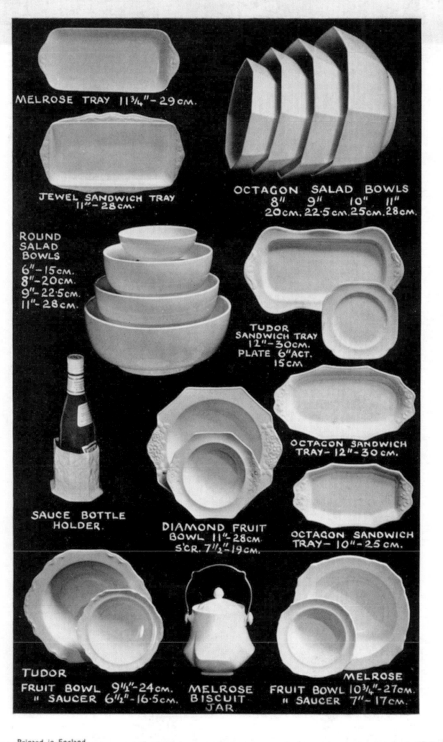

MELROSE TRAY 11¾" – 29 CM.

JEWEL SANDWICH TRAY
11" – 28 CM.

OCTAGON SALAD BOWLS
8"   9"   10"   11"
20 CM. 22·5 CM. 25 CM. 28 CM.

ROUND
SALAD
BOWLS

6" – 15 CM.
8" – 20 CM.
9" – 22·5 CM.
11" – 28 CM.

TUDOR
SANDWICH TRAY
12" – 30 CM.
PLATE 6" ACT.
15 CM

OCTAGON SANDWICH
TRAY – 12" – 30 CM.

SAUCE BOTTLE
HOLDER.

DIAMOND FRUIT
BOWL 11" – 28 CM.
S'CR. 7½" – 19 CM.

OCTAGON SANDWICH
TRAY – 10" – 25 CM.

TUDOR
FRUIT BOWL 9½" – 24 CM.
"   SAUCER 6½" – 16·5 CM.

MELROSE
BISCUIT
JAR.

MELROSE
FRUIT BOWL 10¾" – 27 CM.
"   SAUCER 7" – 17 CM.

CHEESE DISHES

S/S YORK 6" 15 CM.

M/S YORK 7" 18 CM.

8" 20 CM. L/S YORK

CHEDLET 6½"–16 CM.

GRANVILLE 6½"–16 CM

CANADA 6"–15 CM.

DIAMOND 8"–20 CM.

BRAMBLE 7½"–19 CM.

HONEY POTS

DIAMOND BUTTER

DIAMOND

FAST-STAND

MELROSE

FAST-STAND BUTTER

TUB BUTTER

GRANVILLE BUTTER

MAJESTIC COVERED BUTTER

MELROSE EGG-SET

GRANVILLE CRUET-SET

DIAMOND EGG-SET

TOAST-RACKS

5-BAR

3-BAR

4-BAR

DIAMOND PEPPER, SALT & TRAY

DIAMOND CRUET-SET

MAYONAISE BOWL STAND & LADLE

PARIS SUGAR DREDGER

JAMES KENT LTD. SHAPES

Bedroom set

Diamond teapot

Unknown

Melrose teapot

Tudor teapot

Granville cocoa pot

Diamond coffee pot

Unknown

Dutch jug

York jug

Granville jug

JAMES KENT LTD. SHAPES

Unknown

Royal

Eaton

Diamond

Silver

Jumbo

Diamond salt and pepper

Diamond variation salt and pepper

Granville butter dish

Melrose egg cup set

Miscellaneous bud vases

JAMES KENT LTD. SHAPES

Octagon cream and sugar on tray

York cream jug, Tudor covered sugar

Kent cream and sugar

Melrose Cream

Octagon sugar

Diamond honey pot

Granville honey pot

Melrose honey pot

York cheese dish

Diamond cruet set

A. G. RICHARDSON (CROWN DUCAL)
BREAKFAST SET, TEA and COFFEE POTS

Breakfast set

Refreshment set

Georgian Teapot

Teapot

Teapot

Victorian Teapot

Victorian Coffee pot

Black coffee pot

Black coffee pot

Hot water pot

A. G. RICHARDSON (CROWN DUCAL) SHAPES

Hot Water pot with metal lid Victorian Jug Jug

Jug Victorian cream and sugar

Double Egg cup Egg Set

Egg set Lemon Squeezer

A. G. RICHARDSON (CROWN DUCAL) SHAPES

Cruet set

Cruet set

Cruet set

Toast and jam

Sugar shaker

Sugar shaker

Jam pot with liner

Mustard pot

Jam pot

Mayonnaise and ladle

A. G. RICHARDSON (CROWN DUCAL) SHAPES

Rose bowl

Rose bowl

Rose bowl

Comport

Salad bowl

Cedric

Bowl

Bowl

Lily

A. G. RICHARDSON (CROWN DUCAL) SHAPES

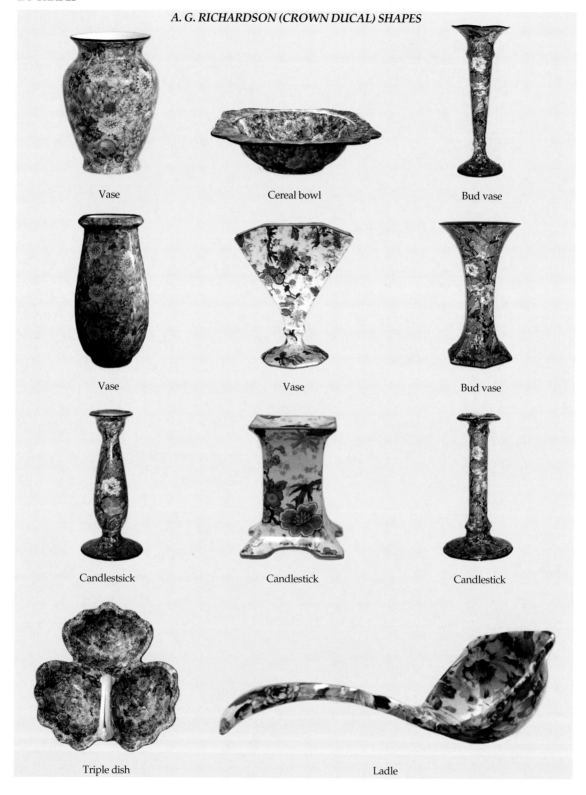

Vase

Cereal bowl

Bud vase

Vase

Vase

Bud vase

Candlestsick

Candlestick

Candlestick

Triple dish

Ladle

A. G. RICHARDSON (CROWN DUCAL) SHAPES

Biscuit barrel

JardiniFre

Biscuit barrel

JardiniFre

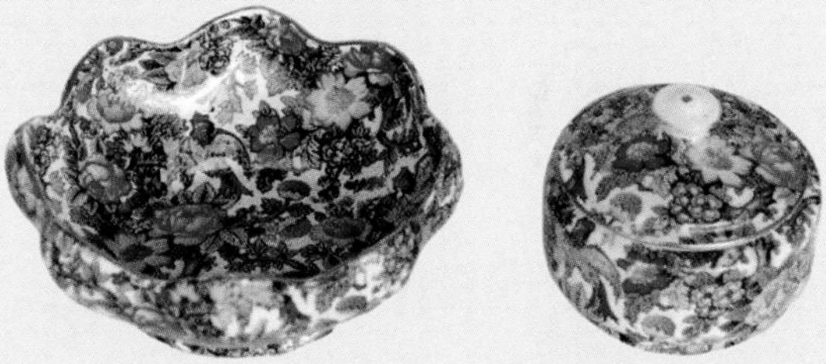

Bowl (left) Covered bowl (right)

Vase

Vase

Vase

Vase

Vase

Vase

SHELLEY SHAPES

Richmond teapot

Richmond cream and sugar

Teapot and stand

Stanley hot water pot

New Cambridge Teapot

Unknown cup and saucer

Oleander cup and saucer

Ripon Cup and Saucer

Cigarette holder

Cruet

Lamp

WADE CERAMICS LTD.

1999 CHINTZWARE BREAKFAST SET

These six-piece breakfast sets come packaged in presentation boxes.

Backstamp not
available
at press time

Item	Pattern	Retail Price
Breakfast tray	Available	$140.00
Cream	in	50.00
Sugar	Butterfly	72.50
Tea cup	Sweet Pea	57.50
Teapot	Thistle	125.00
Toast rack		50.00
6-piece set		245.00

WADE CHINTZWARE

PATTERN INDEX

PATTERN INDEX

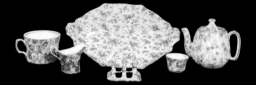

288

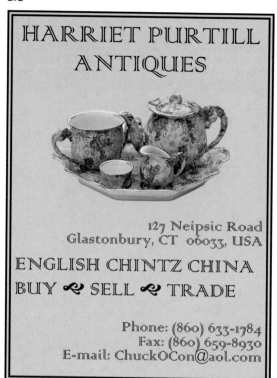

by

OLD FOLEY
POTTERY

FINEST
SEMI-PORCELAIN

"*Du Barry*"
PATTERN

JAMES KENT COLLECTORS CHINTZ

For information, please contact us:
Tel.: +44 1782 597700   Fax: +44 1782 597702
Visit our Web page: www.hadida.co.uk
E-mail: enquiries@hadida.co.uk

Old Foley Pottery
King Street, Fenton, Stoke-on-Trent
ST4 3DH England